Financial Times Pitman Publishing books

We work with leading authors to develop the stronger ideas in business and finance, bringing cutting-edge thinking and best practice to a global market.

We craft high quality books which help readers to understand and apply their content, whether studying or at work.

To find out more about Financial Times Pitman Publishing books, visit our website:

www.ftmanagement.com

The Association of

MBAs

GUIDE TO BUSINESS SCHOOLS

1998/99

Commentary by Godfrey Golzen,
with contributions from Des Dearlove

Listings and text on the accreditation process from
the Association of MBAs

Published with the Association of MBAs

FINANCIAL TIMES
PITMAN PUBLISHING

FINANCIAL TIMES
MANAGEMENT

LONDON • SAN FRANCISCO
KUALA LUMPUR • JOHANNESBURG

Financial Times Management delivers the knowlege,
skills and understanding that enable students,
managers and organisations to achieve their ambitions,
whatever their needs, wherever they are.

London Office:

128 Long Acre, London WC2E 9AN

Tel: +44 (0)171 447 2000

Fax: +44 (0)171 240 5771

Website: www.ftmanagement.com

A Division of Financial Times Professional Limited

First published by Macdonald & Evans Ltd 1970
Second edition 1973
Third edition 1976
Fourth edition 1979
Fifth edition 1981
Sixth edition 1985
Seventh edition 1988
Eighth edition 1990
Ninth edition 1992
Tenth edition 1993
Eleventh edition 1995
Twelfth edition 1996
Thirteenth edition 1997
Fourteenth edition 1998

© Macdonald & Evans Ltd, 1970, 1973, 1976, 1979, 1981, 1985
© Longman Group UK Ltd 1988, 1990, 1992, 1993
© Pearson Professional Limited 1995, 1996, 1997, 1998

ISBN 0 273 63701 0

British Library Cataloguing in Publication Data
A CIP catalogue record for this book can be obtained from the British Library

10 9 8 7 6 5 4 3 2 1

Typeset by Land & Unwin (Data Sciences) Limited
Printed in Great Britain by Bell and Bain Ltd, Glasgow

The Publishers' policy is to use paper manufactured from sustainable forests.

About the author

Godfrey Golzen was appointments editor of the *Sunday Times* until becoming editor of *Human Resources* and later also of its companion magazine, *HR World*. He has written numerous business books and writes regularly on business schools for the *Times* and other national newspapers. He is a visiting fellow at Cranfield University School of Management.

CONTENTS

Introduction
MBAs and their Association

The degree, Master of Business Administration (MBA), is by far the fastest growing postgraduate qualification in the UK. Britain's current output of over 8 000 MBA graduates per year is more than the rest of Europe put together. Though still a long way behind the well over 90 000 graduating in the USA each year, that is nevertheless a huge jump from the total of 2000 in 1985/86. According to Mike Jones, Director-General of the Association of MBAs, enrolments in 1996 were 11,368, of which over half were in part-time and distance learning programmes.

Variation in the quality of the places that offer MBAs is an almost inevitable side-effect of growth of that order. It has to be said that money and 'me-tooism' have played a part in the establishment of some of the MBA courses now on offer in around 110 schools in the UK, plus a growing number in continental Europe. The MBA programme, which runs for either one or two years (overwhelmingly the former) for full-time students and for a minimum of about two years for part-time and distance learners, is a useful revenue generator for financially hard-pressed tertiary institutions. Apart from that, the high visibility of the MBA concept increasingly makes them feel that they have to be able to offer an MBA to be taken seriously in the community and even in the academic world.

The result is that while, until quite recently, just being able to put the letters MBA after your name was sufficient to give you a competitive advantage in the career stakes, commentators now increasingly report that employers and recruitment consultants look at where the degree was earned.

Some MBAs, it is becoming clear, are more equal than others. Consequently, monitoring standards has become one of the key roles of the Association of MBAs. Some of these standards are set out in the pages of this Guide – which is why it has been widely recommended as essential reading for those considering doing the MBA, or indeed for organisations who might be asked to sponsor them.

The Association of MBAs and quality control

The Association of MBAs was founded in 1967, as what was then the Business Graduates Association, by a group of British graduates who had returned from studying at some of the leading US business schools. Their initiative had two main objectives. One was a belief in the need for some kind of pressure group to promote the idea of management education itself, at a time when it scarcely existed in the UK in a formal sense. There were, for instance, no management schools awarding the MBA in the UK before 1965, and the influence of Association members in important positions has played no small part in the expansion of business education in the UK since then.

Their other motive was more social. Experience of the alumni associations of the American schools had shown that they had much to offer their members. The

1

founders of the Association of MBAs wanted to extend to the UK the concept of continuing social contact, informal networking, and exchanges of information through periodic work-shops and members' meetings, strong among business school graduates in the USA.

Both these themes continue to underpin what the Association does, but they have been joined by a third which has become equally important: that of quality control of MBA-awarding bodies through a system of accreditation. Currently 31 out of the 112 or so institutions conferring the MBA in the UK are accredited by the Association. They have been joined by a further 16 on the European Continent.[1] The value attached by schools to such accreditation is confirmed by the fact that even those further afield are beginning to seek it. An average of one school a month is assessed but more fail than pass, according to a report in the *Financial Times*.[2]

The assessment criteria are rigorous, and themselves offer a kind of consumer protection for intending students. Here are some of their principal features:

- the school should have its own discrete identity and physical facilities within the institution of which it is a part
- it should have graduated at least two 'cohorts' (graduating classes)
- the faculty should be big enough to ensure strength in depth – the Association believes that around 40 staff is the minimum needed to provide adequate contact with students during the course
- the staff should be credible in terms of their academic qualifications, their ability to teach business at postgraduate level, the quality of their research, and the extent of their business contacts and consultancy activities
- admission standards for students must be high, and based on work experience as well as academic criteria
- the student body must be large and varied enough to form an intellectually critical mass
- the curriculum must cover core business skills: marketing, the economic and legal environment of a business, accounting and quantitative methods, organisational theory and interpersonal skills, and the processes and practice of management
- examination results must be the principal, though not the sole, measure of attainment.

In addition, accreditation is based on such factors as the availability of language teaching, library and computer facilities, international contacts, and the content and quality of assessment of the project/thesis/dissertation which, towards the end of the course, integrates what has been learned and relates it to a real situation. The extent to which student reactions are taken into account is also considered in the continuing process of course design and improvement.

---

[1] The European Foundation For Management Development (EFMD) has also started an accreditation programme under the heading EQUIS (European Foundation for Quality Improvement). This is complementary to the Association's accreditation, in that it accredits entire business schools, including undergraduate courses, where the Association accredits only MBA programmes. The first schools to have been accredited by EQUIS are ESADE, ESCP, HEC, INSEAD, LBS, SDA Bocconi.

[2] 'Working for the Stamp of Approval,' 2 March 1998.

One of the Association's major roles is to act as a clearing house for enquiries from intending MBAs, or from those who are thinking of doing an MBA; in fact, its staff deal with some 1500 letters and telephone calls per month. However, one area where it is hesitant to give advice, is on matters of opinion. It is, in particular, difficult to judge whether one school is 'better' than another, and it does not provide rankings of schools.[1]

The Association takes the view that the accreditation process in itself provides a broad measure of quality assurance. After that it is up to the individual – or the company thinking of sponsoring an employee to take an MBA – to pursue their own investigations by making personal visits, talking to other sponsors, or talking to graduates of the institutions in which they are interested. However, it does provide very significant services on concrete issues:

- **Events** – it runs regional and national events for Association members, such as evening and lunchtime meetings with nationally prominent speakers, which also give members the opportunity for informal networking.
- **Careers** – it advises on a range of career matters. An important recent development is that, responding to the growing need for information on the job market, the Association of MBAs has linked with Cranfield School of Management to launch *Career Moves*, a twice-monthly bulletin of senior level vacancies, available to members as well as Cranfield alumni. Further career services which have been initiated are the Job Search Service and the Career Development and Advisory Services. The former, developed in partnership with Career Movers Companion (CMC Ltd) helps graduates with job search mechanics and techniques such as CV preparation. The latter is offered by Jo Ouston & Co, a specialist training and working practice that is particularly geared to developing career strategies for MBAs.
- **The Locum Service** – this is offered in partnership with Rent-an-MBA in the growing area of interim management – short to medium term management assignments.
- **Special terms and concessions** – it has negotiated special terms for members with a number of business and social bodies. Concessions have been negotiated for a comprehensive range of insurance products, business and personal travel, and the purchase of car and business books.
- **Special interest groups** – a number of such groups have been initiated among Association members, notably one on small business and another on the Internet. Each group has its own programme of meetings and information exchanges.
- **Publications** – apart from the December 1997 Survey of Salaries and Careers commissioned from Hay Management Consultants, to which we will refer in more detail later in the text, it publishes a monthly newsletter, *Ambassador*, and an annual handbook containing names and addresses of members.

From the point of view of prospective MBAs, its most valuable service is probably the operation, in conjunction with Barclays and the National Westminster Bank, of the Association's Business School Loan Scheme. We will give more exact details of this later in the text, but the importance of the Scheme can be judged from the fact that since 1990, over £120 million of loans have been negotiated. Their average value in the UK in 1997 was £16 344 full-time, £9 860 part-time, and £5 211 distance learning.

Loans can also be raised for study abroad. The average was around £22 400 on the Continent and close on £37 000 in the USA, which suggests that financially, the UK is a bargain, though cost-of-living differentials do also play a part.

The Association of MBAs holds two MBA fairs each year in the UK; the one held at Covent Garden in 1997 attracted an all-time record attendance of almost 2 000 individuals. This and the fact that the Association receives so many enquiries from people interested in taking an MBA, is an indication of the ever-growing demand for the qualification. It also appears that many of those seeking it are funding at least part of their course themselves, and are prepared to invest time and money on their own development. This is a lesson that is not lost on prospective employers.

The revenues generated by the Loan Scheme also benefit the Association's members in other ways. Notably, it enables it to offer all these wide-ranging services without charging a joining fee, though there is a modest, flat rate, tax-deductible annual subscription of £65. The Association of MBAs currently has around 900 members. Membership is growing at around 15% per year and is well on target for the Association's next goal of 10,000 members.

Business schools in the nineties
Even during the recession, the demand for entry into MBA programmes only dipped slightly, and the tendency was often to postpone rather than abandon the decision to take the MBA. More recently, all schools report a marked upturn in both enquiries and enrolments, interest being sparked by the frequency with which management-level job advertisements for people aged 26–38 are listing an MBA as a desirable attribute. According to the Association, there is evidence which suggests that an MBA is fast becoming a prerequisite for a career in management. That view is endorsed by London Business School's former Director, Professor George Bain: 'If you really want to do something, you have to have a master's degree'. A first degree, he argues, is essentially only an entry qualification, and this is becoming true outside the obvious environments of big companies, consultancies and financial institutions. It is noticeable how many managers from the local business community attend the part-time programme of their nearest school.

For their part, rising young managers are voting for the MBA with their feet. Already the Association estimates that there are around 50,000 MBAs living and working in the UK. Such numbers are bound to create their own momentum. One sign of this is the trend, widely noted by the schools, for public sector managers and those from privatised or quasi-privatised spheres (eg managers from NHS Trusts and even medical doctors) to come on to MBA programmes. A local government employee was quoted in the *Financial Times* as saying: 'The MBA is now seen in my organisation as essential, a prerequisite to progression.'[3]

The scope of the guide
Whilst almost 80% of students on the increasingly popular part-time and distance learning MBA courses are supported by their employers in ways ranging from varying degrees of financial support to being given some time off, full-time students are predominantly self-funded. In either case though, doing an MBA is almost always an individual decision.

[3] *Financial Times*, 19 February 1998.

There are a number of issues to take into account in reaching this decision. For the self-funded MBA, there is the question of cost. Annual fees for a full-time programme for students from the European Union (EU) range between £6 000 and £12 000 (those from outside it are often asked to pay 10–20% more), with the top schools at the upper end of the cost spectrum. This is one reason why two-year courses are becoming an extinct species in Europe, with the notable exception of the London Business School (LBS).

Living costs also have to be considered. Schools encourage students to live on campus, even if they happen to live near the school, because of the intense nature of the programme and the emphasis it places on group work both inside and outside the classroom. Depending on location, lifestyle, and family circumstances, accommodation and living costs will add a further £6 000 plus to the cost of the course.

It is estimated that the total outlay on a one-year full-time course is likely to be in the region of £18 000–£22 000, and can be as much as £25 000 at a leading school abroad. On top of that, there are the earnings foregone and the cost of being out of the frame as far as promotion is concerned, for the duration of the programme. Even those taking a part-time or distance learning MBA will have to take their eye off the promotional ball if they are to get through what is universally seen as one of the most demanding of all academic courses. It is true that in many cases employers will be footing at least part of a fee bill which is broadly comparable to the full-time one, and that students will be continuing to earn a salary, be living at home, and remaining visible to their employers, but the worst mistake that can be made is to underrate the amount of work that is involved and the difficulties of reconciling the conflicting demands of job, study, family, and social life. The question is then: is it really worth it?

It is a difficult one to answer for the same reason that as the Association finds it difficult to answer qualitative questions – so much depends on the individual, on individual circumstances and business environments. However, one of the chief objectives of the Guide, which has now again been heavily revised and updated, is to provide readers with enough information about key aspects of the MBA to enable them to draw their own conclusions about whether or not taking the MBA is the right decision for them.

Thus it begins by examining some of the expectations that might lie behind a decision to take the course, and whether these are likely to be met by so doing. Is it, for instance, likely to enhance career prospects, or should it be seen more as a question of personal development?

In either case, what does it actually involve? That may depend on the mode of study. The choices lie between full-time, and a variety of part-time options: chiefly distance or open learning, evening MBAs, executive MBAs (where teaching takes place at weekends), modular programmes (a kind of sandwich course), and consortium MBAs tailored to the needs of a group of sponsors. The first is a short and extremely intensive course of study in a primarily academic setting. The others are longer courses, covering the same ground but spun out over at least two years, that enable students to carry on working – and apply on the job what they are learning – but will place perhaps even greater strains on their time-management skills and possibly on their private lives. We will discuss the pros and cons of each method, and what the learning process actually entails for both foreign and UK students.

Risk factors Apart from the question of whether it is worth it in career terms, what are the risks of doing the course in the first place? What are the chances of failure? How difficult is it all? What is it actually like? How is it changing to adapt to a world of work which over the past year has seen a heightened perception of the threat to jobs in the traditional sense, even at the very top, and a sharpening of concerns with what used to be regarded as luxury issues such as ethics? We hope you will get some idea of this by reading about what is actually involved, but there is one overriding and consoling feature which we would like to point out right away: the hardest part may be getting admitted in the first place.

There is an element of pre-selection in getting on to a course at all. Most applicants are eliminated before they even get as far as the interview, because their application forms show that they do not have the appropriate level of work experience or are unclear about their career aims. Even then, only about 50% of those interviewed are accepted. The consensus of opinion is that once past the admission procedures, notably the Graduate Management Admission Test (GMAT), the chances of anyone with reasonable determination finishing up with an MBA are very good indeed. Because of the importance of GMAT, we will devote a special section to that, though a number of schools are now developing their own tests of verbal and numerical skills.

Is it all worth it from a career point of view? The sounds of the backlash from some of the older and less go-ahead generation of managers are dying down, and as the years go by they are being replaced by a generation of whom many are themselves MBAs. Indeed, the most telling verdict on the value of the MBA comes from the large numbers of bright managers in both the private and public sectors who are voting for it with their feet. They are right to do so, because if the future of businesses is as learning and knowledge organisations – and it is impossible to envisage any other future – then the MBA qualification must be the keystone of that kind of structure.

Questions The Association of MBAs is most often asked – and the answers

Where can I study for an MBA?

With very few exceptions, just about every university in the UK offers an MBA. A number of colleges of higher education and private colleges also offer the MBA – a total of 110 providers. This amount of choice is a problem in itself. See Chapter 3.

How can I ensure I apply to a good, credible, school?

So as to maintain standards, the Association offers an accreditation service. It accredits individual MBA programmes in both the UK and continental Europe. Accredited programmes have met the Association's accreditation criteria. The accreditation process is voluntary; however, if the MBA which interests you is not accredited, then it is reasonable to ask the school why not. A list of accredited programmes and information on accreditation is given in the Guide. See the details on accredited programmes on pp. 144–8.

Where can I apply for an award to finance my MBA?

Unlike undergraduate study, there are no mandatory awards from your Local Educational Authority for MBA study; this is even the case for those who have not studied for a first degree. There are few scholarships available, and the only substantial ones are mainly for study in the USA. However, company sponsorship of employees is prolific. See Chapter 5.

I am paying my own way through Business School. Can I reclaim tax on the expenses incurred in studying for an MBA?

Provided you are a full-time student, and are 30 years of age or more at the date of payment, you can claim tax relief on your tuition fees. If you are a part-timer or distance learner, or if you are a full-time student aged less than 30 years, then you are not eligible. (See Inland Revenue leaflet IR119 – Tax relief for vocational training obtainable from FICO Tel: 0151 472 6000 Ext: 7037). See Chapter 5.

I graduate this year. It seems logical to me to take an MBA immediately so that I can then embark on a career fully equipped with business skills. Will I be able to get a place?

Unfortunately, yes. Some schools, which are unable to attract sufficient well-qualified students with business experience, will make up the numbers with recent graduates. However, an MBA is both a postgraduate and a post-experience qualification and, therefore, an MBA without a track record of success in business is rather meaningless. In a worst case scenario, some employers might consider a 22 year-old MBA overqualified for their graduate trainee scheme, whilst deeming them under-qualified for the senior positions that they have earmarked for MBAs. See Chapter 4.

I've been offered places at both x, y and z. I think that they are considered to be reasonable schools, but how do I choose between them?

Firstly, apply to schools which are highly regarded by industry (see Q2 above). If you are thinking in terms of your marketability on completion, you should remember that your future employers probably already employ MBAs and may be MBAs themselves. They may well have a mental list of what they consider to be acceptable schools. Provided you are satisfied with the school's credibility, then you should look at the programme content (the choice of electives, for example), the teaching style, even the feel of the school. You may also wish to ascertain in which sectors of industry recent graduates are employed, and the length of time it took them to find employment. The important thing to remember is that if you have done your research thoroughly, you should not make a bad choice. Rather, it will become a matter of choosing the most suitable school for you. See Chapter 3.

I have heard that schools require the GMAT Test. How important is the GMAT Test?

American schools require the GMAT, as do many European schools. However, in Europe the GMAT is sometimes replaced by a school's own test or, in some cases, is not required at all. Many part-time and distance learning courses do not require GMAT. First of all, you should ascertain from the schools in which you are interested whether or not they require GMAT. It would be pointless investing time and effort needlessly. If they do require the test, then you should not take it until you have fully familiarised yourself with its content. It would be an unusually talented person who did not benefit enormously from undertaking some preparatory study. Note that where schools do set their own test, the level of numerical and verbal literacy called for is very similar to that of the GMAT, so it might not be a bad idea, if you are not confident of your abilities in this direction, to consider doing one of the GMAT cramming courses shown in Chapter 4.

The GMAT is designed to indicate to admissions officers those who may have problems in coping with MBA study, and low-scoring candidates may be eliminated immediately from the admissions process. However, the average score varies from school to school. Students at schools such as London Business School commonly have an average score of 600–650. At schools where GMAT is employed, the average student's score is a reasonable indicator as to the school's quality. See Chapter 4.

MBA tuition costs vary enormously from school to school. What am I supposed to infer from this?

This is a complex question. To some extent, it is a matter of supply and demand. The better schools do sometimes charge high fees, but still attract excellent students because of the kudos attached to obtaining a prized brand name MBA. However, high fees do not automatically mean a first-rate MBA.

Some schools offer questionable value for money. It has been argued that MBA tuition fees sometimes bear little correlation to the costs incurred in offering the programme or the value of the end result. Whilst a brand name MBA may open many doors, an MBA from some other institutes may fail to impress. See Chapter 3 and the School Profiles.

I have a degree in a non-numerate discipline and I'm worried that I might not be a suitable candidate for an MBA programme.

Some programmes demand higher mathematical skills than others. In general, one would expect any graduate to be able to tackle an MBA, and it is fair to say that many would-be MBAs are unduly concerned about their level of numeracy. However, in some instances some remedial or refresher study might be advisable. If you think you may have a problem, consult your intended school. See Chapter 4.

What are the realistic outlooks for an MBA in terms of salary and career?

This depends on a number of factors and a comprehensive answer cannot be offered here. Suffice to say that Salary and Career Surveys of members of the Association of MBAs,[4] which have been undertaken by a leading company in this field, clearly indicate benefits in the medium- and long-term which are not achieved by other professions. You should, however, be realistic; while the MBA will open new doors to you, the immediate premium may not be enormous. See Chapter 8.

[4] The 1997 MBA Salary and Career Survey is available from the Association of MBAs, price £25.

Part 1

GUIDE TO

MBAs

THE MANAGEMENT SCHOOL
LANCASTER UNIVERSITY

The Lancaster MBA

Where Academic Excellence Delivers Personal and Organisational Change

AMBA Accredited

ACADEMIC EXCELLENCE: Lancaster University Management School's top ratings for Research (5 star) and Teaching (Excellent) place it in an elite group of three business schools in the UK for academic excellence. (Higher Education Funding Council).

PRACTICAL RELEVANCE: Over a period of 30 years it has built a distinctive reputation for delivering personal and organisational change, by a combination of imaginative teaching and practice-driven learning on organisation based projects. Organisations benefit as much as individuals on our Executive MBAs.

INTERNATIONAL SCOPE: Lancaster's rich network of international alliances with leading business schools and companies enables it to offer a more profound international experience than most competitors.

A PLACE FOR REFLECTION AND ACTION: The rural parkland campus and high quality facilities offer an ideal environment for both critical reflection on the more complex issues together with active group learning. Easy access from Manchester International Airport, Intercity train or M6 motorway.

THE LANCASTER MBA: Choose from the 12 month full-time, 26 month executive part-time, or single-company options.

For more information see our entry on page 213 of this guide, or contact the MBA Office for an information pack.

MBA Office, Lancaster University Management School, Lancaster, UK.
Tel: +44 (0)1524 594068. Fax: +44 (0)1524 592417.
Email: mba@lancaster.ac.uk
Website: http://www.lancs.ac.uk/

Thinking it over

In the case of most postgraduate qualifications, you can move straight on from a first degree to a postgraduate course. While it is not absolutely impossible to take an MBA in this way – some non-UK schools do not list work experience among their admission requirements – it is generally regarded as inadvisable. In the words of Mike Jones, Director-General of the Association of MBAs: 'The MBA is focused on themes and techniques applicable to the business world, and demands that students bring to it some business skills and experience. What distinguishes it from other business-led masters degrees, is that it is both a postgraduate *and* a post-experience qualification'. Thus few MBA students in the UK or other Western Europe countries are doing the course without at least three years of practical grounding of some kind, though it need not necessarily have been in a business role. Profiles of recent and current cohorts of students at a typical leading school show, apart from line management in a wide variety of sectors, backgrounds that range over law, engineering, the armed forces, journalism, engineering, financial services, teaching, consultancy, helicopter flying, and television production.

One reason why work experience is important is, as Sheila Cameron wrote in the MBA Handbook,[1] because 'students who have worked as managers tend to be far more excited by their studies than those who have not'. This seems to be particularly true of those who take the course part-time or by distance learning – we will deal more fully with the various options and what they involve in the next chapter. 'Part-time and distance learning courses', she goes on to say, 'offer splendid opportunities for practice for those already in managerial jobs'.

That conclusion is borne out in conversations with MBA students on such programmes. The theme that recurs again and again is that they find that what they are learning in the classroom, in study groups and in their reading, is immediately applicable at work. A student taking a part-time MBA at Warwick Business School is typical. With a degree in computer science, he felt he needed to widen his understanding of general management after taking a principal part in a management buy-out of the firm of which he is a director. 'I was astonished how relevant the programme was, right from the first day,' he recalls. There was also a direct practical value to the company, because he was able to feed actual facts and figures into the discussions with fellow students and faculty. As a result, he has moved from being the primarily 'techie' member of his board, to being able to make a business contribution of real and increasing influence. Indeed, Sheila Cameron argues that you can only get full value out of part-time and distance learning courses if you can actually 'practise the skills in parallel with the course'.

---

[1] Cameron, Sheila, *The MBA Handbook*, Financial Times Management, 3rd edition 1997.

By contrast, full-time MBA programmes are not immediately applicable at work and tend to have a more theoretical orientation. As she points out, they do not allow you 'to experiment with concepts and techniques in a real working environment ... Case studies offer few advantages in this respect when compared with on the job experience'. Some maintain in fact, that they may therefore be more suitable for those who want to upgrade work experience, say in a specialist or functional capacity, into a future role in general management, or for those looking for a change of career direction.

Students: characteristics and profiles

In 1997, the Association of MBAs repeated an exercise it had undertaken in 1992 and 1995: a wide-ranging survey of the characteristics, expectations, motivation, and careers of members who had taken full- and part-time MBAs.[2] With a response rate of 26% among the almost 6,000 members polled, it shows a sharp switch in the direction of part-time and distance learning courses. Whereas respondents are evenly divided between these groups and those who took their degree by full-time study, the trend is very much towards the former modes. Under 20% now do a full-time MBA. That has had a corresponding impact on the percentage who continued to work while studying: over 80%. Associated with that is the age pattern of students. The 31–35 group accounts for over 30% of their number, but over 15% are over 40.

Motivations have changed as well, which probably reflects the acceptance of the notion of employability as the basis of a career strategy in a market where a job is no longer for life or even perhaps for a longer term. On the other hand, the MBA is not seen primarily as a tool for changes of career direction, though it can enhance starting career prospects for people like ex-service personnel.

Significantly, change of career direction is seen as most important among full-time students, who are mostly self-sponsored and who therefore have no obligations towards someone who will, in some form, be footing the bill for their studies. The main motive overall, however, quoted by 91%, is 'improving job opportunities'. The high proportion of those who remained with their employers for at least a year after graduating indicates that, at least in the first instance, the aim is to do that in the organisation in which they are currently working. However, there is a very considerable amount of movement after that.

On the question of funding, no details are available on employer funding of full-time students, but it is likely to be low since 90% of students had financed their studies with an Association of MBAs loan. Anecdotal evidence further suggests that the majority of those entering a full-time course had resigned their jobs to do so. By contrast, 51% of part-timers who were employed during their studies had all their fees paid by their employer. Others were supported by employers in a variety of ways, ranging from some financial assistance to time off work.

However, in other ways, the differences between full- and part-time students were only minor. In both cases, around 80% had a first degree and around 48% had achieved a first or upper second. A significant statistic here was the

---

[2] *The Association of MBAs Salary and Careers Survey*, 1997.

preponderance of those with some kind of science/maths/engineering/ accounting background.

The schools say that this is not because people with this kind of qualification are favoured in their acceptance policies but because they find they need an MBA to break into general management from a blocked specialist role as accountants, engineers, or whatever.

However, for all the shift towards 'soft' management subjects in the MBA (eg interpersonal skills such as communication, negotiation, teamwork etc), students with poor levels of numeracy would be likely to find the course very difficult. Many schools now offer a short preliminary maths course before the start of the MBA programme itself.

There were no marked differences in the employment background of the two groups, except that more full-timers than part-timers came from consultancy, whereas the reverse was true of the growing numbers of those who came from the public sector: almost all of them were taking part-time or distance learning courses. Other interesting features were the wide spread of job disciplines in students' backgrounds, and their relatively high previous levels of responsibility. Forty-two per cent came from senior or middle-management levels, a statistic which ties in with the finding that 70% had more than six years of work experience. This is encouraging because such a large part of the learning process comes from mixing and exchanging views with fellow students from different backgrounds, but with comparable levels of responsibility and experience.

Though the MBA is still not attracting women in numbers which reflect their growing presence at senior levels in organisations of all kinds, numbers are increasing. The Association's figures now show that the average female participation is up to 23% from 20% three years ago. Professor Leo Murray, Director of Cranfield, believes that further growth in the numbers of women may be limited because the post-experience nature of admissions criteria coincides with the age at which women tend to start families.

Some UK schools contain a very sizeable overseas contingent. That may be a laudable move towards internationalisation, but it may also reflect a policy of active recruitment in countries where UK fees seem less daunting, and where the status of a UK MBA has an added cachet. Sitting in on classes with a large contingent of non-native English speakers, language difficulties became immediately obvious to the writer when presentations were being made by some groups. The general view is that a 50:50 mix of UK to foreign students is about right, except in the case of schools which set out to be international and to have an even balance of nationalities in their admission policies: London Business School is a case in point.

Opponents of the MBA often cite the salary demands made by MBA graduates as a reason for their suspicion of the qualification. While it is true that MBAs often expect to, and do, increase their earnings after they graduate (see Chapter 8 for further information on this) – they are, after all, adding value to their business skills and have made considerable personal and often financial sacrifices to do so – the evidence is that money is not a prime motivation for those taking the MBA.

Student expectations and motivation

There seems to be little difference here between the expectations of full- and part-time students. However, it appears that sponsored students are more interested in improving their skills as managers within their current organisation, whereas self-funded students are thinking in terms of career or job change. Only a minority of all students give 'making more money' as a reason for doing the course, though this may be a case of the motive that dare not speak its name. However, one full-time student, a young former navy officer who had no business experience, did say that he expected the degree to be reflected in a higher starting salary in his new civilian career.

So the evidence is that career strategy is the centrepiece in the mix of reasons why people do an MBA. In their controversial report, *The MBA Question*,[3] the headhunters Saxton Bampfylde established some broad characteristics of what lies behind these strategies. Though it was published in 1990, these still hold true and may give prospective MBAs some explanation of their own, sometimes unarticulated, motives and the chance to examine whether doing an MBA is the right career move for them in the light of that:

● **The Big Game Planner** is described as 'often a very driven individual' who may be planning to use the MBA to assemble a set of skills and a network of contacts for some future entrepreneurial activity. Big game planners should be aware, however, that while the MBA does contain a great deal of practical content, it is not a vocational course on running a business – though many schools do offer programmes in entrepreneurship among their electives.
Another category under this heading is the career strategist. Often to be found in the public sector and in some of the professions, they see longer term opportunities in the demand for business skills linked to areas like education or medicine. Most schools have at least a sprinkling of doctors, dentists, vets and educationists among their MBA students and their number is growing.

● **The Natural Next Stepper** often comes from a business like banking or consultancy, where possession of an MBA is the norm for their peer group. However, in a setting where most people have an MBA, where it was obtained will be very significant. Saxton Bampfylde warn, however, that the content of some MBA courses is more readily transferable to another business sector than others. This is particularly true of moves from financial services to manufacturing line management. If you are looking to make a move of this kind, you might consider one of the growing number of specialist MBAs which start from a common core and then go on to focus on a particular area in the electives.

● **The Disillusioned Functionalist** is generally a person trying to move out of a specialism with limited access to general management. Engineers and those seeking a change of career direction fall into this category. Engineering, say Saxton Bampfylde, is the 'single most important professional provenance for MBAs', though accountancy must run it close. The high proportion of engineers and accountants on MBA courses, say the schools, is not so much because it is a natural progression from skills they already have (and by

[3] Saxton Bampfylde, *The MBA Question*, 1990.

implication, more difficult for those who don't have a previous quantitative qualification), but because they most often feel the need to broaden out their skills if they are to advance their careers.

● **The Searcher** is someone with high, but perhaps unarticulated, career expectations who sees the MBA as a way of exploring directions their career might take. Such people are often looking to the MBA to provide a route to a new career direction, though some have reported this to be more difficult than they had imagined. For instance, a graduate who had won a scholarship to INSEAD, acknowledged to be one of Europe's top schools, reported that she was finding it extremely difficult to move from the financial services sector to line management in industry. Relevant experience, it seems, still counts – even for those who can point to an MBA in their CV.

● **Moving up at 35**. The mid 30s are widely seen as a crucial career stage. If you are going to get anywhere in senior management, that is when it has to start. At this point an MBA – generally taken part-time or by distance learning – can provide an invaluable reinforcement to experience and an enhancement of existing skills. The problem is that doing an MBA while holding down managerial responsibilities obviously imposes additional strains, both in work and in study. Those who have followed this course all stress that it requires a good deal of understanding on the part of one's family and employers in order to keep up with the workload.

● **The Cop-out** falls into the category of the perpetual student. Bright enough, he or she is not likely to experience too much difficulty with the intellectual challenge of the course, but is lacking direction and more concerned with study as a way of postponing a career decision. Such people are likely to benefit least from an MBA. While it is not a vocational course, it is not meant to be a set of abstract intellectual exercises either.

To these one might add a further category of people who often come from a public sector background:

● **The Self-developer** is someone who sees gaining an MBA as a way of enhancing a portfolio of skills, or who has simply become interested in management as a subject. One might call this the Open University student attitude, though such motives are to be found among distance learning and part-time students generally. However, self-developers should be aware that an MBA requires commitment of a much higher order than a first degree. It is interesting to note that the 1997 Association Survey referred to previously shows that there has been a slight decline in MBAs by distance learning, perhaps indicating that word has got around about how difficult it is to combine work with a form of study that requires a very high degree of self-discipline.

Since most people take the course in order to advance their careers, either within their own organisation or by changing jobs, the perception of employers of the value of an MBA is crucial. The good news is that attitudes have become much more positive over the past couple of years. Several factors have contributed to this:

Employer expectations · and fears

- the environment of tumultuous change in which organisations of all kinds now operate – deregulation, mergers and acquisitions, searches for core competencies, the impact of IT, to name just a few factors – calls for a need to stand back and take a more strategic view of the future. The MBA is a qualification with a strong strategy content
- global competition has sharpened the need for professionalism in management, in contrast to the cult of the talented amateur which, in Britain at least, prevailed in many organisations until the 1980s
- as the number of MBA graduates has increased, they have moved in growing numbers into senior jobs in organisations where they are in a position to influence hiring decisions. According to the 1997 Board of Directors Study carried out by headhunters Korn/Ferry in conjunction with London Business School, 41% of UK company directors out of a sample of 345 now have an MBA – a huge increase on the percentage five years ago.
- the debate about the MBA itself, though not always conducted in favourable terms, has heightened general awareness of the qualification and often stimulated interest in what it has to offer. Research by the Association shows that there has been a big rise in the number of smaller organisations hiring MBAs
- there has been an increased demand by managers for meaningful training and development, preferably of a kind that confers portable qualifications. Over the past couple of years, it has become noticeable that possession of an MBA has become a desirable attribute in many job advertisements
- the realisation, by organisations as well as individuals, that narrow professional qualifications or functional skills are ultimately not enough in a business environment where there is a need to take an integrated, and increasingly global, view of how a decision in one sphere impacts on others – precisely what an MBA teaches
- sea changes of attitude by the business schools themselves, as they have competed to provide programmes which reflect the needs and realities of business and industry; for instance, in emphasising team and group work and in rooting the dissertation or project (which is a key part of almost all programmes) in the real world, rather than basing it on case studies or academic research. A typical example is that of a student at Imperial College whose project was a dissertation about inward investment in South China; it was sponsored by the China-Britain trade group and a London law firm.[4]

But what about the fears and prejudices of opponents? There have been ill-informed criticisms of MBAs as aggressive, egotistical, job-hopping, know-it-alls with unrealistic expectations of their immediate prospects. Hostility along these lines is still to be found, expressed or otherwise, among the more traditional and less progressive kinds of UK manufacturing firms. Saxton Bampfylde sums up their attitude as regarding MBA courses like a 'finishing school for management consultants'.

To some extent this can be put down to the anti-intellectualism in some quarters of British business. The generation gap and fears about job security from older,

---

[4] *Times*, 16 October 1995.

less well-trained people also play a part. As Sheila Cameron puts it, 'Their own self-esteem depends on valuing experience more highly than the qualifications they do not have'. Conversely, the MBA is the business equivalent of a Commando course, and there is a temptation, natural among people who have gone through an experience of this kind, to be 'cocky' towards those who have not had it.

The business schools are aware of this problem, which is why interpersonal skills now form an important part of the course. But what is it that the more forward-looking employers expect to gain from hiring MBAs? By the same token, what qualities should an MBA expect to come away with, having taken the course? The Saxton Bampfylde survey, conducted among major employers of MBAs, comes up with an interesting picture:

● a breadth of business understanding of management principles across the key concerns of organisations
● specific tools for analysing strategic issues and options
● the ability to identify priorities in courses of action
● presentation and communication skills.

It will be noted from this that implementation and line management ability do not figure here. Indeed, firms are quoted as saying that MBAs are not automatically 'great line managers'. Many of them feel that the real worth of an MBA course is to add value to in-company training. However, the fact that an increasing number now see the MBA as a management development tool – a matter which we shall discuss at greater length in the next chapter – indicates that there can be a congruence between the MBA qualification and employer expectations.

What about the charge of job-hopping, though? The notion that at any level, training is something provided for the benefit of the next employer, is often the underlying, if unstated, reason for not supplying it or regarding it as something employees must provide in their own time and at their own cost.

The evidence of the most recent Association Survey[5] points clearly to the fact that this fear is largely groundless, at least as far as those who were supported by their employers are concerned. Sixty per cent of the Association members surveyed who had been employed while studying – from which one can infer that such support was forthcoming – had remained with their existing employer for at least a year after graduation.

Employers must also recognise that to some extent whether, and for how long, MBAs stay with them, depends on them providing settings and opportunities that will encourage longer term commitment. The Association survey reported that MBA graduates changed jobs when they felt their qualification was under utilised, but the reverse can also hold true. A Report on The MBA Experience[6] (written some years ago, its findings are still valid in many respects) warned that: 'MBAs recruited in some companies are under pressure to perform and produce results fast.' Trial by ordeal is also a way of losing them fast. It can also

[5] *MBAs: Salaries & Careers*, Association of MBAs, 1997.
[6] *The MBA Experience*, Association of MBAs, 1992.

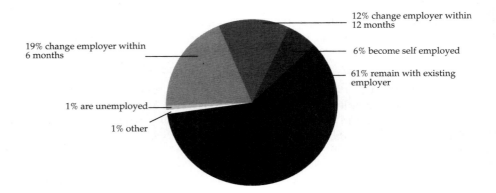

Employment changes after MBA

19% change employer within 6 months

12% change employer within 12 months

6% become self employed

61% remain with existing employer

1% are unemployed

1% other

be argued that investment in training is simply a matter of public interest, which falls into the sphere of the growing emphasis on the importance of corporate ethics.

How the MBA is changing

The changes that are happening in the job market, in the structure of organisations, and in the global economy, have left their mark, both on the method of delivery of the MBA and on its content. Both anecdotal evidence and statistics coming out of the Association indicate that job prospects for MBAs have improved sharply over the last couple of years, but lingering anxieties about the job market have made many students reluctant to embark on full-time programmes because they entail a career break and because they involve a financial, as well as a time, commitment – full-time courses are seldom sponsored by employers. Instead, the trend is moving in the direction of part-time MBAs, where teaching takes place in the evenings, weekends or by day release, over a longer period: 2–3 years is the average.

The most marked increase though, is appearing in distance learning, with over 10,000 students in the UK – 40% of them studying through the Open University Business School (OUBS). Twenty-seven per cent of MBA graduates surveyed by the Association in 1997 came through this route. But in the end, how persistent students will be with a mode of learning that requires a high degree of self-motivation remains to be seen.

As far as content is concerned, there is now a strong demand for relevance. The schools are meeting this in a number of ways:

● increasing the emphasis on practice rather than theory, and strengthening the links between learning and doing at the workplace
● teaching topics not as separate disciplines, but in a more integrated way – showing for instance, the impact of finance on marketing decisions
● greater internationalisation in the student body, the faculty, and the case studies. Alliances between schools in different countries are becoming more

meaningful, with student and faculty visits and exchanges and the opportunity to take modules or electives at some school in another country that has a reputation as a centre of particular expertise in a given field

- greater emphasis on 'soft skills', such as teamwork and leadership
- a heavy accent on group work, replicating what actually happens in 'the real world'; groups are generally put together by the faculty to create a mix of skills, job backgrounds, and nationalities
- facilitating in-company projects, from consultancy assignments to 'internships' which involves actually becoming a temporary member of the host organisation's management team working on a particular problem
- attaching much greater importance to career management and personal development; many schools now include personal development programmes in their course curriculum, and have appointed staff to look specifically after career management matters – they are also actively promoting the growth of alumni associations and other means of networking, with those who have had various connections with the school, for instance through attending executive programmes.

The demand for relevance does not, however, seem to have moved in favour of in-company and consortium MBAs (explained in Chapter 2).

The pattern of specialist MBAs (see the table on p. 366) is that they start out with the same core subjects as the generalist ones. The specialist aspects are developed in the electives. The dilemma facing schools is how to strike the balance between the demands of relevance and those of academic rigour; equally, how to meet the undoubted need for softer skills in an organisational environment where command and control is giving way to empowerment and consent. As Professor Murray says, 'You have to be better than ever at the functional aspects of your job to survive, yet you also have to be able to persuade, to negotiate and to manage your own career development'. These are the directions in which the MBA is moving.

Getting it together

In the absence of direct company involvement in course design, the aims of prospective MBAs and organisations are most likely to meet if both have a clear understanding of each others' views and motives. This means that MBAs must be realistic about the ways in which they can add value to an employer as well as to their personal career aims.

From the employer's point of view, it is important to buy into the notion of lifelong learning and to see its benefits from a corporate point of view. Central to that is using the qualities that MBA graduates can bring to bear. The Economist Intelligence Unit's survey, *Which MBA?*[7] says that many companies have found that using new MBA graduates initially as internal consultants is the best way of tapping into what they have learned, but it adds that 'trying to show traditionally reluctant companies to use MBA graduates effectively' is a key task. The implication is that whether it is worthwhile taking an MBA as an individual – or sponsoring it as a company – depends on the organisation as much as the individual.

[7] *Which MBA? A Critical Guide To The World's Best Programmes*, EIU Addison Wesley 1992, revised annually (latest edition, 1997).

Before you start thinking seriously about taking an MBA, there are a few basic questions you should ask yourself:

- in this book we describe the pros and cons of full-time and part-time study, but whichever you choose, the MBA is a demanding and time-consuming programme. Would you describe yourself as persistent? Are you prepared to curtail severely your social life for the duration of the course? Is your partner prepared to go along with that? (The writer spoke to one student who took the precaution of divorcing her husband before she started her MBA!)
- part-time programmes (where study is combined with a daytime job) need strong employer support because inevitably there will be times, such as just before exams, when the demands of work and study are apt to clash. Have you spoken to your employers? Do they understand what's involved? Are they prepared to be understanding and flexible on such occasions?
- how are your finances? Though some programmes are more expensive than others, none of them are cheap. Have you drawn up a budget? Even a part-time programme may involve a loss of income if the time it takes up affects bonus payments. If your employer sponsors you financially to any substantial extent, remember that this will at least morally limit your freedom to move when you graduate
- what does your job involve? If you do, or are likely to do, a lot of travelling, a distance learning MBA (see Chapter 2) is the only sensible option
- would you consider yourself reasonably literate, numerate and articulate? You will need all these attributes
- are you a bit of a loner? If so, you will have problems, because group work is at least as important as individual study (unlike a first degree or professional qualification), certainly with full-time or part-time programmes
- why do you want to do an MBA? If you want to improve your skills, the middle-of-the-range school nearest to your home might be the most sensible choice. If you want a 'visiting card' MBA that will enhance your career or impress employers, talk to recruitment consultants, human resource managers and headhunters about which they regard as the top schools from that point of view

Choosing the options

Deciding to take an MBA is, as we have seen, primarily a career-building decision. Few people embark on it to pursue knowledge for its own sake so, as with any career decision, the choice of options must start with a consideration of your personal circumstances, lifestyle and values, as well as your objectives. For instance, the choice between taking a full-time course and a part-time or distance learning option may depend on whether you can afford to take a year off work. Within these two latter modes, whether you can operate on the basis of distance learning, or whether you need the stimulation of regular face to face contact with tutors and fellow students, will depend on the workstyle which best suits you.

However, schools increasingly recognise that students' circumstances may alter during their period of study. Switches between full and part-time modes are difficult to organise because of the different speeds at which these programmes run, but transferring from part-time to distance learning and vice versa is quite common, given the fact that over a period of three years, career moves, even within one company, may involve relocation.

The extent to which a course of study allows flexibility between modes is a point worth checking, as is the question of whether part of a course taken at one school might be recognised at another one if you were to move to another part of the country, since not all of them offer the option of continuing study by distance learning. Indeed, whether part of an MBA taken at School X is recognised by Schools Y or Z is itself a good test of the pedigree of School X's MBA.

Let us now look at the various modes in more detail and see what they entail.

The full-time MBA: two year programmes

Originally, most full-time courses were two-year programmes, based on the example of the MBA in the United States. London Business School, Manchester, Birmingham, and some highly regarded Continental European schools, such as Erasmus in Rotterdam, IESE and ESADE in Barcelona and Bocconi in Milan still offer 16 to 21-month programmes, but 12 months is generally the norm in Europe. In fact, the MBAs at INSEAD and IMD run under 12 months.

Though the content and teaching method of the full-time MBA is very similar, irrespective of how you do it, the proponents of the longer versions argue that it gives you more time to digest what you are learning and to combine study with a job search. 'On a one year MBA you've no sooner started when you've got to begin looking for a job for when you've graduated,' says one student at London Business School. 'The two year MBA gives you more time to consider your options.' The other great advantage that is put forward for this option is the summer internship that comes at the end of the first year. In an internship you spend some weeks on an in-depth consultancy assignment in a business or an organisation, at the end of which you produce a report for their senior management which is also an assessed assignment for your MBA. At most schools you get paid for this by the client – and it can be very well paid, to a point where it makes a substantial contribution to programme fees. The other plus factor is that it can, and often does, lead to a job offer from the client. It also gives you a taste – or otherwise – of a business sector or a firm in which you might be interested from a career point of view. Critics of the two-year model have made the point that someone with several years of work experience would have a fair idea of what they want to do anyway and would probably not need an internship to establish that. In response, quite a number of schools, even in the USA (Harvard Business School is a notable example), offer an accelerated version that cuts out the summer internship. On the whole, however, US schools have resisted the call to shorten their full-time programmes and have preferred to expand their part-time (executive) MBAs – in many cases with a massive investment in technological infrastructure – for those who do not want to give up two years to their studies.

The full-time MBA: one year programme

The one-year model is based on the length of time it normally takes to do a master's degree in other academic disciplines, but beware of assuming too much from the parallel. Whereas other master's courses will build to a large extent on your first degree, the MBA will involve a lot of skills that are entirely new to you. This is true even in the case of those who start with an advantage because of the nature of their previous qualification and/or experience. An accountant, for instance, will not previously have had much exposure to marketing, management strategy, organisational behaviour, or human resource management, all of which are part of the core programme all students have to go through. Conversely, a young general manager may not previously have had to get to grips with finance or quantitative methods at the level required by the course.

The common pattern of study events for a generalist MBA – irrespective of the mode by which it is taken – is that the first part of the course will consist of a crash programme covering all the core business skills, which are then examined. This is followed, or in some cases after the opening stages accompanied by, electives which allow students to focus on subjects that particularly interest them – they may, for instance, have some bearing on their future career direction – or where they can best bring their expertise to bear. The final part of the programme is usually a project carried out within a company, possibly their own employer in the case of a sponsored student. That is, or should be, more than a token gesture towards practicality. Students are given access to people and data; they are then expected to undertake a thorough analysis of the problem and to produce an action plan supported by quantified research.

But when all this has to be crammed into a year, it follows that study is very intensive. There is little time to stand back and relate it to your previous experience or to see where it applies to everyday management, and this may have some bearing on the criticisms about the MBA being 'too theoretical'. The schools are well aware of this and combat it in a number of ways. One is to use case studies, simulations and role play in their teaching, and to focus on learning in groups and syndicates, rather than passively sitting in a lecture room. So, right from the beginning of the programme, small groups of 6–10 students are put together by the faculty to reflect a variety of backgrounds, qualifications, experience, and nationalities. As a result, students often comment that they learn as much from each other as in the classroom. A further measure is to ensure that the various subjects are taught in an integrated way, showing how each topic relates to other disciplines; for instance, that a marketing decision will also have financial management implications. Some schools take this as far as teaching through themes – say the management of change – rather than by discipline. Others structure the course so that it all comes together in modules which deal specifically with business strategy.

Yet another way of keeping in touch with the 'real' world is through the project which comes in the final part of the course. In some cases this may involve seconding students to an employer, helping him (we will generally use this personal pronoun in a unisex sense in the Guide, though the proportion of women on MBA courses is around 25%) to solve a problem or manage a project in a quasi-consultancy role, and to write a dissertation based on that experience.

Many schools provide opportunities to take one or more electives abroad, or to undertake projects with a company outside the UK – or, in the case of schools abroad, for students to come to Britain for that purpose. A number of schools offer a direct link with sister bodies, mainly on the European continent, for this purpose. Some of these exchange arrangements, it is said, are little more than an excuse for a 'jolly' in some interesting capital, and need to be taken with a pinch of salt – but at best they offer the opportunity to undertake a term's study abroad, often linked to a project, which may be a way into the international job market.

A more pronounced trend is towards specialist MBAs in a particular discipline or business sector, such as the MBA in financial studies offered by Nottingham Business School, or the Public Sector MBAs at Aston, Henley, Birmingham, Nottingham and Exeter. Another Public Sector MBA is offered by a consortium of schools – Cranfield, the Imperial College and the Manchester Business School in conjunction with the Civil Service College – the students on which are sponsored by civil service departments. There are now said to be about 40 specialist MBAs on offer in the UK alone, including such exotic variants as one in football management at Liverpool University and one in church management at a theological school. Other interesting examples of what may be the shape of things to come are an MBA in luxury brand management offered, with the backing of some very blue chip companies in this field, by the ESSEC Graduate School of Management in Paris, an MBA in legal practice at Nottingham University Law School, another, newly launched MBA for lawyers at Manchester Business School and Glasgow Business School's MBA in healthcare and housing management. The core courses take you through the basic disciplines. The specialist focus is then developed in the electives or, as in the case of the Nottingham Public Services MBA in health and education, both there and through some additional core modules.

Advantages

- Suitable for those who want to switch career direction and to equip themselves with the conceptual management tools they need to do this; for instance, to switch from a functional specialism such as engineering to general management, or to move from the armed forces into a civilian career.
- Good campus atmosphere, based on a spirit of practical teamwork – exactly the direction management is now heading in practice.
- The intensity of the full-time programme, and the experience of living and working together closely during it, fosters a potentially lifelong network of contacts, at least some of whom will be tomorrow's business leaders.

Disadvantages
- In the words of Shelia Cameron in *The MBA Handbook*,[1] 'If the more difficult techniques are not practised while "fresh", there will be insufficient impetus ever to make the effort of applying them. By the end of a year's full-time study a student's head may feel completely stuffed with all that has been covered.'
- Full-time study inevitably means a career break; few employers will hold a job open for that length of time.
- Employer sponsorship is rare; therefore you have to consider loss of earnings.
- You have to live close to or on campus on full-time programmes; you may therefore have to move house for a year.

Watch out for
- The experience and background of current participants on the programme
- Since you will almost certainly be taking a career break, check how much attention is paid to career management aspects. Are job-hunting and self-development skills part of the programme? What is the average length of time it takes to get a job after graduation? Which organisations regularly recruit there, for what kind of jobs, and at which salary package levels?

Part-time courses

UK business schools which offer full-time MBAs generally also run part-time MBA courses. In talking about part-time programmes, one has to distinguish between a number of species and two particular varieties:

The Part-time MBA

The part-time MBA itself is usually taught in the evening, at weekends, or sometimes via day release attendance. Most programmes also include a mandatory residential element of roughly one week per term, plus some weekends. The average length of such programmes is about two and a half years. Most students on them are sponsored by their employers to varying degrees, ranging from full to partial financial support with fees, to merely being given time off at critical periods, such as before examinations. The latter, in fact, is a minimum requirement for anyone thinking of doing a part-time course. There will inevitably be conflicts between work and study, study and family, or other commitments. Part-time courses may also involve a good deal of travel, unless the school of your choice is a local one. A further factor to consider, is whether your job itself involves a significant amount of travel; in that case, a part-time course would probably not be suitable. Part-time MBAs are sometimes confusingly referred to as Executive MBAs (see below).

The Modular MBA

Properly speaking, the Modular MBA – somewhat confusingly also called the Executive MBA by some schools (but see below) – could be described as the management equivalent of a block release course. Modular, in this context is, or should be, written with a capital M to distinguish it from another sense in which the term is used: that of teaching material packaged in such a way that it can be digested in conveniently-sized chunks, or modules. It involves 'fillings' of full-time attendance, over extended periods and on numerous occasions, at a business school chosen by the employer, between layers of normal work. That, for instance, is the pattern at Ashridge Management College. The Modular MBA is usually, though not exclusively, a sponsored form of study, and involves closer involvement by the sponsoring company, who may want to have a considerable input into parts of the programme, notably projects and the final dissertation.

[1] *op.cit.*

Professor Leo Murray, Director of the Cranfield School of Management, described the Cranfield Executive MBA as 'a triangular relationship between the school, the individual, and the sponsoring company'. The course responds to the development needs of the individual, but it does so in the light of the skills and competencies required by his or her sponsor. Thus the latter has a good deal of input into the Executive MBA to ensure that corporate needs are taken into account and that the course content reflects what is happening in the 'real' world of business. Generally, company representatives are encouraged to visit the school on a regular basis. **The Executive MBA**

One advantage of that triangular relationship is that traffic runs both ways. The process of consulting with the school helps the sponsor to define strategic aims, while keeping the school in constant touch with corporate needs 'outside'. The student is the beneficiary of both aspects. Cranfield, indeed, suggests that students on the Executive MBA should have 'some form of written agreement before the programme begins', in which the sponsor should spell out exactly what benefits the organisation hopes to gain by sending the individual concerned on to the course, what support will be provided by the sponsor, and what information on the progress of the student he is entitled to request. As management changes may mean that even an apparently powerful sponsor may not be there by the time the student is halfway through the programme, this seems to be a sensible idea.

Whether or not such an agreement is in place, anyone who takes this kind of executive, modular MBA will need to be certain of company support at every level – not just the financial one, and not just at the top. As in the case of part-time MBAs, your immediate boss will need to be understanding about your need to take time off for study and will, on occasion, have to distribute your workload to allow for your commitment to the course. Some superiors, particularly those who are sceptical about the value of the MBA, or who fear for their own career prospects when you have got your qualification, may be hard to convince.

There may also be practical difficulties about doing this kind of executive MBA in individual cases. As with the part-time course it would not, for instance, be a suitable mode of study for someone whose job involves a lot of travel, unless the employer was able and willing to schedule this accordingly, in line with the programme timetable. However, given that commitment to the concept of the modular or executive MBA on the part of the organisation exists, the schools are nervous about the possibility that he who pays the piper may wish to call the tune; in other words, that academic integrity may be impaired. The fear is that schools which come to be too heavily dependent on direct or indirect sponsorship, may be pressed by sponsors either to lower their admission standards, or to make the degree easier to get, or to make the MBA a glorified form of vocational training rather than an intellectually rigorous business qualification. Here again, the accreditation criteria set out by the Association will help in keeping the triangular relationship an isosceles one.

This is a variant of the modular or executive form, by which a small group of sponsors band together and jointly fund a programme tailored to the development needs of their management cadre, while at the same time allowing **The Consortium MBA** a degree of the intellectually stimulating networking that is one of the key features of open programmes. Some of the leading schools have been reluctant to support consortium MBA programmes because they were worried about the possibility of undue influence on the content by sponsors. But this has not happened in practice, and there are signs that sentiment is changing more in their favour, though consortium programmes have not grown as much as was forecast. The administrative problems of keeping coherent groups of sponsors together are probably a contributory factor here. However, there are examples of very successful consortium programmes: the one which has been run by Lancaster University Management School since 1989 is a case in point.

The Single Company MBA

Single company MBAs are also delivered by part-time study in executive MBA or modular form. Like the consortium MBA, they were opposed by some of the major schools but the schools are having to yield to pressure from the market where the tendency is for big firms to integrate an MBA with their own senior management development initiatives. 'Relationships with companies have become more complex to reflect their own complex needs, often entailing a whole range of interventions,' as the head of one school put it.[1] In fact, some successful examples are already well established – the ones run by Lancaster University Management School and British Airways, and Bradford's with the BBC and Allied Domecq come to mind, while Henley runs single company MBAs with 20 different companies in a variety of sectors. More recent examples are the programme Warwick is doing with Arthur Andersen and Cranfield's with Vickers. Opposition to single company MBAs is based on the concern that when people from one company and one corporate culture come together, the opportunities for learning from diversity are limited. There may also be less openness when you feel that colleagues are looking over your shoulder, noting your progress – and your mistakes. A single company MBA also limits the 'employability' which the degree confers.

These views, however, are very much contested by proponents of the single company MBA. They argue that large organisations already contain enough diversity of culture, activity, gender and culture to overcome these problems. In any case the trend that is developing in the single company MBA is that only some core modules and/or some electives are tailored for the sponsor. The rest are run as open programmes. An example is the MBA that Warwick Business School, in partnership with Manchester Business School, runs for the accountancy firm, Arthur Andersen. Partnerships between schools (not in the past noted for co-operation), possibly even schools in different countries, to run single company MBAs could be a significant new trend.[2]

These varieties of part-time MBA are structurally similar to the full-time course, and are identical in the content of the core material. The main differences are firstly that they take longer, and secondly that they may offer a smaller range of electives. The usual length is 18 months to two years for a Modular MBA, and two to three years for a part-time MBA. Of the various modes, the part-time MBA is by far the most popular.

[1] 'Your Ticket to Ride', the *Independent*, 23 October 1997.
[2] 'How Three Into One Makes the Perfect MBA', the *Independent*, 24 September 1997.

- You don't have to give up your day-time job; there is no loss of earnings.

- You can immediately apply what you have learned; equally, you and other participants can bring 'live' material from your work to the programme.
- Employers are far more ready to sponsor programmes which do not involve a career break.
- Regular attendance imposes its own study routines.
- You come into regular and stimulating contact with participants from other sectors and disciplines.

- There can be enormous pressures on combining work with study, especially before exams and when meeting assignment deadlines; negotiating employer and family/partner support is vital.

- Employer support, whatever form it takes, might put you under a moral obligation as far as your career plans are concerned.
- Where single company or consortium programmes are too employer-specific, what you learn may lack transferability to another organisation, should you wish to move.
- Although participants in part-time programmes do sometimes jet in from abroad, they are hardly likely to come from outside Europe. There is therefore less of a global element in the programme.

- You will need to check carefully how much of the course is taught by full-time, 'first division' faculty members and how accessible they are out of teaching hours.

- Do not forget that part-time programmes may involve travel as well as attendance and study time. An evening programme involving more than an hour's driving each way may not be a good idea. Weekend programmes, running on Friday afternoons and all day Saturday, have proved more popular for that reason.
- Extra expenditure. Does travel add significantly to costs? Does the fee include residence at weekends or during residential weeks (usually one per term)?
- Weekend and evening opening hours of the library and other facilities.

The content and, broadly speaking, the structure, of the distance learning MBA is exactly the same as for other modes, but the method of delivery is obviously very different.

Its most familiar form to the public at large is that of OU courses, and indeed, the OU Business School (OUBS) MBA is now the largest Association of MBAs-accredited programme of its kind in the UK, though the Henley Distance Learning MBA is the longest established and has the bigger worldwide enrolment. Distance learning courses can be undertaken by students at their own initiative, but like other forms of part-time study, they require enormous application as well as support from employers, at least in terms of keeping the normal workloads of one's everyday job down to manageable proportions.

The difference between open and distance learning is somewhat blurred. Some schools say there is none, and indeed, both Henley and the OU have been known to refer to their distance learning courses as 'open learning'. The Association distinguishes between the two types in saying that open learning courses include at least some elements which call for mandatory attendance by students in person. Usually this is of the order of once or twice a term, though the Kingston University open learning MBA has a full-time weekend once a month backed up by its own specially written course material which students use to prepare for these sessions. That makes it closer to a part-time MBA than what is generally regarded as distance learning.

Estimates of student numbers on distance learning programmes vary. The Open University claims to have 4 000 students on its MBA programme, and since it estimates that these make up 40% of total distance learning enrolments in the UK, it follows that there are 10 000 students following this mode of study in the UK. Some claim that the numbers are much larger, but Jill Ford of Henley Management College believes that this is because some non-accredited schools allow students to select modules out of their programme and then count them as MBA students, though they may not intend to do the full degree. Henley Management College, the next largest, says it has about 2 500 UK students and a further 2 500 abroad, making it the market leader in distance learning worldwide. Other schools whose distance learning programmes have been accredited by the Association are Aston, Warwick, Strathclyde and Durham. In addition to these Aston's part-time MBA can be taken off-campus and Kingston's open learning MBA combines elements of part-time and distance learning.

Gaining an MBA by distance learning normally takes at least three years. The students on such courses are often self-funded – though reportedly a high proportion of those at the OUBS are financed wholly or partly by their employers – and they include a considerable number of expatriates. In fact, distance learning is particularly suitable for those whose jobs are mobile, or who cannot make a commitment to specific periods of study, as in the case of the Part-time MBA, or who simply live too far from the nearest business school in the UK. Indeed the Association suggests that an MBA by distance learning at an accredited school might be considered as an alternative to going to a local one that is not accredited.

Distance learning MBAs assume that you can apply and relate what you are learning within an organisation. That can be a problem for those who do not have a context within which to do this. Conversely, though, the feedback between learning and applicability at work makes distance learning, like its part-time counterpart, an attractive proposition for sponsoring employers. IBM, for instance, is reported to be sponsoring as many as 700 students for the Open University's MBA and has switched financial support from full-time MBAs to distance learning ones.[3] The course will provide you with all the materials you need, and a lot of it will have been specially written for the course. The words of Sheila Cameron's *MBA Handbook* cannot be bettered as a succinct explanation:[4]

> 'A good distance learning course will provide you with all the materials you need for your study, saving you hours of time chasing elusive materials. Furthermore, these . . . should be written specifically for the course . . . teaching objectives are made very clear

[3] 'Learning While Earning Income,' *Financial Times,* 19 January 1998.
[4] *op.cit.*

so that the student knows what should be achieved by the end of the part of the course being worked on, material is broken up into 'chunks' which can normally be studied at a single sitting. A study calendar is provided so that the student knows what should be achieved by each point of the course. Most importantly, the material is as interactive as possible, asking the student at regular intervals to think about what has been read, and apply it to his or her own job context. There should also be regular exercises and self-test questions, with answers provided, so that the student can check understanding of one part of the material before progressing to the next. Written text will be supplemented by video and audio material . . . a video has the advantage of allowing replay of difficult bits'.

These are also broadly the criteria applied by the Association in its accreditation policy for distance learning programmes. In particular, these stress the importance of logistical support, tutor contact, the existence of a core staff dedicated solely to the distance learning programme, interaction with fellow course members, and periodic updating – at least every five years – of course materials.

Sheila Cameron's point about checking understanding of these materials goes some way to answering a question which the writer overheard at one of the distance learning exhibits at an MBA fair. The questioner was very typical of someone interested in this MBA mode: an export manager who spent a good deal of his time abroad. He wanted to find out how, working on his own, he would know that he was really grasping what he had read. The answer is that each student has a personal tutor who can be contacted when required, either about the subject matter itself, or about problems such as difficulties in keeping a deadline. That may itself be a problem, however, for students in locations abroad with poor communications.

They may also have a problem with the residential element in the so-called open MBA version, where occasional weekends at which students get together are mandatory. In that case, employer sponsorship may be necessary. For instance, the Standard Chartered Bank, which runs a company-based distance learning MBA with Henley, pays for flights from as far away as Australia.

One factor that is having a big influence on the rapid growth of distance learning, is the speed of developments in information technology. Henley Management College has been particularly active in this area, and pioneered the use of Lotus Notes in its programme in the early nineties. They are a groupware product which enable students and tutors anywhere in the world to keep in contact with each other and with the School: a form of 'electronic classroom' in which participants can communicate by email, exchange study tips, access databases, and engage in conferences and discussions, with the tutor listening and commenting on the proceedings, irrespective of geographical and time zone barriers. Some interaction, incidentally, is purely social – one school even has an electronic 'coffee room' for this purpose. As the Open University Business School's Tony Stapleton comments, the social club element is 'an opportunity for students to familiarise themselves with the medium by sharing thoughts and opinions on topics that are not necessarily course-related'.

Like a number of other distance learning tutors, he believes that the next big move in this sector will be in the direction of video conferencing. At present this is very expensive, but is almost certain to follow the general trend in IT for costs to decrease and speed to increase.

Case studies and reading matters associated with assignments are now also sent via email, rather than as hard copy in the post. This has speeded up turnround time considerably, though some have found that reading from a screen is very tiring. A more telling argument in favour is that it also enables tutors to respond much more quickly when finished work is delivered late. Advances in information technology are also simplifying the administration of programmes, enabling Henley, for instance, to have a fluid programme of starting dates. Lotus Notes have been introduced by Cranfield and Warwick on their part-time programmes, while Henley itself has launched a multimedia course. Other schools, such as INSEAD, are putting case studies on CD-Rom, while at the Open University CD-Roms have been introduced as an integral part of the distance learning programme. Another development being mooted in some quarters is to introduce elements of distance learning into core courses on the part-time programme.

Advantages
- It's ideal if your job involves a lot of travel or if you're a long way from a good school or working abroad.
- You're freer to work at your own pace; distance learning programmes can extend over as much as seven years, though it's been found that students go off the boil if they spin it out over much more than five years.
- As with other forms of part-time learning, you can combine it with your day-time job and what you learn can be applied right away.

Disadvantages
- Not so suitable unless you're working as a manager, because you won't be able to put much of what you learn into context.
- In addition to the time commitment, it requires a great deal of self-discipline to continue if you are studying on your own.
- Face-to-face contact with other students, as individuals or in groups, and with the faculty is limited; indeed, there are some programmes (though not ones that are accredited by the Association) where this is not even a requirement.
- There is a danger that schools may overdo reliance on transmitting learning materials electronically or putting them on CD-Roms; reading from a screen for long periods is very tiring, while downloading on to hard copy is cumbersome unless you have a very fast printer.

Watch out for
- The quality of the study materials; are they specially written or produced for the programme or 'off the shelf'?
- Administrative efficiency. How quickly are assignments turned round? The speed with which your initial enquiries are answered should give you a clue.
- The loneliness of the long-distance student: how accessible are faculty if you run into difficulties? Are there any fellow students nearby who could form the basis of a study group?
- Your computing skills and keyboard speeds; they need to be good if you are to keep up with the work.
- Drop-out rates. Schools will tell you that the drop-out rates are very low, but this is a bit disingenuous where they count inactive participants among their students. They may simply have given up without telling the school. The crunch question is how many of those enrolled are still paying their fees after four years.

Questions are often asked about the transferability of modes of study, say from **Transfer-** part-time to distance learning, or between one management school and another – **ability** sometimes in different countries.

In general, there are no problems if you want to transfer between modes within the same school. It is not uncommon, for instance, for someone on a part-time programme to be relocated by their employer to a place from which attendance at weekly evening classes becomes impractical. Distance learning then becomes the only option. Another situation which schools are now encountering, is when a student on a part-time or distance learning programme loses their job part way through the course. They may then seek to speed the completion of their degree – and possibly enhance their value in the job market – by switching to the full-time mode, sometimes with financial help from their employer as part of their severance package.

Schools are now very flexible about this, and as we indicated earlier, some foresee that MBA courses might in general adopt different modes of delivery for different parts of the programme, and to meet individual circumstances. Bradford, for instance, already has a 'full-time' programme which can be taken at the rate of one term a year over three years.

The difficulty arises when students want to transfer from one school to another – for instance, from a part-time MBA at one school to a distance learning programme at another; not all offer such a programme. Although in theory there are schemes for doing this, in practice, whether or not a student wishing to transfer between schools will be accepted, depends sometimes on policy (Bradford, for instance, will not accept transferees from other schools), or on a subjective view by the programme director of the standing of the course from which transfer is being sought, though the quality of the work the applicant has already done would be taken into account. Therefore, a move between schools requires advance planning, and it would be advisable, even at the application stage, to consider the possibility that your circumstances might change over the three years of a part-time course. You cannot assume that because you have completed two terms at School A, School B will accept you for the final part.

This is also true of the transferability of credits gained from other business courses, such as the Diploma in Management Studies (DMS), to MBA programmes. In theory, the 70 credits obtained for a DMS could be applied to the 120 which are required for an MBA, but in practice these are widely seen as two quite different fields of study. However, some business schools offer the possibility of a transfer from a Diploma in Management Studies to an MBA course. Aston, Durham, Henley and the OU, for instance, come into this category. Indeed, at the latter, taking a Diploma in Professional Management is the route into Stage One of the MBA for those who do not have a recognised academic qualification, while at Bristol Business School a pass of 65% or over in its Diploma of Management Studies gives exemption to the first year of its 30-month part-time MBA.

However, students strongly advise against taking a Diploma in order to 'dip your toe into the water'. Although there is some convergence between certain MBA core programmes and the DMS, the general opinion is that if you are serious about taking an MBA, it is best to 'go the whole hog' from the start.

Exemptions Another question that business schools are often asked, is whether professional qualifications or a specialist degree confers exemptions in any of the core programmes. Do you, for instance, have to take the finance and accounting module if you are a chartered accountant, or the quantitative methods module if you have a degree in maths or statistics?

Practice varies. The OUBS will grant exemptions to Stage 1 of its course to accountants with a qualification from a recognised body, though it stresses that a purely academic exposure to a particular subject, however relevant, would not necessarily be grounds for an exemption from it on the course. Other leading schools take the view that even if you think you know a subject inside out, the programme and the contact with other students will make you see it from a new perspective. They also take the view that the presence of experts in a particular area is essential to effective group work and the trading of ideas that is such an important part of the learning process.

The short answer is then, not to take the availability of exemptions for granted in looking over the contents of a programme. The best assumption, in the case of a major school, is probably to assume that they will not be forthcoming.

The MBA and the Internet One issue that has been widely discussed in the past couple of years is the possibility of offering an MBA in cyberspace. So far there has been only one example of this possible new variant in the UK, at a small unaccredited school. The general view is that the Internet will play a growing role in supplementing traditional teaching, possibly in helping students prepare for a class or syndicate work by putting readings, graphics or directions to relevant websites on an Internet which can be accessed with a password. However, Richard Kerley, director of the full-time MBA at Edinburgh University Management School, makes the point that the sophisticated technology to bring teaching via the Internet or an Intranet up to the standards of television, is a long way from being in place as yet and that very few teachers have mastered the art of talking to camera. Thus, what is available so far is hard copy that can be downloaded or printed out. On the other hand, email is widely and increasingly used by students to communicate among themselves and with the teaching faculty. Indeed one school has already had to issue a set of guidelines to students to warn them about indiscriminately bombarding faculty with emails.

Further incursions by information technology into the sphere of business teaching is perhaps, just a matter of time, which is why the pioneering efforts of schools like the Open University Business School and that of the unaccredited programme at Middlesex University are being at least watched with interest by some schools in the UK. The lead may come from the USA, where leading business schools with their huge access to private funding have the resources that are needed to finance fully fledged electronic classrooms operating interactive courses through a mix of CD-Roms and the Internet, as described by two Wharton professors in a recent book.[5]

[5] J.Y. Wind and J. Main, *Driving Change*, (1998) Kogan Page.

Choosing a school

Accreditation by the Association of MBAs is, as we have said earlier, a significant mark of quality assurance, but out of the list of 33 schools in the UK, and 17 in continental Europe, which offer programmes that come into this category, one of the questions that the Association is most frequently asked is: which school is the best? There are also variants of this: 'I have been offered a place at X, Y and Z – which is the one you would recommend?' or: 'I am thinking of applying to B – is it any good?' Such questions reflect the growing importance of the provenance of one's MBA, but there are good reasons why it is difficult to give a meaningful answer to them.

The situation is more straightforward in the USA, where ranking lists of the top 10 or top 20 business schools are published from time to time in magazines such as *Business Week*, *Fortune* or *U.S. News & World Report*. The most recent survey comes from the latter and was issued on 2 March 1998.

Why is there no similar ranking for Europe, or at any rate, none that has achieved any degree of acceptance? One reason is that the US experience has been that there is a commercial value in being a ranked school – they get both more applications from students and more consultancy assignments for the faculty – so vigorous lobbying by PR firms can have an undue influence. Another is that the quality of a business school depends a good deal on who is on the faculty at the time. The loss – or gain – of one or two key professors can change the standing of a whole institution and make a nonsense of its ranking. Faculty movements can certainly have a considerable impact on your choice if the person concerned is working in the fields in which you are most interested.

The other factor is that judgements about business schools are not only subjective from the point of view of the person making the report, but also from that of the prospective student. The question is not: how good is the school? It is: how good is it in the light of your career development needs, work situation, personal circumstances, and preferred learning styles?

Looking at choice from that point of view there may, for some people, even be a case for considering a non-Associated accredited school, provided that they meet some of the broad criteria set out in this section. A self-funded person who wanted to enhance their general management skills – perhaps in order to run their own small business more effectively – who had rejected the distance learning mode, and who did not live near an accredited school, might well consider a local, unaccredited one. It might not carry much weight in the job market, but if that was not your object, it would undoubtedly help you to be a more effective manager. In such cases, incidentally, it would be important to look at the electives as well as the core programme. Do they correspond to your needs, and are they offered by faculty members with a credible track record in that field?

Graduate Schools of Business ranked by the *U.S. News*

Rank/School	Overall score	Reputation rank by academics	Reputation rank by recruiters
1. Harvard University (MA)	100.0	2	1
1. Stanford University (CA)	100.0	1	6
3. Columbia University (NY)	99.0	9	10
3. Massachusetts Institute of Technology (Sloan)	99.0	2	5
3. University of Pennsylvania (Wharton)	99.0	2	3
6. Northwestern University (Kellogg) (IL)	98.0	2	2
6. University of Chicago	98.0	2	9
8. Dartmouth College (Tuck) (NH)	97.0	11	13
8. Univ. of California–Los Angeles (Anderson)	97.0	11	15
10. Duke University (Fuqua) (NC)	96.0	9	7
10. University of California–Berkeley (Haas)	96.0	7	14
10. University of Michigan–Ann Arbor	96.0	8	4
10. University of Virginia (Darden)	96.0	11	8
14. New York University (Stern)	95.0	16	16
15. Carnegie Mellon University (PA)	93.0	14	17
15. Univ. of N.C.-Chapel Hill (Kenan-Flagler)	93.0	16	11
15. University of Texas–Austin	93.0	19	12
15. Yale University (CT)	93.0	18	19
19. Cornell University (Johnson) (NY)	92.0	14	18
20. University of Rochester (Simon) (NY)	91.0	21	27
21. Emory University (Goizueta) (GA)	90.0	29	25
21. Indiana University–Bloomington	90.0	19	20
21. University of Southern California	90.0	23	33
24. Purdue University (Krannert) (IN)	89.0	21	21
25. Ohio State University (Fisher)	88.0	29	28
25. Vanderbilt University (Owen) (TN)	88.0	23	23
27. Michigan State University (Broad)	86.0	36	32
27. University of Maryland–College Park	86.0	36	44
27. University of Minnesota–Twin Citites (Carlson)	86.0	23	34
30. Georgetown University (DC)	85.0	36	24
31. Am. Grad. Sch. of Intl. Mgmt. (Thunderbird) (AZ)	84.0	33	22
31. Arizona State University–Main Campus	84.0	36	50
31. Case Western Reserve Univ. (Weatherhead) (OH)	84.0	23	35
31. Georgia Institute of Technology	84.0	47	39
31. Pennsylvania State University (Smeal)	84.0	29	29
31. Tulane University (Freeman) (LA)	84.0	47	47
31. University of California–Davis	84.0	53	63
31. Washington University (Olin) (MO)	84.0	23	31
39. College of William and Mary (VA)	82.0	61	40
39. University of Arizona (Eller)	82.0	36	42
39. University of Georgia (Terry)	82.0	36	55
39. Wake Forest University (Babcock) (NC)	82.0	47	42
43. University of California–Irvine	81.0	44	59
43. University of Notre Dame (IN)	81.0	47	30
43. University of Tennessee–Knoxville	81.0	53	58
46. Brigham Young University (Marriott) (UT)	80.0	53	36
46. University of Florida	80.0	36	53
46. University of Pittsburgh (Katz)	80.0	33	38
46. University of Washington	80.0	33	40
50. Texas A&M University–College Station	79.0	47	51

Sources: *US News* and the schools. Reputational surveys conducted by Market Facts Inc. Response rates to reputational survey: academics, 58%; corporate recruiters, 34%. * signifies a *US News* estimate.

& World Report survey

Student selectivity rank	Placement success rank	Average '97 GMAT score	'97 average undergrad GPA	'97 average acceptance rate	'97 median starting salary	Employed 3 mos. after graduation	'97 out-of-state tuition and fees
3	1	674	3.50	13.8%	$82,000	99.1%	$25,000
1	1	712	3.59	7.3%	$80,000	99.1%	$24,000
3	1	670	3.45	13.1%	$88,000	98.3%	$26,180
2	7	675	3.50	13.8%	$75,000	97.7%	$25,800
3	5	674	3.45	14.5%	$75,000	98.9%	$24,570
8	7	673	3.40	16.2%	$75,000	98.0%	$24,351
8	5	676	3.42	27.0%	$75,000	98.7%	$25,255
8	4	667	3.40	11.5%	$75,000	100.0%	$24,900
3	7	670	3.50	15.9%	$75,000	98.9%	$20,093
12	11	660	3.33	18.9%	$71,600	98.8%	$25,362
3	14	675	3.40	10.9%	$75,000	96.0%	$19,378
12	13	662	3.32	22.3%	$70,000	99.5%	$24,185
12	7	660	3.30	15.8%	$71,000	100.0%	$20,429
12	11	657	3.30	19.7%	$75,000	97.0%	$25,500
22	14	640	3.20	29.9%	$70,000	98.1%	$23,100
19	16	640	3.20	18.3%	$68,000	96.9%	$17,017
16	18	645	3.35	28.3%	$65,000	97.8%	$14,912
8	18	679	3.38	25.7%	$70,000	95.9%	$24,305
22	21	637	3.24	30.1%	$68,000	94.4%	$24,260
22	16	631	3.26	31.8%	$66,000	98.7%	$25,092
22	18	630	3.30	31.8%	$65,000	99.1%	$22,800
22	27	634	3.30	37.1%	$64,900	94.0%	$16,229
22	21	640	3.20	34.6%	$67,000	95.6%	$23,466
39	21	615	3.11	26.4%	$61,900	99.1%	$14,872
33	21	621	3.20	26.8%	$65,000	94.7%	$14,058
33	30	625	3.20	36.1%	$64,000	94.7%	$23,140
33	27	614	3.30	42.6%	$59,908	96.0%	$11,828
16	35	646	3.34	26.3%	$55,000	97.0%	$13,011
48	25	600	3.22	36.9%	$61,250	98.3%	$15,176
29	37	631	3.19	34.3%	$64,500	90.4%	$22,870
48	37	590	3.44	55.9%	$60,000	91.9%	$19,890
39	25	609	3.26	40.4%	$62,500	97.4%	$10,710
48	37	608	3.20	41.0%	$55,750	95.2%	$21,000
33	30	632	3.20	45.0%	$55,000	95.4%	$11,440
48	37	601	3.15	24.6%	$58,000	94.1%	$13,809
19	35	637	3.40	34.2%	$56,000	96.5%	$22,066
16	27	660	3.20	30.1%	$60,000	95.0%	$19,450
39	45	606	3.23	35.2%	$60,000	88.4%	$21,900
33	30	620	3.25	34.4%	$58,800	95.1%	$16,042
29	51	610	3.39	34.5%	$54,000	90.8%	$9,712
29	44	630	3.12	22.1%	$53,000	96.1%	$9,630
39	37	615	3.20	44.1%	$53,000	96.6%	$19,300
19	51	637	3.30	29.0%	$55,000	95.6%	$20,011
48	37	615	3.10	42.0%	$60,000	91.9%	$20,640
39	30	610	3.20	27.4%	$55,700	94.3%	$8,112
29	51	620	3.47	47.6%	$57,530	86.7%	$7,460
48	45	600	3.20	39.4%	$55,000	94.8%	$11,294
60	45	612	3.16	62.6%	$55,000	93.5%	$28,354
22	72	630	3.32	30.7%	$54,000	83.7%	$13,166
33	51	605	3.38	37.5%	$51,255	95.5%	$9,841

Reproduced by permission of *US News & World Report*.

The question of what you, personally, hope to get out of it also casts some light on another aspect of choice about which the Association is often asked. What are the relative merits of going to a business school in the USA or in Continental Europe, as compared to the UK? There is no absolute answer to such questions, except to say that going to a school abroad would have an obvious value if you were planning to work in the country concerned.

However, an increasing number of commentators are asking for how much longer, in a world of global trading and IT-based techniques and corporate strategies, we can really think about business education in national terms. On both sides of the Channel, and to some extent the Atlantic as well, an increasing number of schools are establishing a variety of links with their counterparts in other countries.

These relationships are becoming increasingly formalised, as shown by the development of such alliances as the Community of European Management Schools (CEMS) and the Alliance of Management Schools in European Capitals (AMSEC). Another grouping is the European Network of Business Schools, set up between Bradford Management Centre, Groupe ESC Atlantique in Nantes, and the Universidad Commercial de Deusto in Bilbao. Participants spend one term each in Spain, France and the UK, taking courses in the language of the country and undertaking projects with local firms, eventually graduating with a European MBA.

Other schools are going down the collaborative road with varying degrees of directness. One major problem is the difference between the structure of education in different countries, so that, for instance, it takes very much longer to gain a first degree in Germany than it does in Britain. However, some very close relationships with European partners are already in existence, which in the case of Bradford goes as far as offering a Bradford MBA through a Dutch partner, the Netherlands Institute for MBA Studies (NIMBAS). Another variant is the double French and British MBA offered by Cranfield and EM Lyon. A more common route, however, is that of completing the core programme at home, after which participants can spend one, or even two, terms of their course as exchange students in another country, mostly within the EU, though the geographical spread is widening. London Business School's exchange network, to take another instance, covers the USA, Latin America, the Far East, and Australasia, as well as a number of countries in Europe.

It is very likely that various forms of the 'multi-centre MBA' will expand among all European business schools, and possibly US schools as well. The past year has also seen a sharp rise in the numbers of specialist International MBAs, based on a common core and a menu of international electives involving a period of study abroad. The quality of these electives depends on the quality of the other schools participating in such schemes. A further variant is the introduction by Warwick Business School of one-week international modules taught on-site abroad to capitalise on local knowledge of the topic in question.

What these various forms of internationalisation of all or parts of the MBA programme have in common is the opportunity for attachment to, or work on, a project with a local company. One of its main attractions from a career point of view, is that it gives students access to job markets in more than one country.

There can, however, be other good reasons for doing an MBA abroad. Asked why she took her MBA at INSEAD, one recent graduate from there said she thought it would be more fun and also a good way of improving her French.

Though subjective judgements and gut feeling do play an important part in choice, there are, nevertheless, some objective criteria which can also be applied. Some are those used by the Association in its accreditation policy, which we have mentioned in the introduction. In the end though, it is a question of applying one's own set of comparisons to a range of criteria, some of which relate to the programme itself, others of which could be described as contextual:

The crunch quesions

- Reputation
- Campus size and culture
- The selectiveness of its entrance requirements
- Programme content and duration
- Fees
- Quality of faculty and the student body
- Nature and quality of the school's research activities
- Internationalism
- Flexibility of delivery modes
- Administrative efficiency (particularly in the case of distance learning courses)
- Links with business and industry
- Facilities and location
- Accommodation (particularly on full-time programmes)
- Success/failure rates
- Career services, placement record, and exit salaries
- Alumni network.

Let us now focus on some of these factors in more detail.

For a majority of prospective MBA students, reputation is probably the most important single factor in the choice of a school, aware as they are that where you gained your MBA now weighs more heavily with prospective employers than the fact that you have one at all. The problem is that many employers are remarkably ignorant about business schools, and will only have heard of LBS, Harvard, and a handful of others which will probably include those in their own part of the country. The spread of specialist MBAs also means that schools are building a reputation in particular disciplines and functional areas. Some other useful indicators about reputation are:

Reputation

- which companies in any field in which you are interested recruit, fund research, or take students for projects from there
- the extent to which its alumni are currently working in areas in which you are interested; this information can often be gleaned from the school's brochure
- whether blue chip or significant public sector organisations encourage staff to take short courses there

However, the measure that is most often queried, particularly by prospective students abroad who do not have access to the domestic grapevine, is the school's standing in published surveys and rankings. These are less prevalent in the UK than in Continental Europe and the USA, and have generally been attended by fierce controversy when they have appeared. What, to take just one difficulty, is being measured: teaching or research?

Both of these come under the scrutiny in England of the Higher Education Funding Council (HEFC), which awards five grades for research (a starred 5 is the highest), and three grades for teaching: excellent, satisfactory, and unsatisfactory. The last of these has never been used, which rather puts teaching alongside those products which only exist in giant and king-sized packets, but never in small ones. As the *Financial Times* has observed,[1] 'an 'excellent' rating is a genuine feather in an institution's cap, but 'satisfactory' is very broad'.

How useful, then, are the more finely tuned research ratings – bearing in mind that a school like Cranfield, persistently rated as 'excellent' for its teaching, does not quite get into the first division for its research? There is much debate about how to strike a fine balance between practical applicability and the traditional academic view that research must advance knowledge and validate its findings.[2] In a subject such as management, an attempt to do the latter can result in proving the obvious in a blizzard of footnotes and equations in some academic journal only read by other academics.

The schools themselves are divided. Some say that research feeds back into management, consultancy, and teaching; others claim that the HEFC assessments are rather dismissive about what is called 'near market' (i.e. practical) research. Perhaps the best way of evaluating the use of a research rating from a student's or a sponsor's point of view is to look at its current research topics.

In addition to this, there are two acid tests. One is this hypothetical question to alumni: would you go there again, given the chance? The other concerns accreditation. There is catch here. The list on page 359 shows schools whose MBA programme is Association accredited. But some of these schools – they shall be nameless – also offer another MBA, more controversial because of content or method of delivery, which is not. The moral of the story is that MBA accredits individual programmes, not schools. When in doubt, always check the Association of MBAs accreditation. You may even find that a school that had lost its accreditation has subsequently been re-accredited.

Campus size and culture   The importance of the 'fit' between your own values and the culture of the organisation has received growing attention in career literature. It is equally crucial in the case of choosing where to study for your MBA, particularly in the case of the full-time and part-time modes. In the first place, it is essential to visit the school and talk to students and the faculty. All schools have open days for this purpose. Do you actually like the people there? Are you in tune with the way they talk, dress, and behave? What can they tell you about the teaching style? Some places are competitive and confrontational, others have more of a

---

[1] 'Business Schools: An A–Z Guide', 17 October 1994.
[2] *Building Partnerships: Enhancing the Quality of Management Research*, Commission on Management Research 1994.

collegiate culture. There are also differences in the accessibility of the faculty. British schools score well on this one. Many of them have also taken over the American practice of some form of upward assessment on the performance of faculty, such as Cranfield's so-called 'happy sheet'. A good question to ask any students with whom you feel a rapport is whether, given the chance, they would choose that particular school again, knowing what they now know about it. Many would say that an informal visit is advisable, even where a school also holds informal off-site receptions or formal open days, as most do.

From the point of view of personality and temperament, it would be a great mistake to think that a business school is just a place where you learn a set of functional skills and mind your own business the rest of the time. Group and project work is a key part of the course, so interpersonal relationships are important. Admittedly, you cannot forecast the configuration of your cohort of students from the current one, but the percentage mix of ages, genders, nationalities, business experience, and educational qualifications in the current cohort will give you a fair idea of the nature of the student population and the school's admission policy. This can be compared with research produced by the Association on the educational background of its members.

Educational Background

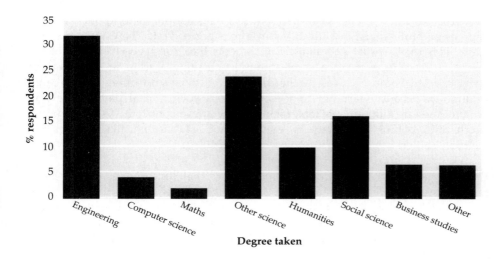

Overall 81% of respondents had degrees, nearly half of which were either Firsts or Upper Seconds, nearly all from UK universities. As with the previous surveys, the bias of Association members is towards the sciences and engineering.

In addition to their MBAs, 27% of repondents have gained some other professional qualification. Overall over 50% have another qualification other than a degree or an MBA. This is in line with current ethos of continuous learning being the only way to stay ahead in today's competitive world.

The size of the cohort is also important. The Association's accreditation criteria call for a minimum annual intake of 75, because it feels that below that a school may not have sufficient resources to run a programme properly. But how big is the maximum? Most established full-time and part-time MBA courses seem to have a maximum of about 100–150 students in each year, though some of the big US schools have cohorts running into several hundreds. The key question though, irrespective of whether courses are part-time or full-time – and this also applies to the residential element in distance learning courses – is the size of working groups in seminars and study groups. Numbers running into double figures become increasingly hard to manage effectively, and may suggest an inadequate staff:student ratio, as do over-large classes. The general opinion is that they should be no bigger than 30–50. Schools with larger cohorts than this solve the problem by breaking them up into streams, though these have nothing to do with ability, unlike the school system.

Selectiveness of entrance requirements

In the nature of the laws of supply and demand, the best known schools are the hardest to get into. One criterion of how choosy they are, is the score they require applicants to achieve in the GMAT and, in the case of non-English speakers, in either the Test of English as a Foreign Language (TOEFL) or the English Language Test. These are dealt with in the following chapter.

The minimum GMAT score you should aim for is around 550, but the requirement may go as high as 650 in some cases. It should be said, however, that not all schools use GMAT as an entry requirement. Some have devised their own tests on lines similar to GMAT; others give exemptions to applicants with degrees or professional qualifications in a relevant subject. The GMAT has two main sides to it: verbal and numerical. Schools look for a good balance of the two, and there have been cases of students achieving a score in the 600s, but being rejected because it was too heavily skewed in one direction, as compared to another. Because learning from each other is such a vital part of the way programmes are run, schools look for people who can contribute to that process. Single track boffins and loners, no matter how bright, are not likely to get into the best schools.

Programme content

Though they may attach different terms to the concepts involved, MBA programmes, whether full-time or part-time, consist of a core programme of basic business skills, which take up on average one-third of the course. They are followed by electives from which you can make your own choice, though in some schools certain mandatory subjects run on into the elective phase. In the final part, there is usually a project on which you will be asked to prepare a report. In the case of part-time and distance learning courses, the project is often one which bears a direct relation to something in your own organisation. Together these form the 'credits' which are the building blocks of the course.

Among the criteria for the Association of MBAs accreditation is that a school should be able 'to provide students with a common body of knowledge in business administration'.[3] That is generally taken to mean core courses in:

---

[3] *Course Accreditation*, The Association of MBAs.

- Managerial Economics
- Financial and Management Accounting
- Marketing
- Quantitative Methods
- Human Resource Management
- Operations Management
- Information Systems
- Business Strategy.

Though what is taught may be coloured by the tendency of a school to build up a reputation in a particular functional discipline or in relation to a particular sector of business activity, these topics are not, or at any rate should not be, taught as separate subjects. Business schools have been accused by their critics of breaking up management topics as if they were distinct academic disciplines. Many professors will admit privately that this may have been the tendency at one time, but the emphasis nowadays is very much on integration – looking at the implications of decisions in one sphere of the business for its other components. Some schools have moved some way down the path of teaching core themes (e.g. the management of change), rather than individual disciplines.

The electives can cover an enormous range of subjects, though students should check that these relate to those in which they are interested. Electives may vary from year to year, depending on demand, so it is important to look at the latest brochure if that is one of the reasons for your choice of a particular school. A recent article in the Association's own magazine, *Ambassador*, stresses that electives are important from a career point of view: "The content of an MBA was not felt to be significant *per se*, but electives or specialist subjects which did relate to the job being applied for were a distinct asset."[4]

Given the number of schools and the variety of methods of delivery of the MBA, it is of course impossible to lay down any platonically ideal structure for the course. In particular, there are differences in the way the one- and two-year MBAs are structured. There are also differences in the way part-time courses are delivered. Some schools have a dedicated part-time path; in others, part-timers simply attend the full-time programme, but over a longer period.

Distance learning MBAs have a similar structure, but here it is important to look at the way the content is delivered. See Chapter 2 for some points you need to consider. The crunch question here may be how much experience the school has had in the field of distance learning.

Duration

Full-time courses at Association-accredited schools in Europe range from 10 months at INSEAD to 21 months at LBS and some continental schools. The norm, however, is 12 months. Some executive or modular MBAs can be completed in two years. Part-time and distance learning MBAs usually take three to five years, though some of the latter have a theoretical duration of seven years. The general opinion, however, is that there is a distinct danger of the trail growing cold if you take too long to go down it.

---

[4] Are You Making The Right Impression With Your MBA?' *Ambassador*, March 1998.

Fees Tuition fees for EU students at a sample of accredited schools are given in Chapter 5. However, for full-time courses, these are not the whole story. Living costs – not to mention lost salary – can add appreciably to the real cost, which gives a competitive advantage to those in parts of the country where rents and living costs are cheaper than in major cities.

In the case of part-time courses, you will need to take the cost of travel into account if you do not live near the school of your choice. A further hidden cost is the £1 000–£2 000 for a good PC if you do not already have one, because this is increasingly becoming a must in all types of programmes. You should always check what a quoted fee covers, and whether there are hidden extras. For instance, if the programme includes study trips abroad, who pays for the fares and accommodation? According to the *Financial Times*: 'Two years of course fees, living expenses, and the cost of not being employed, will cost more than £100 000'.[5]

However, it seems that few people seriously interested in taking an MBA are put off by the cost factor, though there is a certain amount of shopping around when it comes to all-up costs for schools of equivalent status. Conversations indicate that when it came to the final choice, quite a few prospective students from outside London were put off by the problems and costs of finding accommodation in the capital.

The faculty A criticism that is sometimes made of some of the top schools on both sides of the Atlantic, is that the star teachers and/or management gurus who are billed as attractions of the place may seldom be seen by students – they are too busy with lucrative consultancy assignments or jetting around the world on the guru lecture circuit.

While this is less true of the UK and other European countries, you do need to check how much the big name teachers are around, and how much actual teaching they do, if that is why you are thinking of choosing a particular school. Anecdotal evidence suggests that this can be a problem with some of the more glamorous schools. In most cases, fortunately, what you see in the brochure is what you get in the classroom, and though you will find that most of the faculty have consultancy or research assignments, they generally do their fair share of teaching and project work. In fact, the usefulness and relevance of teaching is generally considered to be in close correlation to the amount of consultancy undertaken by the teacher. Not only is it a sign that he or she is taken seriously by the business community, it also ensures that they keep in touch with the real world. Business school students benefit from the real life feedback of private courses and consultancy, and increasingly, too, from the depth of faculty members' international experience.

On the guru question, Professor Bob Galliers, Chairman of Warwick School of Management, makes an interesting observation. With one or two exceptions – Professor Charles Handy (who no longer teaches) is a case in point – Britain does not have high profile gurus with a large business following and a high media profile of the kind found in the USA. British gurus tend to have more of a reputation in their subject among their academic peers than with the general

[5] *Financial Times*, 21 February 1996.

public. Then there is the question of the reputation of particular tutors among the students themselves. In the profiles section of the current edition, we have included the names of tutors who were highly rated on this basis. One student made the interesting suggestion that you should look for the names of the tutors who were most frequently chosen to supervise the dissertations in the final part of the course. These were often the best and most highly respected teachers.

It is also important to check that the teaching staff are 'dedicated' to the business school; not in any psychological sense, but in that of being attached to the school itself, rather than to another faculty. This is a particular drawback of small, newly established business schools. They are apt to draw at least some of their teachers from other faculties within the institution of which they are a part. Some MBA students in this situation would say there is nothing less useful to a manager than being taught economics by someone from the economics faculty, rather than the business school! Here again, accreditation provides a degree of quality assurance, in that it calls for a minimum of 40 staff, of whom 75% should be dedicated to the business school itself.

The student body

The average age of students is reported by business schools to be between 28 and 35, and to be lower in full-time courses than in part-time and distance learning modes.[6] Generally, students will have had at least three years of work experience. Indeed, some schools specify this as an admission criterion, though others will accept a professional qualification, and a few take people straight from a first degree. However, Professor Carnall writing in his book *MBA Futures*,[7] expresses a widely held view in saying that 'real work and managerial experience are a vital 'resource' the member brings to the course'. Without them he lacks credibility with other members, and he may not be able to derive full benefit from the interchange of ideas with other participants, which is said to be almost as important a part of an MBA course as its formal elements. Other criteria to apply to the student body are their career histories, their functional disciplines, their industry sectors, and their nationality. Many schools publish an annual book of profiles of their students, which contains such information. Though mainly intended as a marketing tool to send out to recruiters and potential employers, it would also give someone considering an application to a particular school a good idea of the kind of students it attracts.

The age/experience profile of the student body

Anecdotal evidence suggests that this is an important factor for many prospective students. Having regard to the fact that 'learning from other students' is an important part of the overall learning process, prospective applicants want to make sure that others on the programme are going to be on the same wavelength, and have reached a similar level in terms of age and experience, to themselves.

One acid test of choice was suggested by a student at IESE, the leading Spanish school. He had checked out several places before making his choice, and his advice was: 'See whether people laugh in class. That's a good test, both of teachers and the kind of students you're likely to meet'.

[6] It should be noted that this is an *average*; most cohorts have a sprinkling of forty pluses and even the occasional fifty plus.
[7] Carnall, C. (1992) *MBA Futures*, Macmillan.

Research   A ranking of business schools in terms of their status as research centres has been issued jointly by the various UK Higher Education Funding bodies – see pages 34–5, for a list which, it should be noted, includes all UK MBA schools, including many not currently accredited by the Association. Research is sometimes thought of as an abstract academic activity, but in the context of business schools, largely dependent on client funding, it generally has to have practical, and often very direct, applications. The value of such research is that it then feeds back into teaching programmes and learning activities. A further implication in the case of the HEFC rankings, is that much government funding is based on the outcome achieved by the school in question, and that may be reflected in the resources on campus.

Internation-   Internationalisation is one of the buzz words of management education in the
alism   nineties, and rightly so, but what does it mean in practice? Some schools take it to mean having an international student body and a faculty drawn from the nationals of many countries. The prime examples of the latter are schools such as LBS, INSEAD, IESE, Rotterdam, and IMD. Elsewhere, schools increasingly aim to assemble study groups and syndicates made up of students from many different countries. Critics say that overcoming the language and cultural barriers inherent in this approach can slow down the process of learning the core skills it is meant to impart.

In addition to growing intakes of foreign students in both UK and continental schools, the trend is to foster internationalism through exchanges with schools in other countries and the multi-centred MBA referred to previously. Many schools in the UK claim to offer schemes of this sort, but the acid test of the effectiveness of internationalism in a school is more likely to be how many of its alumni obtain jobs with multinationals or foreign companies, and whether there are regular exchanges of faculty and shared research with schools with whom a special relationship is said to exist – and the standing of those partner schools.

The other valuable clue as to how seriously internationalism is taken is in the approach to foreign languages. Some schools offer an MBA closely tied to a foreign language, such as Manchester's MBA with a diploma in Japanese, or Bradford's electives in French or Japanese. Most schools have language laboratories and offer the opportunity to learn foreign languages which, especially in the case of schools attached to a university, can be a very wide range. Many students do take advantage of language learning facilities, though where languages are not assessed subjects, it requires a good deal of determination to persist with such courses on top of all the other work the programme always entails.

If you really want to be international, and have your sights set on a career as a Euro-manager, your best course of action would probably be to attend either a multi-centre programme, or to take your MBA at an accredited school across the Channel.

Flexibility of   One of the trends that has developed in the MBA in the nineties is that of greater
delivery modes   flexibility in delivery. Particularly in the case of part-time programmes, your career over a period of three years or so may be affected in ways that you cannot

control, but which will have an impact on your ability to study in the way that you had originally envisaged. You may be relocated, promoted or made redundant, or change jobs. In any of these cases, you may want or have to switch the way you take the MBA, and you should make sure either that this option is available, or that any work you have done on your course to date is recognised by other schools.

Administrative efficiency matters most in distance learning. How quickly material is sent to you, relative to the schedules that have been laid down, is important, as is the turn-round speed by tutors of the work you send in, and whether residential courses are properly structured and organised. **Administrative efficiency**

In full-time and part-time courses, efficient scheduling of classes is important – and by no means easy when you may have several streams going through the same year. Students at one school said that the staff at times rationalised what looked to them like inept scheduling by saying it was part of the pressure MBAs had to learn to take! By contrast, the comment from students at good schools was that the scheduling of topics followed a natural flow that made it easier to make connections between them.

Another important test of efficiency arises in project work. It is not always easy to get businesses to take on an MBA student for this purpose. Efficiently run schools have proper procedures for doing this; for others it is more of a scramble. The usefulness of the exercise will be very limited if the employer concerned is reluctant or unsuitable.

How do you know whether a school is efficiently run or not? As we said earlier, the look of the place is often significant. Professor Carnall of Henley Management College suggests another measure: how promptly the school replies to your initial enquiry.

We have indicated some of the measures earlier in the text – which organisations recruit or send people on short courses to the school in question, fund chairs, research or part-time MBAs there, come as guest speakers, and – most importantly from the point of view of prospective MBAs – have, over the past couple of years or so, taken on students for their in-company project. **Links with business and industry**

Location is said to be one of the key elements in the success of an enterprise. Big city business schools such as London, Manchester, or Strathclyde, do benefit from being in a metropolitan area, but this has more to do with their physical proximity to contacts in business and industry than to the bright lights. The fact is, that the intensity of the MBA course means that students have very little opportunity to sample these. Indeed, some would say that schools which are not particularly conveniently situated, such as INSEAD or Cranfield, are good places to focus on one's studies – real life examples of Michael Porter's theory of competitive advantage arising out of what can appear to be unfavourable environments. However, for full-time residential students, it is then important that suitable accommodation is available at a reasonable cost, reasonably close to the campus, and that the school can facilitate finding this. For part-time students, though, convenience and proximity to their workplace are important. **Facilities and location**

So far as facilities are concerned, you should look at the range of literature available in the school's library, and whether it can access the databases in which you are most likely to be interested. The size and condition of lecture theatres and seminar rooms, the convenience and general state of care and maintenance of public areas – what might loosely be described as the general look of the place – are all signs of the morale and well-being of the school.

Success/ failure rate

Business schools all say that their failure rate is very low; that is because the pre-selection process seems to be highly effective. Although the GMAT or its equivalents are not the only criteria used for admission, if you achieve the score demanded by the school of your choice, it means that in theory you can cope with its MBA course. We will deal in more detail with the GMAT in the next chapter.

Business school faculty maintain that the very small percentage of students who fail do so because they have, for one reason or another, lost the motivation to put in the work the course requires. When this happens, it is often the policy of the school to persuade the student to discontinue the course: that way no stigma is attached when they apply for jobs, since a decision to break off one's studies can be ascribed to any number of reasons. However, procedures on this point are worth checking, if you feel that you might be a marginal case, as are the criteria of what constitutes failure. Some schools will award the degree on overall performance, even if you have not passed in every subject; in other cases, there may be a consolation prize – a number of schools offer a Diploma in Business Studies to those who have successfully completed significant parts of their MBA programme.

First degree graduates should note that success is measured differently from first degree processes: there are no firsts, seconds or thirds, although some schools end up with much the same effect by placing MBAs in 'quartiles' on completion of the course. There may also be special recognition for outstanding per-formances, such as the LBS' awards of distinctions to the best students. In some other schools, outside sponsors award prizes, usually for the best performance in some subject in which the sponsor has a particular interest. However, schools in Europe do not disclose grades to a prospective employer without your permission.

Career services, job placement record and exit salaries

Sponsored students generally go back to their organisation – at least for a while, but schools are becoming conscious of the importance of helping those who have financed their own studies to get back into employment. Some form of career management service should be in place, not only advising students on career opportunities, but also proactively marketing its graduates to business and industry. This has become increasingly important as the demand for MBAs from such previously reliable sectors as management consultancy and financial services has, in some years, come under pressure with the move towards downsizing and outsourcing.

You should establish whether the career management service, or placement service as it may also be called, provides individual counselling on career possibilities, and on job search mechanics such as CV preparation and interview techniques. It should also have active and systematic contacts with recruiters, headhunters, and influential alumni. However, the old boy network, powerful though it can be, is not really enough these days. It ought to be backed up by a website through which prospective employers can search for MBAs with specific skills. In many cases, this is provided as hard copy in the form of a book of profiles of the current cohort (worth looking at, incidentally, by prospective students, because it gives a very good overall picture of the sort of people they are likely to be meeting). There should also be a proper programme for presentations by key companies and appropriate interview facilities.

How effective all this is proving to be should be reflected in two measures:

- What percentage of students get jobs, and within what length of time, after completing their MBA?
- By what percentage did they increase their previous salaries?

These are questions often asked at MBA fairs, and an effective careers centre should be able to supply this information. In the end, much depends on how a school is viewed by potential employers. As we stated earlier, there are no established rankings of UK business schools, though there is a general perception among recruiters of certain schools as being in the premier division, whereas as others perhaps fall into a notional first or even lower division. That status is the informal product of such factors as track record, the subsequent business performance of their graduates, the reputation of individual faculty members, relevance of their course content, the amount of press coverage they receive, the strength and level of their links with business and industry, the quality of their research and for which clients it is being undertaken.

The alumni network

One of the big advantages of US schools is the strength of their alumni network. The American management guru, Rosabeth Moss Kanter, recently pointed out to the writer that at the World Economic Forum there is a regular Harvard dinner for world industrial leaders, at which most of the guests are Harvard Business School graduates. In Europe it is surely no coincidence that, according to a recent *Financial Times* survey of the top European 500 companies[1], by far the largest number of their directors got their MBA from INSEAD. Until quite recently alumni associations were a neglected area in the UK, except, of course, for the umbrella role of the Association of MBAs. Now all the major schools are developing them, and some have appointed support staff to the faculty specifically to look after alumni associations, to produce regular newsletters, and to organise alumni events.

Their value from the point of view of alumni is that they serve as a contact network at dinners or other social or professional meetings. A future role for them, currently being explored by Warwick Business School and others, is as the basis for refresher courses and other areas of continuing professional development. Indeed in an interview with the writer, Dave Wilson, president of the USA's GMAC, has suggested that they might become the focus for continuing professional development courses requiring MBAs to "recertify" their qualifications after a certain length of time.

[1] 'The Best For Visibility', *Financial Times*, 19 January 1998.

The 10 key
questions

- Does the school deal with enquiries promptly and efficiently?
- How discriminating/intelligent are its selection procedures?
- Which organisations recruit at the school, participate in its projects, or send their own managers on short courses there?
- What is the age, experience, and nationality mix of the student body?
- What do the students think of the teaching standards?
- Are the school's claims to internationalisation real, or are those parts of the programme token gestures?
- Do the fees represent most of the cost, or are there hidden extras to consider such as travel or accommodation?
- What are the toughest parts of the programme for those without prior work experience or qualifications in that area?
- Does the school run preliminary courses to bring you up to the required standard in verbal, numeric or computer literacy, if that's what you're going to need?
- What is the average starting salary once you graduate?

Getting in

4

The best shows in town are always the hardest to get into, and so it is with MBA courses. All of them receive more applications than the number of students they can admit, though the ratio between applications and admissions is not necessarily a decisive measure of how good the school is. A great many applications are rejected because they do not meet the basic criteria: generally a first or second class honours degree, or its equivalent, plus at least two years' work experience, or, in the absence of academic qualifications and in some fairly rare cases, at least five years' work experience at a significant level of achievement. The best schools – or at any rate the ones that rate highest in published rankings[1] or on the unofficial grapevine among leading employers and recruiters – tend to be the ones which have the toughest admission standards for those who are, prima facie, eligible. The ratio between those who meet admission criteria and those who are actually admitted therefore provides the clue as to how choosy a school can afford to be.

Making your application

In reply to your initial enquiry, you will be sent an application form. It will show a deadline, and reports indicate that applicants are tending to work very closely to this, possibly because they are trying to negotiate support from their employers or are making comparisons between schools. However, if you want to get into one where you think there might be a pressure on places, or if you want on-campus accommodation on a full-time programme, it is best to apply early. Where the academic year begins in September/October, as it generally does in the case of full-time courses,[2] the deadline in Europe is in April/May, but unofficially the best advice is to apply at the beginning of the calendar year for the academic year in which you would like to start your course. In the case of part-time or distance learning programmes, which often begin in January, you should ideally apply at least six months ahead.

Applying early gives you a number of advantages. Firstly, schools tend to fill places on a first come, first served basis among those whose applications are accepted. Secondly, scholarships, a list of which is given in the next chapter, are also allocated in this way. All other things being equal, the early bird gets the grant. Finally, since most schools operate a moving process of admission – applications are dealt with as they are received, rather than processed after deadline day – if you are turned down by your first choice, you still have time to apply to other schools.

It is important to understand here that at postgraduate level there is no common applications procedure as there is for first degree courses through the

---

[1] European schools are sometimes ranked in business magazines, though there is no officially authorised ranking, except for research programmes.

[2] Not universally, though; for instance, the Ashridge programme runs from January to December.

Universities and Colleges Admissions Service (UCAS). You have to make the application yourself, direct to the school in question.

That raises the question of whether you should make multiple applications. Anecdotal evidence suggests that you need not feel any misgivings about doing so, and indeed, the director of the full-time MBA at one leading school told the writer that he would be 'extremely concerned' by a candidate who applied only there. However, three is about the maximum, and an increasing number of schools now charge an application fee of £30–50, partly to discourage the 'just looking' brigade, and partly to defray the costs of what, for most schools, is a selection process which is at least as sophisticated as that used in job applications. It also seems to be the case that MBA students are in the main a very focused lot, who form a clear idea of what they want from a school, and who do a lot of homework on what is on offer before they send in their application.

This may range from a systematic evaluation of the criteria set out in the previous chapter, to a gut feeling about the school and its culture. Thus a young UK doctor who chose the INSEAD MBA looked first at a number of blue chip American schools before deciding that INSEAD provided the most interesting and compatible mix of students. His initial intention had been to apply to Harvard, but he was deterred by its buttoned-down collar, Wall Street-related image. As we said in the previous chapter, compatibility between your own values and the culture of the school is as important as the hard facts of fees, course content, location, student:faculty ratio, and so forth.

Incidentally, the example quoted above makes another point about admission policy – your experience does not have to have been in business for you to be considered for a place. On the contrary, schools rather like applicants with unusual backgrounds, such as that of a police officer attending Bradford's full-time MBA, or the submarine commander featured in Henley School of Management's magazine *Newslink* – provided they can demonstrate that they can both benefit from the course and bring an unusual and interesting perspective to it.

Application forms

One commentator has described the admission procedures to business schools as a two-way beauty contest: the school is as keen to find out about you as you are about it. One of its main instruments in the judging process is the application form. This is a very searching document – rather more so than most job application forms. Here are some of the things the school will want to know about you in addition to the usual personal details:

- details of current job, its level of responsibility and salary
- similar details of previous jobs
- subjects taken in secondary and higher education courses, and results achieved in them – some schools, notably in the USA, may ask for certified copies of degrees, diplomas etc
- non-curricular/extra-professional activities, and the role you took in them (e.g. as club treasurer, etc)
- international experience, either in a private or job-related context
- your financial resources – how your studies would be funded
- knowledge of languages. Applicants to UK, US and many Continental schools, whose first language is not English will have to show their score,

either in the British Council's International English Language Testing System (IELTS) or in its USA equivalent, TOEFL

- GMAT score, particularly in the case of applicants from abroad, or those whose qualifications and work experience fall outside the obvious areas of relevance to a postgraduate business degree.

Some schools do not use the GMAT as an admission criterion, but have devised tests of their own which are taken if the application proceeds. These tests cover very similar areas of numeracy, literacy, and verbal and numerical reasoning as the GMAT.

The score on the GMAT, or its equivalent, is generally seen as the cornerstone of your application – you will not be considered unless you achieve the score the school has set as its admission criterion – and we will deal with this in more detail shortly. However, schools stress that they are not interested in number crunchers and logic machines – in fact, it is quite possible to achieve a high GMAT score and not be accepted, though by contrast a good GMAT score can offset a more modest academic record.

Schools are also interested in 'softer' attributes of motivation, character, and personality. One school asks the following questions, which are fairly typical of what you might expect to find on an application form:

- What are the main factors which you believe account for your academic and professional development to date?
- What do you feel are your major strengths and weaknesses? Please provide examples to illustrate these.
- What do you feel you would contribute to the MBA at this school?

Some schools ask for such information in essay form, which also tests your ability to analyse your personal characteristics and actions, and draw coherent conclusions from them in terms of your career aims. INSEAD, for instance, asks you to describe not only your main achievements – and why you regard them as such – but also situations where you felt you failed to achieve your objectives. It asks you not only to consider how the MBA course would develop you as a manager, but also what alternative means of pursuing your personal and professional goals you have seriously contemplated. American schools may ask questions which probe your views on business ethics. A major British school leaves a whole page in which it asks you to 'add any other information which you believe may influence our decision on your application'.

How honest should you be in giving your replies to application form questions? A number of books on how to handle job applications have given hints on what are allegedly favoured answers to questions about personal attributes; for instance, they recommend that you should say that your greatest weakness is to drive yourself too hard, or to expect the same high standards from others as you set yourself. Admissions administrators are, however, a pretty sophisticated and creep-resistant bunch. They can readily spot applications from those who are labouring to create the right impression, or those whose answers are inconsistent with other aspects of their application.

People who advise on job application procedures suggest that it is a good idea to make a photocopy of the document first, and to draft your answers on that. These forms are very similar to business school admissions applications, and the same advice applies to these. You may have second thoughts about some point or other, or find that you cannot fit the information you want to give into the available space – a problem that often arises if you type your reply, as some forms specify (look out, however, for those that specifically ask for your replies to be handwritten, a sign of graphologists at work). An untidy document, or one thick with eraser fluid, creates a bad impression immediately. 'Your application is an important part of the total package you present', warns one writer. He goes on to add that attention to detail is very important. Before you send off your completed form, check that you have answered all the questions, and keep a copy – you may need to refer to it if you are called for an interview.

Another writer, John Byrne, who is responsible for one of the main ranking lists of US schools, advises particular care over essay questions. He suggests that applicants should look at the school's brochure to see which qualities it seems to emphasise, and to orient their essay answers towards these. Thus, if a school places obvious value on internationalisation, you should focus either on your international experience, or your desire to acquire it.

Indeed, the general opinion of commentators on the admissions process is that evidence of an intelligent awareness of how an MBA could add value to your present job and your future career as a manager is one of the points for which admissions administrators look. They also look for evidence of what you have done about self-development so far. The MBA course calls for a very high level of commitment and sheer hard work, so anything you can bring in to show that you are prepared to do more than your job in the personal pursuit of excellence, is favourably noted.

References

As with job applications, business schools do not work on your version of your career record alone. References are a very important part of the process, and some schools call for specific information from referees. Usually they will ask for two sets of references, one from an academic source concerning your intellectual ability, and at least one other focusing on your performance at work.

The latter can be a problem if you are intending to leave your job to do the course on your own. If that is the case, you should explain the circumstances to the admissions administrator, who may well be prepared to make your acceptance subject to receiving a satisfactory employer's reference, rather than requiring it in advance.

Some reference forms specify what information they require; others leave it more open, though in the latter case, the admissions office will be looking for similar information to that sought in the former (bear in mind that we are using 'he' in its unisex sense!).

What schools want to know from referees

- How long the referee has known you, and in what capacity
- How he rates your intellectual ability in areas such as analytical and communication skills, often in a range of 1 to 5 between poor and excellent

- How he rates your competence in the job you are now doing, or in the job areas in which he has known you
- How he rates your personal attributes such as social skills, perseverance, and emotional maturity
- What he considers to be your principal strengths and weaknesses
- How good your written and spoken English is, particularly if this is not your first language; in the case of a non-English school, this question would apply to your ability in the language of the country concerned
- Whether and how he thinks you will benefit from an MBA

If these questions are not asked in the form provided for referees, it would be a good idea to brief the people you have nominated that the above is the kind of information the school will want to have. Character references as such are of little use, as are vague statements about performance, even if they are complimentary. As far as possible they should be backed by facts. This makes giving a reference a modestly time-consuming experience for the referee. You should warn the people you are intending to nominate that you are going to do so – and make sure that they will return the reference form quickly.

The Graduate Management Admissions Test (GMAT)

The proof of one of Euclid's easier geometrical theorems used to be called the 'pons asinorum' by schoolmasters of an older generation: the bridge of asses, or rather the bridge which asses fail to cross. The role of the GMAT is somewhat similar. Failing to achieve a respectable GMAT score does not make you an ass, but it does cast considerable doubt on your ability to complete an MBA. It does not, however, test specific subject areas which would be related to the actual contents of the course. Rather, it is a test of verbal, quantitative, reasoning and communicating skills which, in the words of the GMAT *Bulletin of Information*, 'are good though imperfect predictors of academic success in the first year of study at graduate schools of management'.

The mention of a 'first year' of study assumes a two-year course, which is the usual length of the MBA in the USA, and indeed, the GMAT is a US-based test, sponsored by an American body, The Graduate Management Admissions Council, and administered by the Educational Testing Service (ETS). Enquiries about it should be addressed to:

Graduate Management Admissions Test
Educational Testing Service
PO Box 6103
Princeton NJ 08541–6103, USA
Tel: +1 609 771 7330
(or faxed to +1 609 883 4349)

Graduate Management Admissions Test
CITO – Sylvan Promatic
PO Box 1109
6801 BC Arnhem
Netherlands
Tel: +31 26 352 15 77

The fastest response is, however, via email – gmat@ets.org

Another Web site, that of the MBA Explorer at http://www.gmat.org provides a mass of useful information, including quick answers to commonly asked questions about GMAT, sample test questions, more than 100 previous GMAT essay topics, a list of testing centres and their phone numbers, the Web sites and databases of hundreds of business schools and the latest news on the GMAT generally.

The GMAT is used as an entry requirement by most major US business schools, and has spread its net throughout the world. Even schools which have an admission test of their own, will exempt applicants from it if they have taken the GMAT and achieved a good score. Schools which do use the GMAT will generally send you its current *Information Bulletin* with your admissions pack. However, if you intend to study in the USA, you can obtain a GMAT Bulletin by sending an A4 self-addressed envelope, stamped for 80 grams, to your nearest Fulbright Commission. The UK address is:

Educational Advisory Service
Fulbright Commission
62 Doughty Street
London WC1N 2LS
Tel: 0171 404 6994 Fax: 0171 404 6874

The fee for taking the test is $160 outside the USA, and can be paid in your local currency at the prevailing rate of exchange. The GMAT used to be offered four times a year only, which made it necessary to plan some time ahead if you were thinking of applying for admission to an MBA programme, but since October 1997 the Test has gone from being a paper and pencil exercise to a computer adaptive model, taken on a continuous basis by appointment at a computer-based testing centre. A list of these centres is printed in the GMAT *Bulletin of Information* and is also shown on the Web site referred to above. All you have to do is to phone for an appointment, and you can take the test within a matter of days. Score reports, too, will be a matter of days, rather than weeks as is the case at present. In circumstances where acceptance on to an MBA programme depends on your GMAT score, it is still advisable to take the GMAT well in advance of your interview – or even of sending in your application, where this information is one of the things the form requires.

Taking the GMAT The Test is not related to a knowledge of business or any specific subject area or academic discipline, though those without school maths at O level do tend to find some of it rather daunting. It measures the ability to read, understand and reason logically in both verbal and quantitative terms. In addition to sections of multiple choice questions which test these particular competencies, there are two 30-minute essays, which measure your ability to think critically and communicate complex ideas in writing.

The test begins with the two essays, the subjects for which you are given one at a time, one setting out an issue about which you have to explain your own views, and the other analysing an argument whose strengths and weaknesses you are asked to examine. Answers are marked in a range of 1-6, a grading of 4 being 'adequate'. Gene Romer, who runs a long established UK-based pre-GMAT crammer called GTAC Associates, suggests that in spite of the limited time you are allowed, you should begin by spending about ten minutes thinking about and making notes on your answer before you start writing – or, as will now be the case, turning to the keyboard. Minimum generic computer skills are, of course, required to do the GMAT in its adaptive form but the vast majority of test takers would be familiar with the keyboard at this level.

After a short break, the essays are followed by the multiple choice questions, one set of which is mathematical and the other, verbal. Each set runs for 75 minutes, with another short interval between the two. GMAT administrators reckon that the verbal and quantitative questions take about two and three-quarter minutes respectively to answer. It is important to keep an eye on the time as you take the test and indeed time pressure is one of its chief hazards.

Though the pattern of results has proved to be broadly similar, there are some important differences between the old paper and pencil test and the computer adaptive one. Under the former system you could first pick off the ones you thought you could answer and move back and forth among the others at will. With the computer-adaptive test, this is no longer possible. You can only move to the next question when you answered the one preceding it. Consequently, if you don't know the answer you will have to guess it, though there is a simple strategy for intelligent guesswork. Gene Romer says the multiple choice options always include some that are patently wrong. If you eliminate those that you know fall into this category, you have a one in four, or even one in three chance of guessing the right answer. The snag, however, is that if you subsequently realise that you got it wrong, you cannot retrace your steps and go back to it.

A correct answer will be followed by another, more difficult question. Because the CAT is tailored to the ability level of the test taker, fewer questions are needed to arrive at a GMAT score, which means that it is possible to give you your result much faster than used to be the case.

See the Appendix for a sample of GMAT questions and answers, courtesy of GTAC.

When the test is marked, separate scores are attached to your numerical and your verbal skills, though a total score is also given out of a possible maximum of 800. A very small number of people do reach that, but anything over 700 is considered to be excellent.

The more demanding schools look for a score of 580–650. The average score of students at LBS, INSEAD, and Rotterdam School of Management is reported to be 620–650. In percentage terms, a score of 600 is equivalent to around 67%, which is achieved by the top 15–20% of those taking the test.

Five hundred is equivalent to 50%, and is generally regarded as the absolute minimum you need in order to be able to tackle the course with any confidence. All schools would echo the words of Cranfield's Professor Colin New: 'We try not to pick people who may fail'. He says that he seldom considers applicants with scores much below 580. He adds that as well as looking at the total score, schools take into account the balance between numerical and verbal results. There should be a reasonable balance between them, though by all accounts if there is a bias, it should preferably be slanted towards the numerical end. You do not have to have A level maths to succeed in the GMAT – and by extension in the MBA programme – but an arts graduate with weak O level maths would undoubtedly struggle to get through the course. Read *Snapshots From Hell, The Making of an MBA* (Nicholas Brealey) for a cautionary account of what it's like for the innumerate.

Someone whose written and spoken English was poor, would also have a problem in a school where English was the main medium of instruction. Those who are in this position would probably be required to take a preliminary proficiency test. This would either be the Test of English as a Foreign Language (TOEFL), also adminstered by the ETS, whose address has been given above, or the British Council's International English Language Testing System (IELTS), which is increasingly the one favoured by UK-based schools. The latter takes 2 hours and 45 minutes, and tests listening, reading, writing, and speaking. Grading is in bands of 1–9, and most schools look for a minimum of 6 or 7. The British Council produces a booklet, *How To Prepare For IELTS*.

ETS produces a brochure on TOEFL, similar to its GMAT Bulletin, which is also available from the Fulbright Commission in the UK. This test is of reading, writing, and comprehension, primarily of American English, and is administered five times per year at centres all over the world. Most schools who ask for your TOEFL score will be looking for a minimum of 580.

Preparation for the GMAT Michelle Collias of The Studyworks, another GMAT crammer, makes the valuable point that although you cannot do much about admission criteria which relate to your past history, you can do something about your GMAT score, and that a good one can make a decisive differerence if your academic qualifications are a bit shaky. There are a number of ways in which you can get yourself in shape to take the GMAT and to get a foretaste of the kind of questions you will encounter. This is advisable, even if you are thoroughly confident of your verbal reasoning and mathematical skills, because the GMAT is not, strictly speaking, a test of either maths or English in the accepted sense. It is rather like the driving test where, even if you think you can drive, it is advisable to take some lessons from a qualified instructor who knows what the examiner will be looking for.

It is not generally considered a good idea to take the test itself as a dress rehearsal. Although you are allowed to resit if you fail, taking the test itself does not give you enough feedback on what you need to do to improve your answering techniques or your weaker areas. There are a number of books and courses that can help you in this respect, often advertised in *The Economist*. Such sources include:

GTAC Associates
55 Gunnersbury Avenue
London W5 4LP
Tel: 0181 993 3983
Fax: 0181 993 5380

The Studyworks
46 Queens Gardens
London W2 3AA
Tel: 0171 402 9877
Fax: 0171 258 0417

Kaplan
The London Centre
3 Charing Cross Road
London WC2 0HA
Tel: 0171 930 3130
Fax: 0171 930 8009

Test Analysts
14 Woodville Road
London E18 1JU
Tel/Fax: 0181 532 2967

The most widely used book on the GMAT is the *Official Guide For GMAT Review*, produced by ETS itself. This contains more than 1 000 actual GMAT questions, with answers and explanation. From the same source you can also get some Test Preparation software, called POWERPREP, two actual tests which you can run on your own computer. However, if you feel more comfortable with face-to-face tuition, the companies listed above conduct training courses on how to prepare for GMAT. GTAC's course, for instance, runs over several weekends and eventually simulates and scores the test itself. It costs £365. Kaplan is the leading American company in test preparation and is now active in the UK, as well as in other European countries.

This raises the question of whether preparation for the GMAT is beneficial. GTAC's Gene Romer believes that it is, even for those who are confident about verbal and numerical skills, and certainly for those who are phobic in either field. Maths phobia is, of course, the more common, but experience of tutoring GMAT candidates over many years has led him to the conclusion that someone intelligent enough to get an honours degree should, given the right kind of intensive coaching, be able to handle the numerical reasoning sections in the Test. Equally, he maintains that even people who are comfortable with maths would benefit from coaching in the type of questions asked, because they are not like, for example, A levels. The ability to see the essentials of a problem and analyse it quickly is what is being tested, not the detail of how you arrive at the answer. Another argument in favour of formal preparation is made in *Marketing Yourself to the Top Business Schools.*[3] The authors, themselves MBA graduates, make the point that 'when you take the exam, you should not be wasting time reading directions for the various sections – you should know exactly what is required of you for each type of test question and be able to plunge in right away'.

Given that there are several GMAT tutorial-type organisations in the market, how do you choose between them? Some suggested guidelines are listed below.

- What do the facilities look like?
- How much experience do the instructors have of the requirements of the GMAT itself, rather than general teaching qualifications in maths or English?
- How many hours of coaching do you receive for your money?
- Can they substantiate any claims they make about significant improvements in the score people achieve as a result of coaching? (Also significant here is whether they have been able to move out of the sub-500 range into the 500–600 field, while still maintaining an even balance between numerical and verbal sections)
- What is the nature of the follow-up to the practice exams, which must be a key part of the course?
- What literature is provided to support the learning process?

GMAT crammers – a checklist

A good GMAT score, well balanced between the numerical and verbal aspects, is a strong indication that you can do the work. Language tests, where these apply, show you can understand what is going on in lectures and seminars. However, these are not the only criteria which schools use in their admission procedures. Work experience and personality are equally important, because the teaching methods the schools use place considerable emphasis on students learning from

Other admission criteria

[3] Carpenter, P. & C. (1995) *Marketing Yourself to the Top Business Schools*, Wiley.

each other, most notably in group work. Presented with a significant record of academic and work achievement, schools will, within reason, accept that a GMAT score below their normal expectations reflects the fact that you may have had an off-day.

In such a case, they would probably call you for an interview, but that is not as universal a condition of acceptance as it is for a job. As with jobs, interviews for business school places are built around your application form, so it is a good idea to study what you have said in that before you go; as we said earlier – make a copy before you send off your application.

Normally, as we stated earlier, you need to make your application well in advance of the deadline and to line up all your preliminaries, such as taking GMAT and contacting referees, with that in mind. However, if you are turned down because you are slightly too late in applying, there is always a chance of last-minute admission if someone who had been promised a place drops out because they have changed their mind, or because they have applied to several schools and had an offer elsewhere which they would prefer to accept. If you are in either position, do let the school know. Confirm your acceptance to the school of your choice if you have had more than one offer, and let the others know that you are not coming.

Financing your MBA 5

Reports indicate that most students on full-time programmes fund their own fees and living costs. Few employers want to pay to lose the services of a high-flyer for one, or possibly two years – especially when there is no guarantee that they will return to them at the end of that time. Part-time and distance learners fare rather better – the OUBS has stated that over half of the students on its MBA programme are sponsored or supported by their employer. The recent Association survey[1] says that such support varies from the payment of all fees, to a contribution to the cost of books, but it seems that only a small minority of employers refuse to provide any help at all.

The joys (and griefs) of being sponsored

The MBA is not a cheap course, wherever it is taken, or by whatever mode. In the UK, tuition fees per course, irrespective of the mode in which it is taken, average at around £8 000–£10 000, but can be over £15 000, so the principal difference is that in the case of part-time or distance learning courses, that cost would be spread over 2–3 years. (Fees are generally higher for non-EU nationals, though under EU rules, citizens of member countries cannot be charged more than locals.)

A one-year residential MBA at a leading UK school may work out at as much as £30 000, taking living expenses into account – more in the USA and on the Continent, though the rise in sterling against European currencies has altered the picture somewhat, though possibly on a temporary basis. To all of these figures you have to add the opportunity cost of lost income. Does this indicate that, wherever possible, you should try to persuade your employer to pay?

The chances of obtaining sponsorship for a full-time course are slim, for the reasons stated earlier. However, as we have indicated, sponsorship from employers for part-time and distance learning courses is quite widespread among employers who have a concerted policy for management development. If you are intending to make your career with them for a foreseeable spell – these days that is realistically for about 5 years – it is worth attempting. There is, however, a catch with consortium MBAs, and even more with those where many of the contents are company-specific to a particular employer. Indeed, even in open part-time programmes where employers have sponsored students, they may have quite a lot of influence on the contents of what is taught. The risk with such programmes is that they might then become a type of academic golden handcuff – what has been learned can be hard to transfer.

The other point about sponsorship, is that it leaves you with at least a moral obligation to stay with the employer who has paid for your course for a reasonable period after graduating, and possibly on his financial terms.

[1] *op. cit.*

On the plus side, the employer also has a moral obligation, which is to deploy the skills of MBAs properly. If he fails to do so, the unwritten, psychological contract can reasonably be regarded as broken. 'If someone who has completed an MBA does not obtain recognition and change, they are unlikely to put in 100% for the firm', comments a recent graduate.

Sponsored students often comment on the fact that they have to work at 'selling' the idea to an employer. The question is: what's in it for them? Schools are well aware that this will be an issue, either openly or by implication. You should ask for their advice on how to handle it before you raise the sponsorship issue with an employer. There are good answers – for instance, the project which is a feature of many MBA courses can, in effect, be a piece of in-company consultancy, often with the weight of experts from the business school faculty behind it.

The Association is sometimes asked by prospective students for a list of organisations known to sponsor MBAs, rather on the lines of being sponsored to paddle across the Atlantic in a canoe. There is no such list, and the chances of getting sponsorship from anyone other than your employer are just about zero. In fact, the question itself marks you as someone with unrealistic expectations.

Another question often asked of the Association, is whether awards for postgraduate study are available to non-graduates who have been accepted by a business school on the basis of work experience and record. In principle the answer is no, even though local authority grants to go to university for a first degree are given to anyone eligible. The Association advises, however, that appeals against such decisions have been known to be successful.

Financing your own studies

Taking the figures for Europe, according to the most recent EIU survey,[2] 40% of those who financed their own MBA did so from savings, 44% from private or bank loans, and the remainder by a variety of means – which included redundancy payments, sending their spouses out to work, and parental help.

For the majority of students from the UK, bank loans through the Association's Business School Loan Scheme are the most cost-effective method. Another possibility would be through a Department of Employment backed Career Development Loan.

The Association of MBAs Business School Loan Scheme

The Association of MBAs Loan Scheme was set up as long ago as 1969, and is operated through NatWest bank. To apply, the bank requires you to be a permanent UK resident aged between 18 and 40 years. In practice, it would be unusual for anyone under the age of 24 to be eligible under this scheme. You must also have been offered a place at an Association accredited school in either the UK or continental Europe, or in some leading US business schools. A condition in the latter two cases is that you plan to return to work in the UK. Apart from that, the criteria for eligibility are basically the same as for being accepted on a course in the first place – a minimum of two years' relevant work experience, a good honours degree or its equivalent, and so forth.

You can borrow up to two-thirds of your pre-course salary, plus tuition fees for each year of full-time study (but less any other grants), so the amounts can be

[2] *Which MBA*, (1997) 9th edn, EIU.

quite large. For part-time and distance learning students, the loan can cover tuition fees, study equipment and course expenses. In the case of full- and part-time study, no repayments are required during the course of study, during which time interest is rolled up to principal. After that, the capital sum, plus interest at a preferential commercial rate, has to be repaid, usually within seven years from when you first draw down the loan.

Distance learning students can apply for a maximum of £10 000 to cover tuition fees and study equipment. Unlike for full- and part-time study, to qualify you must be in full-time employment and repayment commences one month after drawing down the loan.

How do you apply for one of these loans? For a copy of the appropriate application form, you should contact (UK only):

NatWest: Freephone 0800 200 400

Loan terms from Nat West:

Full-time study   6% fixed for term of study, 7.5% variable thereafter

Part-time study   6% fixed for term of study, variable thereafter

Distance learning   7.5% variable for term of loan (pricing correct as of May 1998)

When you have completed the application form, it must be stamped by your school to prove that you have been offered a place there. In the case of overseas study, you will not need a stamped application form – a photocopy of the place offer will do in the first instance, though the bank will require more proof later.

The school, or yourself, should then return the form and any necessary enclosures to the Association. The Association does not actually *approve* the loan. They process the application to ensure that it fulfils the required criteria, answer any general queries that the bank's loan manager might have, and offer helpful advice. You may be a prospective MBA, but it's easy to get your figures wrong when working out the cost of study. Omitting an important cost can lead to a cash crisis, and much anxious gnawing of finger nails, just when you are already stressed out half-way through the course, says the Association's Peter Calladine, citing a typical example of the type of things prospective students get wrong.

If the Association is unable to process an application because some important detail has been omitted, they try to speed things along by contacting the applicant by telephone. If all the eligibility criteria are met, then they forward the application form direct to a designated branch or office of the bank. They also inform you that the application has been approved. The bank will then ask you in to sign the necessary documents. Usually the bank will also wish to interview you to discuss terms and conditions. If your application is approved by the bank, they will then ask you to sign the necessary documents.

Loan applications are forwarded to regional offices of NatWest. Applications for overseas study are dealt with from offices in London. Regional offices are listed in the bank's booklet. If the loan has been agreed by the bank, 1% of the total loan agreed is added to the sum of the loan, and is payable to the Association of MBAs to cover its administrative costs.

Career Development Loans

If you are not accepted for a loan under the Association scheme, or if the school to which you are applying is not approved by the Association, there is an alternative route. Provided that you (a) live or intend to train in the UK, and (b) that you intend to use that training for work in the UK or elsewhere in the EU or the European Economic Area (EAA), you can apply for a Career Development Loan (CDL) to Barclays, the Clydesdale Bank, the Royal Bank of Scotland, or the Co-operative Bank, a scheme they operate in partnership with the Department for Education and Employment. You can borrow up to 80% of your course fees, plus the costs of books, materials, and other course expenses (subject to a limit of £8 000).

Students may apply for support for up to two years of their course. If it is going to take longer than this, which might be the case with some part-time and distance learning MBAs, application should be made only for the final two years, because you have to start repaying the loan a month after the agreed term is up, unless you are unemployed. Even then the start of repayment would only be extended for five months. Obviously you would not want to be burdened with repayments before the end of your course, and the banks may not be willing to provide a loan in such circumstances anyway.

Full written details on CDLs are available from:

> Career Development Loans
> Freepost
> Newcastle upon Tyne
> NE85 1BR

The ABN/AMRO Bank: investing in an International MBA

This is a loan scheme intended to enable students from Eastern and Central Europe to attend a top European business school: INSEAD, IESE and London Business School are at present in the scheme, and others have applied to join. It is jointly operated by the ABN/AMRO Bank and the European Bank for Reconstruction and Development. Repayment periods can stretch out over as long as 13.5 years. The idea is that students repay the loan out of future earnings, which are likely to be greatly enhanced by having an MBA. However, a condition of the scheme is that borrowers should return to their home country within three years of graduating, though the assumption is that by virtue of having an MBA you would be earning a "foreign" rather than a domestic salary package. For further information, contact the admissions offices of the three schools concerned.

MBA loans in the USA

There are some low interest MBA loans schemes in the USA, run in conjunction with the Graduate Management Admission Council. They are mainly for US citizens studying at a school in the USA, but they can also now be obtained for study at selected schools abroad. For further details on this, visit the GMAC Web site, MBA Explorer at http://www.gmat.org or another one at http://www.salliemae.com.

In certain circumstances and under very strict conditions, these loans can also be obtained by foreign students studying in the USA.

Loans have one big snag – they have to be repaid, whereas with sponsorship, the **Repayment** only obligation at present is a moral one. Furthermore as the previous table shows, though the terms of the Business School Loan scheme offer flexibility during the period of study and for three months afterwards, they do require a structured repayment plan thereafter.

Although the terms are below the normal lending rate, you should recognise that the need to repay the capital and interest may have some impact on the remuneration you will need to seek on completion of the course. This may inhibit your freedom of choice in the job market when you qualify.

Students aged 30 or over who are UK taxpayers are entitled to Vocational **Tax** Training Tax Relief (VTR) on course fees for one-year full-time courses. The claim **deductibility** is submitted by the school on the student's behalf. You can get tax relief as well **of tuition fees** as a Career Development Loan or an Association of MBAs loan.

While strictly speaking tax relief is not available on fees for part-time and distance learning courses, there is at least one school that has managed to find a way round this. VTR is available for courses leading to a National Vocational Qualification. By designing modules in such a way that they are also qualification courses for an NVQ, the school has successfully claimed for tax relief on behalf of its students.

Scholarships are few, and reserved for full-time students. There are more **Scholarships,** available for study in the USA than the UK. They may cover tuition fees only, but **awards,** in some cases maintenance costs are covered as well. Examples are Fulbright **grants and** Awards, Harkness Fellowships, Kennedy Awards etc – refer to the Useful **bursaries** Contacts section at the end of the Guide.

A comprehensive listing of scholarships, grants and other awards appears in the *Grants Register*, published by Macmillan, and is to be found in all academic and public reference libraries. Check that it is the latest edition, though, which may not be the case these days because of budget cutbacks. *Study Abroad*, published by UNESCO, is another source of information.

Bursaries are sometimes available from individual schools. They may be allocated on a first come, first served basis, according to need or as a means of attracting specific types of applicants – for instance women, who are still generally under-represented at graduate business schools. A case in point is the *Sunday Times*/Lancaster University Management School Scholarship for Women, which pays full tuition fees and accommodation on campus for the 12 month full-time course. There is no central register of bursaries, and enquiries should be made to individual schools, who will give details in their literature.

Many overseas full-time students are sponsored by their governments. The local British Council is often able to inform local prospective students about such schemes (see below).

Unless otherwise stated, the following awards are restricted to holders of first **Awards/** degrees. Only organisations which offer a significant level of funding are included. A **funding for** comprehensive listing of awards is to be found in the *Grants Register*. **MBA study**

TUITION FEES AT A SAMPLE NUMBER OF ACCREDITED SCHOOLS

The tuition fees are valid for EU students and cover the entire course of study (unless stated otherwise). Some of these schools have not actually fixed their 1998 fees and the figures below may be subject to some slight adjustment. All the schools below offer at least one accredited course.

UNIVERSITY/ COLLEGE	FULL-TIME MBA	PART-TIME MBA	DISTANCE/OPEN LEARNING
Ashridge Management College	£16,000	£16,000	n/a
Aston University	£8,750	£8,750	see part-time
Bath University	£11,000	£14,000	n/a
Birmingham University	£7,500	£7,700	n/a
Bradford University	£9,250	£8,750	n/a
Bristol (Univ. of the West of England)	£5,950	£8,211	n/a
Bristol University	£12,500	£14,000	n/a
Cambridge, Judge Institute	£18,000	n/a	n/a
City University	£13,000	£18,000	n/a
Cranfield School of Management	£15,000	£19,000	n/a
De Montfort University School of Business	£6,000	£6,000	n/a
Durham University	£8,750	£7,950	£6,800
Edinburgh University	£9,300	£7,000	n/a
Glasgow University	£9,750	£2,600p.a.	n/a
Henley Management College	£14,000	£15,500	£8,995
Imperial College	£13,500	£18,800	n/a
Kingston University	n/a	£9,000	£9,000
Lancaster University	£10,500	£11,200	n/a
Leeds University Management School	£7,500	£6,000	n/a
London Business School	£26,000	£25,000	n/a
Manchester Business School	£16,000	£14,940	n/a
Manchester Metropolitan	n/a	£9,000	n/a
Middlesex University	£8,000	£4,000pa	n/a
Newcastle University	£7,500	£7,500	n/a
Nottingham University	£7,980	on application	n/a
Open University	n/a	n/a	£9,000
Sheffield University	£6,820	£11,500	n/a
Strathclyde University	£10,750	£8,925	£8,100
Warwick University	£14,000	£12,164	£7,210
Westminster University	£7,750	£5,204	n/a
SDA Bocconi	Lit32,000,000	n/a	n/a
EAP	Ff125,000	n/a	n/a
Ecole National des Ponts et Chaussées	Ff110,000	n/a	n/a
ESADE	Ptas4,400,000	Ptas3,400,000	n/a
Helsinki	Fim 65,000	n/a	n/a
IE, Instituto de Empresa	Ptas2,200,000pa	Ptas2,200,00pa	n/z
IEP, Sciences Po	£12,000	n/a	n/a
IESE	Ptas4,600,000	n/a	n/a
IMD	SFr33,000	n/a	n/a
INSEAD	Ff155,000	n/a	n/a
ISA at HEC	Ff125,000	n/a	n/a
Groupe ESC Lyon	Ff99,000	Ff120,000	n/a
Nijenrode	DFL38,000	n/a	n/a
NIMBAS	DFL37,500	DFL47,500	n/a
Rotterdam	DFL42,500	DFL67,500	n/a
Harvard	$25,000p.a.	n/a	n/a
Stanford Graduate School of Business	$23,100p.a.	n/a	n/a
Amos Tuck, Dartmouth College	$24,900p.a.	n/a	n/a
Darden, University of Virginia	$ 20,249p.a.	n/a	n/a

© Association of MBAs, May 1998

Contact addresses are listed in the appendices at the back of this book.

The Association of MBAs/Hobsons Publishing Scholarship
An award of a £10 000 scholarship to an applicant to an Association accredited school anywhere in Europe. Contact Rachel McClure at Hobsons Publishing, 159-173 St John Street, London EC1V 4DR. Tel: 0171 336 6633, fax 0171 608 1034 or email rachel.maclure@hobsons.co.uk.

British Council
There are a limited number of grants for study in the UK funded or administered by the British government. Information on these and on application procedures can be obtained through the local British Council, High Commission or Embassy. Competition for grants is intense, and you should apply at least a year before the start of the programme. It is essential to apply before you leave your own country, and that is where you will be interviewed. You will not be eligible once you arrive in the UK.

British Universities North America Club (BUNAC)
For students who already have funding, BUNAC offers ten 'topping up' awards to recent British graduates; tenable in USA and Canada only. Application deadline: end of March. Contact: BUNAC.

Career Development Loans
Barclays Bank, Clydesdale Bank, the Co-operative Bank and the Royal Bank of Scotland offer loans of between £300 and £8 000 to assist in paying for up to two years' vocational education or training, plus (if relevant) up to one year's practical experience where it forms part of the training. Contact: individual banks.

Charles R. E. Bell Fund Scholarships
Awards for UK domiciles engaged in commerce and for teachers in commercial education; also available for non-graduates; tenable for one year; not to exceed £1 500 in the first instance, but with possibility of additional £1 500. Application deadline: 31 December. Details from: London Chamber of Commerce.

Frank Knox Fellowships
Four awards for UK citizens who are graduates of a UK university or polytechnic, for study at Harvard; tenable for one year, with possible renewal for a second; includes a stipend, plus health and tuition fees; persons already in the USA are ineligible. Application deadline: mid-October. Details from: Frank Knox Fellowships.

Fulbright Awards
Fifteen academic awards covering round-trip travel and maintenance for graduates

with a minimum 2.1 grade from a UK university to spend one academic year studying the MBA at a US business school. If you wish to complete the two-year US MBA, you have to arrange your own funding in the second year, but an increasing number of Fulbright Awards are now sponsored by blue chip employers, many of them US firms active in the UK, in which case there is no difficulty obtaining further funding. Deadline for applications, leading to an interview, for the 1999/2000 academic year is 6 November 1998. Send a self-addressed A4 envelope with a 39p stamp to the British Programme Administrator at the address given in the Appendices, or check the Fulbright Commission website for futher details.

Fulbright Commission, Educational Advisory Service

Provides comprehensive list of awards for postgraduate (and undergraduate) study in the USA; same organisation but separate office to that which administers Fulbright Awards. Details from: Educational Advisory Service, Fulbright Commission.

Kennedy Scholarships

Up to 12 scholarships annually for study at MIT or Harvard; open to individuals who are in their final year at university, or who have graduated not earlier than three years prior to applying; stipend, plus travel and tuition fees. Application deadline: 25 October. Details from: Kennedy Memorial Trust.

Marion and Samuel T Pendleton Fellowship

Award covering tuition fees, cost of living stipend, and travel expenses for MBA study at University of Virginia; applicants must be under 26 years of age. Application deadline: January. Details from: Colgate Darden Graduate School, University of Virginia.

Rotary Foundation Ambassadorial Scholarships

For one year's expenses (with top limit), including round-trip transportation, on-campus board, tuition fees, and limited expenses; applicants must be sponsored by a local Rotary Club. Application deadline: April. Details from: Rotary Foundation.

The Mary Lugard US $20,000 Memorial MBA Scholarship

Offered by Edition XII, this award is open to anyone applying to and accepted by one of 50 leading international business schools. With your application you must state that you are applying for the Edition XII award, since the sum is paid directly to the school. Contact the Scholarship Administrator, Edition XII Ltd, 10 Regents Wharf, All Saints Street, London N1 9RL. Tel: 0171 833 0120, fax: 0171 923 5505 or website http://www.edition xii.co.uk.

The Sainsbury Management Fellowship Scheme

This scholarship is for UK citizens between 26 and 34, who have a first or upper second in engineering or a closely allied subject and either have Chartered Engineer status or be on the way to achieving it. It covers the course fees of an MBA at INSEAD, IMD, Theseus, the Rotterdam School of Management or in some circumstances at another business school of similar status outside the UK. There is an initial shortlisting stage, sometimes followed by an interview, and then a final selection process once your place has been confirmed. Applications can be made at any time, but preferably four months before the start of the MBA programme. Further details from: The Sainsbury Management Fellowship Scheme, The Royal Academy of Engineering.

Thouron Awards of the University of Pennsylvania

12 awards tenable at the University of Pennsylvania; covers tuition and fees, plus monthly allowance of $860; contact university direct for course information and application forms. Application deadline: November. Details from: Thouron Awards.

Applying for a scholarship

The Fulbright Commission has produced a guidance note for those applying for Fulbright Scholarships, but the advice they give is also generic for those applying for scholarships generally.[2]

- Know the funding body's mission. Why do they want to shell out the money?
- Try and find out who is on the interview panel. They may be listed in *Who's Who* or on the Internet.
- Focus on how your studies correlate with your career path and explain what you will contribute to your field and to the programme generally.
- Think of the possible questions and research and rehearse your answers.
- Try and get hold of other previous winners and ask them how the interview was conducted and how they handled it.

Some scholarship awards may be partly based on a short essay. If the choice of topic is left to you, it's a good idea to show that you know your way around what is being written in places like the FT, *The Economist, Human Resources* and the business pages of quality newspapers and to draw on your personal experience of management.

[2] 'The Interview', *Transatlantic Study*, Spring 1998, The Fulbright Commission.

6 | Surfing the learning curve

A first or second class honours degree, or an equivalent professional qualification, or a diploma in management studies, or the foreign equivalent of any of these things gained at a recognised institution abroad is, except in a rare number of instances, a prerequisite to being accepted on to an MBA programme, irrespective of whether the mode of study is full-time or one of the numerous part-time options. However, there are some big differences between studying for an MBA and for a first degree, or indeed between an MBA and other forms of postgraduate degree.

One difference is that for a large part of the time you are learning as a member of a mutually supporting or self-help group, rather than by solitary study. This is to a large extent true also of distance or open learning and the faculty will encourage you to form such a group with people living near you. The other big difference is the sheer amount of work involved in an MBA programme. If you have done a first degree, you will be aware that it is quite possible, if you are fairly bright, to get a good second or even a first without a huge effort, and without attending boring lectures or those held too early in the morning or too soon after lunch. This is simply not the case with the MBA. The work keeps on coming at you in the form of reading, preparation for group and individual assignments and case studies, as well as actual lectures. The universal opinion is that if you don't keep up with it all, you are soon left hopelessly behind. It is not something you can put aside and swot up at critical points.

So, what happens if you are ill, or if, as happens with part-time or distance learning programmes, you simply get swamped with the demands of your day job? Your first line of defence in that case is the self-help group mentioned above. 'We try to see that no one fails', is a widely repeated comment, and members do help each other with lecture notes and with coaching if one individual in the group misses a class or preparation for an assignment, or has difficulty in an area where another has experience and expertise. It is for this reason that many schools are extremely reluctant to give exemptions to those who, because they already have a professional qualification in a particular field, see no reason to take that part of the course – besides which, experts often discover they knew less than they thought they did when challenged by an intelligent fellow student from another area of endeavour. Finding out that they knew less than they thought they did about their own subject, is a reaction reported by many MBA students.

On distance learning programmes too, your tutors should be able to advise and help you in these circumstances – provided, of course, that you tell them what is happening. With the increasing flexibility of programmes, he or she might, for instance, suggest that you drop out of that part of the programme temporarily and join another group at a later date.

However, the heavy work commitment right from the start of the programme does give rise to a number of suggestions from students in the light of experience, and, in some cases, with the wisdom of hindsight.

- Brush up on knowledge, and develop computer skills before you start. The knowledge area which is most often quoted, is statistics. Keyboard skills are the other important technical skill to develop. There are plenty of people around in business schools who will spring to your aid with software problems – indeed, many of the schools have a help desk in their computer suite – but no one can help you churn out pages of word processing, though in fact there is more to it than that. Students report that the appearance of your written work also matters. You are given better grades for a well laid out, attractive-looking document, than for one that simply consists of slabs of indigestible-looking typescript. It has also been noted that case studies, a key part of the learning process on MBA programmes, are being increasingly presented in a form that presupposes considerable familiarity with IT skills.[1]
- Don't underestimate the workload. Sheila Cameron of the OUBS, reckons that students taking a distance learning MBA should think in terms of 12–15 hours per week of study, in other words an additional day and a half per week over and above your daytime job. If you have a partner or a family, make sure they know and will go along with what you are letting yourself (and them) in for; they will not be seeing much of you until you have completed the programme, and if you need to give them some of your quality time, make sure that you all agree with the agenda for that, and for the time and space you need for studying. Some spouses say that MBA stands for 'Married But Away'.
- If you are on some form of part-time or distance learning programme, make sure that you get at least moral support from your employer and your immediate boss. This is obviously somewhat easier if they are sponsoring you, but it by no means follows automatically. On the contrary, there is a disturbing amount of anecdotal evidence that employers are not as understanding as they should be about the need to go easy on your work-load at times – especially before examinations – or about the logistics of attending a part-time course, such as the fact that you may have to leave the office early on certain days of the week, especially if you have some distance to travel. It is therefore a good idea to get your immediate boss, as well as his or her superior, involved by encouraging them to visit your chosen school on an open day. Many also advocate that you should endeavour to enlist the support of a company mentor or personal champion during your course.
- Before you sign up for an MBA programme, consider how it will fit in with your career, and with what you know of your employer's plans during its duration. Are you likely to be relocated or moved to another job which could clash with your studies? Is the person who is championing you likely to continue being able to do so?
- If you have any personal commitments such as fixing your flat or your car, attend to them before you start. You will not have the time thereafter until you have completed your course.

[1] 'Bringing Case Studies to Life', the *Financial Times*, 20 April 1998.

Culture shocks

An interesting point made by full-time students, is that the conditions of acceptance on a programme – at least three years' work experience (many have more) and a good track record – mean that they were probably earning a good salary at the time they started the programme, and that they have to get used to being a 'poor student' again. One student said, 'My company car was a BMW, and now I get about by bike'. Another commented that, like many of his colleagues, he did not even have the right clothes when he started: 'I had lots of suits and sports clothes, but nothing I could wear in class'. He recommended that in your preliminary visits to schools, you should take note of what people wear and lay in the appropriate wardrobe.

That however, is only one, and perhaps superficial, aspect of the return to student life. More important is to acquire the right mind-set for participation. Many people who have had some success in their careers and seem set for higher things in their organisations are by nature competitive, but the MBA is not a competitive course. Some schools do award distinctions to the top 10% or so at the conclusion, but there are no 'firsts' or 'seconds' as there are in undergraduate degrees, and the emphasis is on collaboration rather than competition. Trying to climb to the top by withholding information or knowledge from others in your group is not only frowned upon, it is positively counter-productive, because business schools do not see management as an activity for loners, no matter how bright.

Indeed, they make the point that if it were otherwise, there would be no reason why you should attend a business school at all – you could just as easily get all the technical knowledge you need from one of the growing number of textbooks claiming to replicate the content of an MBA programme. That, incidentally, is why the Association does not accredit distance learning programmes that do not call for at least some face to face contact between participants and tutors.

The five- to seven-strong group or syndicate with whom you will be working, will be assembled by the faculty at the start of the programme or at the start of particular parts of it, and in distance learning or part-time modes, they will endeavour to group together participants who live near each other, so that they can meet informally as well as during actual study sessions. They will also try to strike a mix of complementary skills, industries, backgrounds, and nationalities. The latter also applies, incidentally, to those on full-time programmes and residential modules of part-time or distance learning ones. Some syndicates, schools readily admit, work better than others. Participants do not always get on equally well, though the success of groups, and hence the basis on which they are graded, does depend on the members eventually finding common ground. In other words, they are just like the real business world, and that is the object of the exercise.

Learning to study

The MBA, as previously stated, is a post-experience qualification. It follows, therefore, that it will be some years since you studied material in a formal sense, and that is a skill which needs to be both re-learned and adapted to the demands of this particular kind of programme. One of the key features mentioned by students is the enormous amount of reading that is required, not just of textbooks, but of case material in preparation for assignments and lectures. You will have to be prepared to be overwhelmed with facts and figures. The art is to be able to prioritise and pick out the points of real importance, and rely to some extent on team members who, by virtue of their previous experience, are able to point others in the right direction. It takes practice, which explains the widespread comment that the first term is, or appears to be, the hardest.

These skills develop during the course of the progamme, and you will learn to focus on the points tutors look for, both in class discussion and in written work: the ability to analyse the information, grasp the problem, show evidence that you have mastered the appropriate techniques, and be able to present your findings clearly and persuasively. However, there are seldom any right or wrong answers, except in the case of purely quantitative questions, which is something students with a numerical or scientific background sometimes find hard to come to terms with. Equally, 'poets', whose previous study and experience was in less precise fields, find it hard to assemble and present numerical evidence. For a good, if chilling account of their difficulties, read Peter Robinson's *Snapshots From Hell: The Making of an MBA* (Nicholas Brealey). It is actually about taking an MBA at Stanford in the USA, but many who have read it say it strikes a familiar note here as well.

Exams and assessments

The core modules of the programme are examined, though in some cases the exams may be of the "open book" variety – that is, you are allowed to bring in and consult books in order to answer the questions. You will usually have to pass all the exams, but your overall assessment will depend not just on the exams, but also on written assignments, the work of your syndicate and your contribution to it. Electives are generally not examined, but assessed on written papers.

The dissertation

The dissertation at the end of the programme is where you are expected to show that you are able to relate what you have learned in groups, in the lecture room, and in your reading, to a real business or organisational problem. For this reason, it is regarded as an extremely important part of the programme, and there have been instances where students have failed the entire course because of an unsatisfactory dissertation. However, if you mastered the techniques of producing written assignments earlier on, the dissertation should not hold any undue terrors, because the faculty look for much the same criteria. Most schools also hold seminars on the preparation of dissertations, and at Strathclyde, a module on project methodology is an assessed part of the dissertation itself.

Schools recommend that you should start thinking about a topic fairly quickly, during the second stage of the programme, because you have to get approval for the subject from your tutor as well as find a company or organisation who will let you do your research there. This is much easier for sponsored students, whose project will generally be an in-company one, but you will have to make sure that the person who agreed to your topic at the time is still there when you start work on it. In the case of a distance learning or part-time programme stretching out over three years, that is by no means certain these days. One student, in fact, reported that two changes of management in her company meant that she also had to change the subject of her dissertation twice.

Britain is the world's major provider of MBA courses for students from abroad. There are a number of reasons for this:

- **Language** – for most of the world, the language of business is English, which rules out a number of otherwise excellent programmes in non-English-speaking countries. Also, from a purely convenience point of view, students from anglophone countries are likely to find it easier to adjust to living conditions in an English-speaking country
- **Cost** – average fees and living costs are lower in the UK than in the USA; differences between the UK and the rest of Europe have narrowed with the rise in sterling, but don't rely on this lasting during your period of study
- **Availability** – in some European countries, notably Germany, there is only a very limited availability of MBA programmes – though this may be about to change
- **Reputation and prestige** – though there are business schools in many newly industrialised countries, notably in the Asia-Pacific region, they do not as yet match European and North American schools in this respect; the franchised operations of some European and US business schools in Asia should be approached with caution. Here again, whether a school offering a franchise is itself accredited by the Association would be significant.

A major difficulty experienced by students from abroad, is actually choosing a school without being able to see it for themselves first, though quite a number do make the effort to do so, and talk to several schools before making their choice. Reputation, in the areas of management in which they are particularly interested, is a major factor here, though other circumstances can also play a part. For instance, a student from Iceland who is a single mother, took into account the availability of suitably priced accommodation, and the proximity and quality of schools for her offspring, when making her choice.

British Council offices do little more than provide lists, and the absence of rankings makes it difficult to choose between business schools. A growing number of schools do make presentations in centres abroad, and these can be useful in terms of providing answers to the 'crunch questions' set out in Chapter 3. You should also ask whether they have any local graduates to whom you can talk – they are more likely to give you an unbiased opinion than the representatives of the schools themselves. Once again, the key, bottom-line question is: 'If you had the choice again, would you go to that school? – or have you heard of another one that you now feel might have been better?'

For their part, the main questions a school will ask of you, will be about your CV, your qualifications, work experience, and references. If your qualifications are borderline in terms of the demands the programme will make, you will be asked to take a GMAT – expect that a score of at least 550 will be required, with an equal balance between the verbal and numerical scores. If they judge that your English is not up to the required standard, you will have to take either an IELTS or TOEFL exam. Remember though, that both understanding and being understood is extremely important, because so much work takes place in groups and syndicates.

Some students from abroad also comment that, at least initially, they have difficulty in understanding regional accents, both inside and outside the school.

Although English does not have any real dialects in the way some European languages do, getting street directions from, say, a Glaswegian, can pose problems even for a Londoner, never mind a foreigner.

In general, reports from overseas students who are over here are very positive, though the weather is a frequent complaint among those from warm countries. Manchester Business School, which produces a booklet for overseas students, warns them that extra clothing may be an unanticipated cost. Cultural differences can also be problem – not racism, but differences in style. 'We're used to helping each other more', says a student from Pakistan. 'Things are a bit less comradely in Britain'.

Another important point about cultural differences, made by both students and tutors, is about learning styles and attitudes. In some cultures – notably, it is said, some Asian ones – confrontation and disagreement with teachers and colleagues is regarded as disrespectful. British students take a more robust view on this, and lively argument is seen as an important part of learning. Foreign students do get used to this after a while, but one Asian student then made the comment – with which others in his group emphatically agreed – that he would have to 'unlearn' that style of discussion when he returned to the company which had sponsored him.

A confrontational approach to learning is at least equally pronounced in US schools, but an American student compares the atmosphere in her UK school very favourably with the highly competitive environment in the US where, she says, 'People have their eye on the job market from the very beginning, and are very concerned about their grades'. She does, however, remark that students from abroad have to make an active effort to mix. 'There's a tendency for national groups to stick together. I share a house with Americans, and most of what I do socially is with other Americans'.

She says she is 'having a ball' doing a term at a leading UK school; others see the social aspect differently. An Australian student, combining a modular MBA here with a demanding job in Africa, talks of the conflict between work, study, and leisure, and says that the price of an MBA is giving up your social life for the duration of the course. 'If you start dropping behind, you've lost it', he warns, but, like others, he says that the work is not actually difficult – there's just a great deal of it. 'Don't treat it like a year out', says a Moroccan student. 'It's much more intensive than a year at work'. He also advises brushing up on maths. 'In spite of what they say about the importance of soft skills, maths is an important aspect'. This is a view echoed by many British students, though there is an additional dimension of difficulty for those whose native language is not English. A Korean student made the point that problems of comprehension in reading assignments and case studies added about 20% extra time to his workload, at least in the early stages of his course.

So what about the business advantages? For a German manager taking a modular programme, it's not just the quality of the course at a blue chip school selected after a lot of research (which did include looking at rankings in German magazines), it's the contact with fellow students. 'You come on a course with a lot of stereotypes about different nationalities. You correct some of them. In others, there's an element of truth and you learn to live with that – very important for anyone operating in an international business environment'.

A New Zealander who left a highly paid job as a banker and is sponsoring himself on a one-year programme adds to that. 'You get a cultural mix I just wouldn't get at home, but which reflects the way a global business like the one I'm in is going. It opens up a whole range of possibilities for employment anywhere in the world, and I'm making contacts here with fellow students, with faculty, and with people coming on short courses who one meets round the bar at night, that are opening up the kind of opportunities I'm eventually looking for'.

School profiles

The best way of giving readers a feel for what it is actually like taking an MBA, is to present profiles of a number of different schools, showing a variety of modes of delivery of the course. The choice is by no means intended to indicate rankings; it is merely a representative sample – which is rotated in each edition of the Guide – to give readers some idea of what they might expect to find at a variety of Association of MBAs-accredited schools. However, in the words of one of the periodic *Financial Times* surveys of business schools: 'The best course is to visit the institution – and wade through the literature, not just for the course description, but basic facts about duration, cost, placement success and so on . . . word of mouth, surveys and consultants go so far, but there is no substitute for meeting deans and directors face to face', to which list we would also add students and recent alumni. Ask about open days which will give you a chance to do that and get your sponsor to go along with you, if you are looking for sponsorship.

Ashridge Management College

Ashridge Management College is one of the leading management and organization development centres in Europe. Its primary activities are the delivery of short-executive courses, research and consultancy. Its MBA programme is small in comparison to other leading business schools, but is seen as a flagship programme. **General background**

Ashridge preaches the small is beautiful view of the MBA experience. Places on its full-time MBA are limited to 30, which means class sizes are much smaller than on most other MBA programmes. Unlike the large lecture theatres of some other business schools the classroom atmosphere is up close and personal.

The profile of Ashridge MBA participants is also considerably older than that of other MBA programmes, with an average age of around 33 or 34, compared to an average of 27 or 28 on other programmes. This is no accident. Ashridge firmly believes that the MBA should be a post-experience degree, and insists on a minimum of five years' work experience.

Its executive development heritage and history – it is the UK's best known non-university business school – also gives the Ashridge MBA its distinctive 'hands on' character. A number of factors differentiate the programme from others in the UK.

A particular feature of the Ashridge MBA is that it is structured around a year-long consultancy project carried out in a real company. The programme is modular, with learning alternating between intensive periods in the classroom and assignments carried out in the host company. This unusual approach reflects the Ashridge philosophy that learning should be practical and relevant to the real world of business. (Members of faculty have all spent time in industry before becoming academics).

For this reason, it appeals to more mature participants: many Ashridge MBA participants have already risen to senior positions. Many of those who apply to Ashridge report that they also apply to take the prestigious Sloan Master's Programme offered in Europe by London Business School, and which also attracts more mature managers.

Self-development is a key element of the Ashridge approach, and this is driven by the notion of a three-way learning contract – between the individual, the college and the sponsoring company. The Ashridge MBA also places great emphasis on team work, and the development of soft skills to complement the hard analytical components of the traditional MBA. In particular, Ashridge regards the development of leadership skills as one of its core competences, and boasts that a significant proportion of its MBA graduates make it onto the main board of their organizations within two years of graduating.

Although the term is more usually applied to part-time programmes, Ashridge describes its full-time MBA as an Executive MBA, reflecting the more senior status of participants.

The Ashridge MBA is also among the most expensive in the UK, with the basic cost of fees around £17 000. However, for self-sponsoring participants the high cost is partly offset by a fee from the sponsor company for their consultancy project. In 1998, for example, the minimum fee was £10 000.

Although the school can justly claim an international outlook in terms of its teaching and does draw applicants from as far afield as China and parts of Africa, the majority of participants are from Europe. Of those on the 1998 MBA programme, for example, some 88 per cent of students were European, with just over half (51 per cent) coming from the UK. Of the remainder, another five per cent were from Eastern Europe, four per cent were from Asia, with just over one per cent from the Middle East and Africa. Just over a quarter of those on the MBA programme in 1998 were women. Around 30 per cent of Ashridge MBAs are sponsored, with the remaining 70 per cent paying for themselves.

Admission procedures and criteria

Ashridge places great emphasis on the idea that MBA is a post-experience management qualification. Successful candidates are drawn from a variety of organizational and cultural backgrounds but are required to have at least five years' relevant work experience and to sit the GMAT exam as part of the application process (Ashridge doesn't specify a GMAT score).

With only a small number of places available on the MBA programme, Ashridge can afford to be fussy about who it takes. Successful candidates typically possess a first or second class honours degree. However, with its emphasis on work experience, Ashridge will consider candidates who do not have a first degree providing they demonstrate the necessary level of written, oral and analytical skills to cope with the intensity of study. A rigorous selection procedure involves telephone and face-to-face interviews.

According to the College, the ideal Ashridge MBA participant will:

- have a minimum of five years' relevant work experience at a middle to senior level in either a managerial or specialist role (usually in an international or multi-cultural environment)
- have demonstrated outstanding career progression to date
- in most cases, have a degree or equivalent professional qualification
- have senior management potential
- be committed to self-development
- be a minimum of 27-years-old
- have a good GMAT score and TOEFL (if appropriate).

The one-year, full-time programme commences in January and the two-year, part-time programme in October. Consideration of applicants is on-going for both programmes, and places are offered, after interview with the intake director, on a first-come, first-served basis. Applications can be made in tandem with registration to sit GMAT.

Applicants employed by charitable organizations are invited to apply for a college bursary. Ashridge offers bursaries to applicants from Eastern Europe under its Eastern European Bursary Scheme.

Course content

The Ashridge one-year, full-time MBA is modular, something which seems to attract many of those who apply there. As such, learning alternates between intensive periods in the classroom and time spent on project and assignment work.

Unusually for an MBA, the programme is built around a major consultancy project which is carried out for a sponsoring organization and lasts a whole year. The main project addresses an issue of real strategic or operational importance to the host company. On the two-year programme, this means that the sponsoring company benefits from a useful piece of internal consultancy as well as developing a high flying manager.

On the full-time programme, participants are typically able to negotiate a fee of between £10 000 and £12 000, which helps cover the cost of the course. This component gives Ashridge its highly practical focus – something which is central to its philosophy.

As well as the main project, participants complete 12 assignments, 11 of them in the host company. The assignments are functionally-based and provide the 'building blocks for the consultancy project'. They cover six key areas: business policy; finance; human resources and organization behaviour; IT and decision science; marketing; and operations management. In all, students are expected to spend about 40 days on the assignments, and 80 days on the consultancy project.

A key element of the Ashridge approach to the MBA is that learning should be relevant and placed in the context of the real business world. The programme places great importance on the practical application of the techniques taught in the classroom. Along with the analytical skills of the traditional MBA, Ashridge prides itself on the development of soft skills, especially leadership, and communication.

The design of the MBA programme reflects the College's extensive experience in the delivery of executive development courses. Teaching is deliberately cross-functional, with each module combining several management disciplines. Ashridge makes effective use of a range of techniques including the case study method (which accounts for roughly 25 per cent of teaching), workshops, business games, computer simulations, and outdoor leadership development exercises.

Module One: 10 Jan. – 5 Feb.

- Key Learning Areas: The Business Environment; The Marketing Concept; The International Economy; Financial Concepts and Analysis; Production Management; Market Research; Measuring Business Performance; Marketing Analysis; Social and Technical Change; Analysing Operations; Marketing Segmentation; and Business Modelling.
- Personal Skills Development: Presentation Skills; Time Management; Computer Literacy; Information Retrieval; Working in Teams.

In-company module.

Module Two: 28 Mar. – 16 Apr.

- Key Learning Areas: Marketing Tools; Human Resource Systems; Sources of Finance; Information Systems; Marketing in Action; Quantitative Techniques; Long and Short-term Investment Decisions; Planning and Controlling Production; Forecasting; New Product Development; Recruitment and Selection; Cultural Differences; and Branding.
- Personal Skills Development: Leadership and Team-building; Giving and Receiving Feedback; Influencing; Interviewing; Project Planning; Research Methodology.

In-company module.

Module Three: 6 Jun. – 2 Jul.

- Key Learning Areas: Industry Structure and Competitive Analysis; Organisational Culture; Globalisation of Industry; Capital Investment Appraisal; Corporate Re-engineering; Management Accounting; Service as Competitive Advantage; Activity-based Costing; Diversification; Core Competencies; Quality Management; Industrial and Consumer Marketing; Customer Profitability; International Business; Designing a Marketing Plan; Mergers and Acquisitions.
- Personal Skills Development: Project Management; Media Handling; Appraisal and Counselling; Critical Thinking; Decision-making; Creativity.

In-company module

International study week

Module Four: 5 Sept. – 1 Oct.

- Key Learning Areas: International Finance; Organisational Structure and Design; Strategic Modelling; Relationship Marketing; Corporate Transformation; Supply Chain Management; Implementing Strategic Change; Financial Engineering; Strategic HR Management; Implementing New Products, Processes and Technology; Marketing Across Borders; Currency Management; Theory of Constraints; and Business Ethics.
- Personal Skills Development: Project Implementation; Negotiating; Mentoring; Cross-cultural Awareness.

Examinations (Oct.)

In-company module

Final project submission (Dec.).

The degree (validated by City University in London) is awarded on the basis of a number of methods of assessment, including four days of examinations.

Founded as the College of Bonhommes, a monastery of an order of Augustine canons, Ashridge Management College enjoys a magnificent setting on the edge of the Hertfordshire Chilterns. The architecture and feel of the campus, which includes the original monastic cloisters, contribute to a reflective mood that will appeal to any one with a sense of history. **What it's like**

Although it is just a few miles from the M1 and M25, and within easy reach of Heathrow airport, the location is somewhat isolated as far as night life is concerned. The College does have a good bar, however, and there are also a number of local inns providing good fare.

Students talk about the close-knit community of the MBA programme. With fewer than 30 students in each intake, classes are exceptionally small by MBA standards and allow a high level of access to members of faculty and facilities. Students get to know each other well.

With an average age of 33 to 34, the profile of Ashridge students tends to be slightly older than other MBA programmes. The College tends to attract more senior managers in both senses of the word, and there are a few grey hairs evident around the class. This also contributes to a more co-operative atmosphere where team work is emphasized as much as individual achievement. As one student put it: 'We don't have to prove that we could be good managers. Everyone here already has a solid track record in management.' On the other side, some students say that more competition between students might add to the experience. Balancing this, however, is the emphasis the programme places on developing interpersonal skills, especially leadership.

The learning process is heavily centred on the individual driving their own development. This and the maturity of participants means Ashridge MBAs require less spoon-feeding than those at other schools, and have an opportunity to develop a capacity for independent thought that can serve them well in their future careers.

In recent years an international study week has been added to the full-time programme. In 1997, for example students spent time in Budapest and Vienna, where they visited enterprises, met local business leaders and sampled the cultural highlights.

Ashridge offers excellent facilities including an impressive Learning Resource Centre, which is open 24-hours a day. It also has a well-equipped health and fitness centre and acres of scenery.

0830–1300 Lectures **A day in the life...**

1300–1400 Lunch

1400–1800 Lectures and discussion groups

1900–2130 Dinner (sometimes with guest speaker)

After dinner – Self-managed learning/preparation for next day's lectures.

Career management aspects Ashridge places great emphasis on the importance of self-development, an approach which also applies to career management. The college does not have a dedicated placement office, but provides good library facilities to help students research prospective employers.

The small size of the one-year MBA intake makes it harder for Ashridge to persuade recruiters and headhunters to make the trip to the College campus. Many students receive job offers from their project companies. (Participants on the two-year programme are company sponsored.) The constant flow of senior managers attending executive courses at Ashridge also provides a rich networking opportunity for full-time MBAs who keep an eye on the notice board.

A special career development centre in the Learning Resource Centre (LRC) allows students to access books, journals, specialized information files and a multimedia guide, relating to the issue of personal career management and development. The LRC also offers access to a number of financial and press databases, including Dun & Bradstreet, 'FT Discovery', 'Reuters Real Time' and 'Reuters Business Briefing', to assist students in researching target companies.

Faculty highly rated by students Steve Seymour (Finance)

Narendra Laljani (Marketing)

John Constable (Strategy)

Anthony Mitchell (Operations Management)

Jack Hardie (Information Technology)

Aston Business School: The Full-time MBA

General background Aston is one of a number of business schools within a 50-mile radius of Birmingham. From a student point of view this has the advantage that competition keeps them on their toes. The feeling among those questioned about their reason for choosing Aston rather than say, Warwick or Birmingham, is that it offers a well-regarded MBA that is also good value for money – the school rated a 4 in the 1996 Research Assessment exercise, which represents a steady improvement over the years.

Fees of £8 000 (£9 750 for students from outside the EU) are pitched at around the average, while living costs in Birmingham are reasonable. There is plenty of accommodation on and around the campus, ten minutes away from the city centre, and Birmingham has transformed itself visually and culturally in the last 25 years. It is also a major business and industrial centre, as it has been since the last century. In fact one of the advantages of the school is that it has strong links with some major companies who have headquarters in the Midlands – Powergen, Rover and Lloyds TSB, to name just a few.

Aston Business School is part of Aston University which was established in the first wave of 'new' universities in the mid-1960s. Its MBA programme has been going for over 20 years and although the numbers on the full-time course are fairly small – about 60 students, of whom 30% are women – there is now a 3000 strong body of MBA alumni, not to mention those who have graduated from the school's various MSc courses. Aston has established alliances with other schools on the Continent in offering European study weeks or the option of doing a term abroad as part of the programme.

The Aston MBA has two unusual and welcome aspects. One that applies to its part-time programme is that modules of in-company or tailored courses can count as credits towards the MBA itself or towards the award of a certificate or diploma, which meets the criticism, often expressed by managers that they have nothing to show for taking a course that doesn't offer 'letters after your name'. For prospective MBA students this form of training has the further advantage that it enables them to put a toe in the water, before making the decision to plunge into a total commitment to an MBA. The school as a whole is one the leaders in continuing professional development in the area.

The other interesting feature is the emphasis on flexibility of delivery, which means that in practice it is possible to introduce at least an element of distance learning into one's study – apart from the fact that the school now runs a fully fledged, Association of MBAs accredited distance learning programme. All lectures are videoed as a matter of course and faculty members are trained in video techniques. This means that if you miss a lecture, or find that your attention has wandered during it, you can catch up by getting the video. The technology for preparing them seems very sophisticated and students describe them as 'very impressive'. You also have some flexibility of choice. Though the Aston MBA is a generalist one, you can choose your electives in such a way that your MBA degree can be awarded in one of several designated specialisms.

Admission procedures and criteria

The admission criteria are the usual ones of an honours degree (or equivalent professional qualification) from a recognised institution in the UK or abroad, plus at least three years of work experience – indeed some students clearly have a good deal more than that, since the age range shown in the book of student profiles (sent to prospective employers as part of the school's career support) runs from the early 20s to the late 40s. Foreign students whose first language is not English – and again the profiles indicate that the student body is quite multinational – will normally be required to have minimum TOEFL score of 600. The school may also require a GMAT score of at least 550.

The ratio of acceptances to applications is about 1:5, but the school may suggest, if you do not meet the MBA criteria immediately, that you enrol in a business-related MSc course in the first instance. A wide range of these is available at Aston and they will generally count as credits towards the foundation modules of the MBA, as will completion of certain short executive courses.

Course content

The full-time course starts in October. In each term there are four modules. The first set of modules are the basic building blocks of management – finance, marketing, operations management and organisational behaviour. These are followed by a further set of 'integrating' modules which introduce a more strategic and broader viewpoint, for instance in examining the economic environment of business. Performance in each subject is assessed, either by examination or coursework.

The electives follow in the third term. You have to take four out of a choice of around 30 subjects, which vary slightly each year, according to demand. In the final term comes the project, completed by a dissertation. The school prides itself on the fact that its excellent contacts with local businesses – many of whom now have global ramifications – enable it to provide challenging live projects, which in many cases open the way to a future career. The project is part of the overall process of assessment, which is based on individual work, coursework, exam results and the project itself.

What it's like

Faculty at Aston say the course content is 'not over mathematical'. There is no overall agreement amongst students about any part of the programme being more difficult than others. Some say that the degree of difficulty you experience depends on your work background and personal skill sets. However, they say that the curriculum is well thought out, with each topic leading into the next one and putting it in context. Various pre-course programmes are however available, for instance in English language for foreign students. The overall workload – lectures, syndicate work and private study – is estimated to amount to 50–60 hours per week. Ademola Andu (see below) stresses that you shouldn't consider work as the only objective. 'Making contacts and building relationships is an important part of the process,' he says. He is a member of a six person syndicate group, which he reckons will stay together for the rest of the course. Though a new group can be formed if the members wish this, he says about 70% stay together.

A day in the life...

One day a week consists of an intensive programme of lectures, interspersed by syndicate groups, from 9am to 9pm. There is also a day of morning lectures, from 9am to 12.30. The other days are taken up with private studies, reading and preparation for syndicate group meetings. Ademola Andu, a full-time student, reckons on a 50-plus hour week. 'You fall behind very quickly if you don't keep up with the reading,' he says. Because of family commitments – he is the father of a 7 month old baby and his wife is also studying – he sometimes goes in as early as 4 or 5 am to use the university library, which is open around the clock.

Career management aspects

Practical career help comes in a number of ways. One is directly through counselling, workshops on presentation and interview skills. Indirectly, the 3 month project – a 'live' organisational assignment carried out with the help of an academic supervisor – often leads to a job offer, or defines an area of job interest or opportunity. In addition, major employers visit the campus throughout the year and there is an active network of alumni contacts. 'Look on your year as an investment in your career,' advises Ademola, who is adding an MBA to his first degree in law.

Ossie Jones (International Business and Technology)

Peter Burcher (Operations)

Bridget Nicoulaud, Visiting Lecturer (Marketing and Law)

**Faculty
highly rated
by students**

The Australian Graduate School of Management: An Overseas MBA

Australia is beginning to match Europe in the number of MBA courses on offer. Indeed, the 40 programmes currently running there probably represent a higher ratio, per head of population, than anywhere else in the world. However only a few have the 'visiting card' status of being taken seriously by recruiters. Market leadership is a toss-up between Melbourne Business School and the Australian Graduate School of Management (AGSM), a part of the highly regarded University of New South Wales in Sydney. The rivalry between these two cities, Australia's principal commercial centres, goes back to the 19th century when, thanks to the discovery of gold, Melbourne was for a time the richest city in the world.

**General
background**

Sydney may now have the edge on Melbourne as a business and financial centre. It unarguably has a better climate, an advantage which in the case of the AGSM is reinforced by its location at Coogee, a seaside suburb about 20 minutes drive from the centre. The school attracts about 125 students a year into its 21-month full-time programme or its alternative, an 18-month accelerated programme, both of which start at the end of February.

As in Europe, the student mix is global. The Asian contingent makes up 52%, Thirty per cent are from Australia and New Zealand, and the rest come from North America, Europe (including some Brits) and Africa. They have on average six years work experience in a wide variety of fields, though business, science and engineering are the predominant ones.

For those from outside the region, the big career attraction is that going to an Australian business school can be a way of getting a job in what is, by general consent, one of the world's best places to live and work. This happens because the visa students must have to study in Australia covers the summer internship which takes place in the summer break for those doing the 21-month course. This work assignment often leads to a job offer and once an employer puts in a request for you, it is virtually certain that you will get a working visa. Otherwise it can be very difficult to get past Australia's very restrictive immigration rules.

The other advantage of the summer internship is that it is a paid assignment. That helps to set off the tuition fee, currently A$22 500 per year, half of which has to be paid as a deposit. On top of that you have to allow about A$1 200 a year for books and materials and A$1 000–1 500 a month living costs. There are, however, quite a number of scholarships and sponsorships available which cover all or part of the fees: as many as 20% of students receive some financial support of this kind. Details are sent out once you get offered a place. A major criterion here is the GMAT score. The average is 630, about the same as top schools on the global MBA circuit. AGSM has links with several of them and runs exchange programmes with places like Wharton, Chicago and London Business School, which also have two-year programmes. Indeed, the aspiration of AGSM is to be the LBS of the Asia-Pacific region.

Like the top European schools, it has built up excellent contacts with local business and industry. Many of the great and good of Australian business serve on the school's Council and also give lectures there. Another point of contact with the business community is through the school's large part-time MBA programme, through those attending executive courses there and of course the substantial number of alumni who have graduated from the school since it started offering MBAs in 1977. All this means that securing summer internships, mostly organised through the school, is not a problem.

Another strong point of AGSM is the financial payback. Ninety per cent of students have a job offer by the time they graduate. Data collected by the school suggests that the average start salary is A$86 500, a hefty 71% increase on incomes at entry.

Admission procedures and criteria

The admissions criteria are the ones that are almost generic for business schools – a good first degree or professional qualification, plus at least two years work experience, accompanied by references which indicate your ability to contribute to the teams and syndicate groups round which the learning process takes place. All this is set out in the application form which comes with the school brochure. Applications have to be in by the 30 November, though overseas students are advised to apply earlier than this because you also need to get a student visa, which you will only get once you are accepted. Offers of places are made as early as April in the year preceding the start of the programme.

The ratio of applicants to places is 4:1. About 1 in 4 applicants are accepted. There is no interview. Suitability is judged on the application, plus the 630 GMAT score, though this may be waived if you have a good degree from an internationally recognised university.

Course content

The full-time MBA is a six term course. Each term lasts ten weeks. The first term covers six subjects which provide what are called 'Management Foundations and Perspectives': the basic building blocks of hard and soft managerial skills. Some exemptions are available for a high level of prior knowledge in some of these subjects, though the primary aim is that everyone should have covered the same ground. That is then followed in the second and third term by a more detailed study of six out of eight 'Gateway' subjects, which focus on major management functions in more detail.

The summer placement comes at the end of the third term, though students on the accelerated programme go straight on to the next stage: an optional ten week in-company project, carried out by teams of four supervised by a member of the faculty, and other electives. These will be related to the six Gateway subjects you chose previously. For instance, where the Gateway subject is 'Marketing Concepts', the relevant elective is 'Advertising Management.' You have to do 14 out of 35 electives – an unusually large number – and two of them have to be general management topics. In the final term come the exchange visits to another leading business school, mostly in Europe or the USA, though only 30 or so students are selected to go on one of these.

What it's like

The AGSM MBA is unusual in not calling for a dissertation at the end of the programme. Otherwise the method of learning and programme delivery is the familiar one of classwork, syndicates, case studies, projects, discussion, games and simulations. Assessment is also on a broad range of criteria, mixing examination with more general assessment of contribution to the progress of the programme and to class and syndicate discussions.

Students learn from each other rather than from formal lectures, so much of the classroom work, even in the lectures, is interactive. However the programme offers a high amount of face-to-face contact with the faculty who, like the student body, have an international background. There are also frequent presentations on specialist topics by leaders of the Sydney business community and by political and government leaders.

As might be expected in a country where respect for authority is by no means automatic, assessment is a two-way process. Faculty are assessed by the students half-way through each term and again at the end of the term, not only for their teaching, but for administration and the quality of their research. The results are available for public inspection and taken seriously by course directors.

The intensive nature of the course, even when spread over two years, leaves little time for leisure, but the University campus is well equipped for every kind of sporting activity and the beach is close by. Accommodation is fairly easy to find – there is help available about this from the UNSW Housing Office – and less expensive than closer to the centre, though students from abroad are advised to begin flat hunting early. Sydney is regarded as possibly the most expensive Australian city. British students are currently getting the benefit of a favourable exchange rate but it would be wise to remember that currencies can swing sharply both ways – as Asian students discovered during 1997.

A day in the life...

0830–1300 Lectures

1300–1400 Guest lectures, on campus presentations by potential recruiters

1400–1800 Tutorials, discussions, syndicate and group work relating to morning lectures

1800–2100 Dinner and relaxation

2100–2300 Individual preparation for next day's lectures

Career management aspects

One reason why AGSM graduates seem to do so well financially upon completing their studies may be because there is strong backup on job search related aspects from the school's Career Management Office almost from the start of the programme. It ranges from practical advice on job search techniques and general career guidance (e.g. for those aiming at a change in career direction), to facilitating the summer internships which often lead to an eventual job offer. Many of these come through the 3 000 strong network of AGSM alumni, who are scattered throughout the Asia–Pacific region, and with whom the school maintains active contact in a number of ways. The prestige of AGSM also means that it is an automatic source of management recruitment for a wide variety of blue chip organisations throughout the region.

Faculty highly rated by students

The assessment procedure mentioned earlier act as a built-in form of quality control, but the following were particularly singled out:

Professor Frederick Hilmer (General Management)

Professor John Roberts (Marketing)

Professor Robert Kohn (Operations and Statistics)

SDA Bocconi: The Full-Time MBA

General background

SDA Bocconi in Milan, the business school of Bocconi University, belongs to the select band of the ten or so European business schools, regarded by headhunters and recruiters as being in the premier division. Bocconi is, in common with other leading Italian universities, a private, not a state institution – Italian state universities are vast places which by law have to admit large student numbers and have an appropriately high drop-out rate. Bocconi's status is closer to that of one of France's *grandes écoles*.

The business school was founded in 1971 and has been offering MBA programmes for more than 20 years. However, it is also home to some 30 business research centres, and as well as the bilingual Italian/English MBA, it runs an English language master's programme in international economics and management, as well as numerous executive courses held in Italian.

The MBA is a 16-month programme, starting at the beginning of September and going on to the following December. In fact its real length is somewhat longer, because it begins in June with a so-called 'prelude' of videos, CD-roms and disks for home study. These take you through some of the basic concepts of the course and some of the skills you will require in quantitative methods and accounting. The prelude, as well as learning in earlier parts of the programme, can be carried out in English, or in Italian. The faculty is predominantly Italian, though there is now a requirement for them to have studied or taught abroad. The student body, however, is much more international. Only about 50% are Italian. The others, representing some 27 countries, come from the rest of Europe as well as countries further afield. The big attraction of Bocconi, apart from the reputation of the business school, is the idea of studying in Italy. Milan is not actually one of Italy's more beautiful cities, but it is at the centre of one of Europe's most economically vigorous regions. Furthermore, many think that the entrepreneurial Italian management style, with combines a strong sense of regional identity with a global outlook, is a business model for the future.

Another attraction, especially for UK and US students, which may however be temporary, is that the decline of the Lire has made the SDA Bocconi fees of L32 million, payable in five instalments – considered high by Italian standards – look very reasonable for a top-notch MBA.

The deadline for admission each year is the end of April. The process begins with filling out a 15 page application form, which you can do in English, though Italian language skills are 'noted with interest' in the words of one faculty member. Since parts of the programme are taught in separate sections, you will have to indicate your language preference on the form.

You will have either to do GMAT, achieving a score of around 600, or Bocconi's own test of verbal, analytical and numerical skills. Equally important, though, is your ability to contribute to the programme in terms of leadership qualities and personal skills. Generally you will also need to have had two to three years of work experience, though in a small number of exceptional cases high academic grades may be accepted instead. These details emerge from the application form and the school makes a general evaluation from the information about yourself that you give it. Final decisions on admission are made in an interview which, abroad, may be conducted by alumni.

The course falls into five parts, beginning with the self-study prelude, the object of which is to create a level playing field of knowledge for participants from a wide variety of backgrounds, nationalities and kinds of work experience. The teaching part starts with what the school calls the 'pillars', which deal with the fundamental techniques and concepts of management. This part of the course is mainly taught in a traditional classroom setting, though there is some interaction between faculty and students and some work done in small groups of six to eight. At the end of the Pillars stage in November there is a traditional closed book exam, in which you have to pass all subjects.

In the next stage, Functional Management, which goes from November to April, there are core courses in the key management functions – finance, information systems, marketing, operations management and so forth. At this point the teaching become more interactive and there is greater emphasis on group work. The trend towards the use of both languages increases as the course goes on, accompanied by intensive language classes from this point on, though you can still choose to do all written work in English. Assessment is based on general performance in the class, in group work and on exam results.

The fourth stage is in May and June. Coming under the heading of General Management, it is essentially a process of tying together what you have learned so far and applying it to real business situations in the form of case studies on such topics as product launches and the implications of global markets. Here, too, there are further exams and assessments.

This ten-month period of study is a preparation for the final six months of 'Itineraries' from June – December, that are perhaps the most innovative part of the programme. While following the Functional Management course, you will have been asked to choose between taking an 'Exploration' or an 'Orientation' itinerary. Both are carried out in English and Italian. The former means a mix of study activities, which includes following two out of eight electives, individual projects, workshops on specific topics like business ethics or negotiating skills, a turnaround study and:

- *either* an internship or a more extensive in-company project carried out as a group with faculty supervision, *or,*
- for about 20 selected students, a 3 month exchange programme at one of several schools, mostly in the USA and other European countries, with whom SDA Bocconi has exchange agreements.

The other route, that of Orientation Itineraries, focuses on two specific business sectors: information systems and fashion and design. These also include a consultancy assignment involving a detailed in-company project and various workshops. Students do not get paid for project work carried out during the itineraries and in earlier parts of the course, except for expenses, but the school does get some funding from this source. This, however, does ensure that the school will work hard to set up these projects and assignments.

What it's like Students reckon that the programme involves about 30 hours contact time a week, either with faculty or within firms where they are carrying out projects, or in the study groups of eight or nine through whom much of the work, such as assignments, are carried out. In addition to that, there are about three hours of private study a night, though these figures are variable – they go up before exams and during assignments.

As in other business schools, the students learn a lot from each other, in terms of functional knowledge, management style and business culture. Even within Italy there are considerable variations in the attitude to these matters. Faculty comment on the fact that students' behaviour changes during the programme, as they adapt to each others' ideas and methods. Contact between students and faculty is good. Students are able to rate faculty performance, their comments are listened to and taken into account in exam results and assessments. Faculty also have a helpful input in counselling students about choices in the direction of their studies, especially in the case of the final itineraries.

There seems to be more time for socialisation than in the more hectic 12 month programmes. The school reckons that in addition to tuition fees, a single student should allow 1.8 million Lire for living costs. There is no accommodation provided by the school, but it helps them to find apartments, shared by groups of students.

As far as English-speakers are concerned, the big question is how good your Italian has to be. There is no doubt that you can't get far in ordinary life in Italy without reasonable fluency – English is spoken to about the same degree as in France. Students say that by the time they get to the phase where some lectures are in Italian they are proficient enough to follow the lectures without difficulty – but that Italian students in informal situations, like workgroups, tend to talk very quickly.

A day in the life... 0830–1600 Lectures and case studies, with an hour's break for lunch

1600–1800 Twice weekly language lessons

1830–2000 School events and guest lectures

2000–2100 Dinner

2100–2300 Group work and preparation for the next day's lectures

SDA Bocconi's status as a leading European business school means that a large **Career** number of consultancies, financial institutions and leading European **management** multinational companies recruit there. Between September and December about **aspects** 100 organisations make their presentations on campus and the school reckons that 99% of them make an offer while they are there. Statistics collected in 1997 showed that 80 out of 126 students had signed contracts on graduation and a further 20 had had job offers for which they had not yet signed up. Salaries in Italy ranged from L80million–L150million in industry and L120million– L210million in consulting and finance. In addition, some had received signing-on bonuses. The students who had not yet had offers were mainly those who had been on exchanges abroad and had therefore not been around during the peak recruitment period. Others who had experienced job difficulties were those looking for a career change, especially past the age of 30.

However, the school itself is proactive in career management, not only in the form of courses and advice, but also in sending out student profiles to leading companies, facilitating contacts and above all through the way it maintains a strong alumni network which is itself a source of job offers. Over 1600 managers employed around the world are SDA Bocconi MBA graduates.

Professor Panunzi (Industrial Economics) **Faculty**

Professor Tava (Quantitative Methods) **highly rated**

Professor Grando (Operations Management) **by students**

Professor Darsi (Accountancy)

Professor Mercier (Accountancy)

Professor Predovitch (Finance)

Professor Mundell (Organisational Behaviour)

Bristol Business School: The Part-Time MBA

The first thing to say about Bristol Business School (BBS) is that its MBA should **General** not be confused with that of the University of Bristol's Graduate School of **background** International Management, which has recently been Association of MBAs- accredited. Bristol Business School is part of the University of the West of England, ranked both by the *Times* and the *Daily Telegraph* as the most highly regarded of the 'new' universities which have been developed out of the former polytechnics. Its status has been further enhanced by an 'excellent' rating for teaching by the Higher Education Funding Council – though its research grading was a more modest 2. BBS is now working on this by increasing its focus on research and it has established a number of research institutes in fields like strategic management, organisation learning and change, marketing, management accounting and operations management. Their clients, and those for

BBS's consultancy services activities, include some impressive names among the blue chip companies located in the West of England.

BBS started offering a part-time MBA ten years ago as a natural next step for its large and well-established department of management studies. There are in fact over 600 students engaged in various postgraduate business studies at masters' level, and the university itself is bigger than is realised by outsiders. It has some 28,000 full and part-time students, many of whom come from the growing number of industries and corporate headquarters buildings surrounding the campus on the outskirts of Bristol – itself a favourite relocation destination. These numbers mean that UWE is very well-resourced. There is huge library which not only has a large book and periodical stock, but is extremely well-equipped in terms of IT – in both hard and software and data access provision, some of which is available around the clock. Some library services can also be reached by remote access through a modem.

The part-time MBA cohort is fairly small – only about 100 students in all are doing the part-time programme, though a full-time MBA, also small, has recently started (for which Association accreditation will be sought). By contrast the faculty is comparatively large – over 80 combine research with teaching full-time on the programme. There are obvious advantages in the high faculty:student ratio.

The part-time MBA runs over 30 months, on one evening and one afternoon per week during the first two years. The final six months are taken up by a dissertation. On average students are in their late 30s and most are sponsored by their employers, a significant proportion of whom are in the public sector, where an MBA is coming to be seen as an entry qualification to appointments at director level. They are in the open programme with students from local companies in a wide variety of manufacturing, service and high tech sectors, but BBS also runs a single company MBA, specially tailored for the construction company Kvaerner (formerly Trafalgar House).

Though it has developed student and faculty links with some schools in Germany and France and one in the US, at present BBS has a mainly regional orientation, which differentiates it from its most obvious competitors, the business schools at Bath and Bristol universities (though there is talk of closer links with the former). Students who have made the choice say that in the context of their personal circumstances and career aims they preferred a school with a firm grounding in the regional scene.

The fee for the programme is £8 211, a relatively modest figure which includes the cost of the residential sessions and the core texts.

Admission procedures and criteria
The basic admission qualifications are the usual ones: a good honours degree, plus at least three years of work experience. If you do not have a degree you will probably be asked to get a GMAT score of around 550, or a similar grade in BBS's own test. An interesting variant, though, is that a good score in the Diploma of Management Studies exam (DMS) can get you direct entry under strictly controlled conditions into the second year. The School also accepts transfers from the Open University MBA programme, but there are no exemptions for non-MBA qualifications in subjects such as accountancy which are part of the course. This is because the group and syndicate learning process

requires participants to bring their knowledge to the team. Indeed one of the things that the school looks for from applicants is their ability to function as members of a team. About two-thirds of those whose application is seriously considered are accepted on to the programme.

Course content

The part-time MBA begins in September with a three day residential induction course which provides an overview of the programme and the learning processes that it involves – notably the importance of groups and syndicates. There is a further two-day induction course, some of which consists of an outdoor, teambuilding exercise, at the beginning of the second year.

The BBS MBA has a rather higher than usual proportion of mandatory core courses. There are 12 of these, but only two electives out of some seven options. Basic management skills form the first year of core programmes. In the second year, the programme takes a broader, more strategic turn into subjects like decision and business policy analysis and strategic management itself. The two electives also form part of the second year. The final six months are taken up by the dissertation, though students start preparing for it and thinking about it in the second year. It is usually related to a topic which, while meeting the academic demands of the faculty, is of interest to their sponsor organisation, as well as to themselves, and is agreed between all three.

Some quantitative subjects are formally examined, but assessment is mainly on the basis of contribution to group work and written assignments. Like the dissertation, these can be and usually are tailored to the circumstances of the sponsor organisation or to projects going on in the organisation. There are about 12 of these assignments in each year. They are quite demanding, with an average length of 5000–8000 words, but the ability to relate academic work to your job and vice versa is one of the attraction of the MBA to sponsors – as is the fact that you can combine work with study. The various teaching modules, say students, are well linked together so that what you learn in one session generally follows logically from preceding ones.

What it's like

The part-time MBA involved 8–12 hours study per week as well as six hours of on-campus learning. In addition to this are the assignments, which students reckon take 20–30 hours each, with most of the work done over weekends. 'It's a demanding schedule, but the fact that it's hard gives it value in the eye of employers,' says one student, who adds that prejudice against MBAs as a spoiled elite is rapidly disappearing and being replaced by a real appreciation of what MBA graduates have to offer.

Much of the work and preparation is done by and in groups. BBS is somewhat unusual in that the groups are not selected by the faculty but are self-selected by students, often on the basis of geographic proximity, personal chemistry as well as complementary subject knowledge. Apparently the arrangement works well and there is no sign of the less talented participants being left on the shelf in the process, since the initial admission criteria mean that everyone turns out to have a talent. The groups also meet outside the campus and provide mutual support and backup if, for instance, one member misses a teaching session through illness or work commitments.

Students also speak highly of good administrative back-up from the school itself and of support over matters like parking spaces which are in short supply on the campus (MBA students are guaranteed free parking spaces). Although public transport is available most prefer to come by car. The campus, while some way out of town, has good access to the motorway.

A day in the life... The afternoon session begins at 13.30 and consist of lectures, syndicate work and group discussions until about 20.30. Students say they sometimes meet in the mornings to prepare case studies and for presentations in class. Part 1 of the MBA takes place on Tuesday (or Thursday) afternoon and evening whilst Part two students attend on Wednesday afternoon and evening. Most taught sessions are of two hours duration with short breaks for comfort, refreshment and utilising the library, etc. Part 3 students (i.e. those working on their dissertation) operate more independently, though facilitated group sessions are run to assist in the process of completion. In addition, Part 3 students will have regular contact with their dissertation tutor. Each part of the programme has its own year tutor (all of whom teach on the programme) and along with the Course Director are visible and accessible in supporting students through the programme.

Career management aspects Since most students are sponsored by their employers, career management is not a formal part of the programme, though informal advice on career options is sometimes offered by tutors to students who are thinking of eventually moving into a different sphere or who are mindful of the fact that the old notion of a career no longer holds true. There is also a good deal of career-related networking among alumni – BBS has an active alumni network – and between programme participants themselves. In addition the South West regional branch of the Association of MBAs holds regular meetings on campus. Surveys of MBA graduates have shown that a good many go on to advance to senior positions, and a recent report in the *Financial Times* also indicated that BBS MBAs scored high in the impact the degree had on their salaries.

The feeling is that having an MBA is itself a career advantage and that in the public sector it is prerequisite for promotion into jobs at director level. Public sector bodies pay less attention to where the degree was obtained, provided this was at an Association-accredited school.

Faculty highly rated by students Stuart Bowie (Strategic Management)

Jack Castle (Operations Management)

Paul Goodwin (Quantitative Methods and Decision Analysis)

Julian Lowe (Strategic Management)

Ken Russell (Strategic Management and Programme Director)

Marie Thorne (Organisational Behaviour and Management of Change)

De Montfort University Business School: The Part-Time MBA

De Montfort's Dean of Faculty, Professor John Coyne, describes the School as 'one of the best-kept secrets in higher education' and it is certainly true that its MBA programme, established 20 years ago, is among the leaders of those being offered by the 'new' universities. It achieved a very high rating in a somewhat controversial *Times* survey of business schools a while ago, but what is more to the point is its 'excellent' rating for teaching from the Higher Education Funding Council and its Association of MBAs accreditation. Its research rating is a more modest 3a and 3b, but the school points out that this has to be seen in relation to the large number of staff putting their work forward for this purpose – they were in fact the eighth largest community of business researchers considered by the Higher Education Funding Council. The School of Business is also a 'centre of excellence' or a recognised development centre for a number of professional bodies, such as the Institute of Personnel and Development (IPD) and the Chartered Institute of Management Accountants (CIMA). **General background**

The part-time MBA's student body is drawn largely from the area within a 50 mile radius of the school, which now also delivers an MBA on two other campuses. One of these is at Milton Keynes, which puts De Montfort in competition with Cranfield, but students who have considered both options have generally chosen De Montfort because of costs. Fees are £6 250 for the whole programme.

The school caters largely for managers in private and public sector bodies in the East Midlands area. About 60% of the fairly small cohort of part-time students are sponsored by their employers, who are balanced evenly between these two kinds of organisations. However, though the school makes no claim to direct internationalisation in its part-time MBA, it has been quite enterprising in extending its activities abroad, with part-time programmes run in conjunction with schools in South Africa and Indonesia. Both of these award a De Montfort MBA and faculty links with them and with a number of other schools abroad have given its UK course an international dimension.

Contact with the 'real' world of business is maintained through strong links with local firms and the School's own commercial activities. Its runs a variety of consultancy, research and management development initiatives under the name of Business Solutions, a company which is run by the school and has an annual turnover of £5m. Evidence of De Montfort's healthy financial state is an extensive building programme and generally well-resourced facilities within the business school.

Apart from a good honours degree or equivalent professional qualification, there is a minimum requirement for four years of work experience, though about 80% of the participants have a good deal more. The GMAT standard is 550–600, but the school actually uses its own somewhat similar diagnostic test to assess numerical and verbal analytical skills. All applicants are interviewed and about 60% of these are accepted: a high ratio, but the faculty point out that many are screened out after putting in their application. Primarily what interviewers look **Admission procedures and criteria** for is a willingness by students and their employers to commit to an arduous course involving 6 hours a week attendance over 30 weeks. You can choose between attending two evenings a week, from 6pm to 9pm or one single weekly session from 2pm to 9pm. Most students prefer the latter. There are also two residential weekends during the programme, as well as some optional workshops on such subjects as study skills.

There are some exemptions on the core modules to those with a Diploma in Management Studies (DMS) or a professional qualification in the relevant field, but in practice most students opt to do the full programme.

Course content The programme begins in October with an induction period where you get to meet your fellow students and are introduced to the way the programme works – through seminars, study groups, written assignments and participative classroom learning, rather than through the teaching approach of undergraduate courses. The first semester takes you through 6 core subjects – the building blocks and basic skills of management – concluding with a strategic management module which integrates the various topics.

The second semester also begins with an induction period. Though it contains two more core modules – a further one on strategic management and one on financial analysis – the emphasis is now on the electives, where you have a choice of four out of some 24 topics. These enable you to focus on your own particular interests or career direction. There is also a module on research methods, in preparation for the final part of the programme, a dissertation of about 15,000 words on a subject agreed with your supervisor and, in the case of sponsored students, often with your employer. An alternative option is to take eight electives and do a rather shorter dissertation, but most students prefer the first route.

Assessment is by a mixture of exams – these take place about two-thirds of the way through the programme – assessed individual assignments and contribution to the work done in seminars and study groups. There are only two grades: pass and distinction.

What it's like Students reckon that in addition to the 6 hours a week of contact time, study and preparation takes a further 12 hours. Some of the study is individual and private, but a good deal also takes place in study groups of five to six students. Working in such groups is part of the programme, but they also meet informally. Students form these groups themselves – in some schools they are put together by the faculty – and you are encouraged to combine a mix of skills and backgrounds with geographic proximity so that you can meet out of contact hours. Group members support each other in various ways, from bringing individual expertise in a particular area to bear on an assignment, to providing back-up when a member misses a lecture because of illness or pressure of work. However, missing more than one or two lectures can be disastrous because of the speed and pressure of work. Generally there is a feeling that it is unwise to add to the burden of study by living too far from the school – about an hour's drive is considered to be the maximum, hence no doubt De Montfort's decision to open up campuses for the part-time MBA away from its main site.

Students particularly value the interaction with participants from a wide variety of backgrounds and the interactive process in classroom learning – quite different, they point out, from first degree studies. They found no particular difficulties with any part of the programme, though one participant suggested that a pre-course training in computer skills would be useful.

One of the weekly sessions looks like this:

A day in the life...

1400–1700 Group exercises, case studies (e.g. examining a set of accounts), developing 'soft' skills

1700–1800 Break

1800–2100 Finance – part lecture, part computer simulation. Marketing lecture and case study

Sixty per cent of students on the part-time MBA are sponsored and therefore look for career progression within their organisation rather than outside. A recent alumni survey conducted by the school showed that a third of MBA graduates did actually get promoted as a result of getting the degree. The remainder of the graduates eventually moved on from their organisations. However, having an MBA obviously enhanced their salary prospects, irrespective of their career decisions. Another survey, this one conducted by the *Financial Times* showed an uplift of nearly £7 000 from pre- to post-graduation.[1] The school's internal alumnus survey indicated that 56% of respondents were earning over £30 000.

Career management aspects

There is no alumnus association as such at present, though some form of continuing professional development is under discussion. Careers advice is through the university's careers service and by way of Association of MBA seminars, which are thought to be very useful.

Students thought the overall quality of teaching was high and they did not wish to single out any particular members of faculty.

Faculty highly rated by students

University of Edinburgh Management School: The One Year Full-Time MBA

The first thing that has to be cleared up about this school is the confusion between its MBA and the very similarly named, though not accredited, suite of programmes offered by the Edinburgh Business School, which is affiliated to Heriot-Watt University. The latter is best known for its large distance learning MBA, though it also offers a small full-time and part-time programme.

General background

The University of Edinburgh, quite separate from Heriot-Watt, is unarguably one of the world's leading universities, a fact which automatically gives authority to its MBA, regarded as being in the top tier among UK schools. Though unlike

[1] 'Learning while earning income', *Financial Times* 19 January 1998.

many of its peers these days, it has not pursued international links, about half its cohort of 100 students is drawn from outside the UK and from a wide diversity of nationalities. The average age of the students is around 30 and there is a somewhat higher than usual percentage of women on the programme: around 35%.

The faculty, too, is an international one. The teaching staff of 60 is drawn from 12 different countries. A good many of them have a practical business background and the school maintains active links with Scottish business and industry through consultancy and various university-based research institutes. The Forth-Clyde area is one of the most vigorous regional economies in the UK and Edinburgh's financial community has a global reputation.

Another attraction of Edinburgh is that it is widely regarded as a good place to live. It is big enough to support a wide range of amenities of all kinds from sport to culture, but small enough to get out of easily, and it is not expensive. There is plenty of accommodation within walking distance of the school, even though it is close to the centre of town. Some students even buy flats for the duration of the one year programme, which starts in October. Fees for students from the EC countries are £9 300 and £9 900 for those from further afield. Living costs are estimated to be about £9 000 for the year.

Admission procedures and criteria

Edinburgh University's reputation means that applications for the MBA programme are quite high: about 700–800 a year. Satisfactory applicants are interviewed, preferably in person, though in some cases this can be done over the telephone.

Basic admission criteria are the usual ones of a good first degree or its equivalent, plus at least two years of work experience, though the average is about eight. The criteria are set out in the application form in which you also have to write a short essay on why you want to do an Edinburgh MBA. You may be asked for a GMAT score in the high 500s or required to take the school's own admission test, which is somewhat similar to the GMAT in focusing on numerical and verbal reasoning ability. Non-English speakers may also be asked to produce a TOEFL score of about 580 or to do a dedicated preliminary course in English (English for the MBA) before starting the programme. There is no particular pre-course reading list, but Richard Kerley, the full-time director, suggests that reading *Business Week*, *The Economist* and the business pages of at least one quality newspaper is a good preparation.

Course content

The programme starts in October and has a somewhat unusual structure inasmuch as the core programme of mandatory subjects – the building blocks of management – are largely concentrated in the first term, at the end of which they are examined. Not surprisingly students report that the first term is very tough. Apart from 18 hours of faculty contact, study carries on into most evenings and a large part of the weekend.

In terms two and three you become more adjusted to the pace of work. There is a core course in strategic management but otherwise you proceed to the electives, choosing a minimum of four (many students take five) out of twenty options. These are grouped in clusters, which means that you can go for an emphasis in either finance, marketing, entrepreneurship or operations management. Students link their choice to their individual interest in a particular aspect of business or to their post-MBA career strategy. Alongside these electives there are also a number of other optional courses in languages and in 'soft' skills, such as negotiating and communication.

In the first term classes are divided up into two cohorts of 50, but in the electives they will be much smaller and throughout the programme much of the work is done in small groups and syndicates put together by the faculty to produce a stimulating and complementary mix of skills, backgrounds and nationalities. The lectures, too, are much more interactive than is the case in undergraduate courses.

There are different groups for different subjects – again unlike the more common practice of keeping the same groups together for all topics. Links with the Scottish business community are emphasised by the 'Lothians project' which take place in the second and third term; small teams of four students work together on a local consultancy exercise. In the case of students from abroad, the school has developed opportunities for them to work with local companies that have international interests and connections.

There is a final exam at the end of the third term and that is followed, between July and September, by a dissertation of approximately 14 000–20 000 words. The assessments on the basis of which the degree is awarded are a mix of exam results, individual work and contribution to groups and syndicates.

What it's like

The management school has made considerable strides in its use of information technology. Email is in general use among the students on the programme and it is also now used by alumni as a way of staying in touch. All teaching materials are available on an intranet which can be accessed with a password. There are also excellent computing facilities and the general learning environment at a university as important as Edinburgh is as good as anywhere in the world. It is, for instance, one of the two universities in Britain that has a Cray supercomputer.

Students all comment on the pressures of the first term, when it's difficult to keep abreast of the schedule of lectures, meetings, private study, plus non-assessed but important modules in areas such as language learning and career management skills. There is also the problem of learning to work together in groups where individual members at least start out by having their own agenda. In the end, though, everyone does learn that collaboration is the only way to make meetings productive.

Students speak highly of the outdoor exercises held at a university-owned site on the edge of the Highlands, where they mix with students on the part-time MBA programme. These are all part of a wide-ranging syllabus, some of it assessed, which brings in games, simulations, workshops and other less formal ways of learning. 'The programme teaches you to think like a manager,' says one student. 'You don't become a functional specialist in any one area, but you learn what to look for and to ask the right questions. By the time you've finished the course, you've hit all the bases you're likely to encounter when you go back into the real world.'

A day in the life... A typical schedule for one second-term student.

0900–1100 Lecture on managing people at work

1100–1300 Lecture on Japanese management techniques

1300–1430 Lunch and group meeting on a case study

1430–1600 Business French

1600–1800 Case Study Preparation

1800–1930 Working in the computer suite

1930–2030 Shopping and dinner

2030–2230 Study

2230–0200 Relaxation

Career management aspects Although there are career management seminars and a lot of contact with local employers through the Lothians Project and a programme of visiting lectures by business leaders, students are somewhat critical of this aspect of the programme. At the same time, it must be said that conversations with recent alumni indicated that job opportunities did filter through the alumni network. The School is very conscious, however, that more needs to be done on career management aspects and is taking active steps in this direction.

Faculty highly rated by students Simon Cook (International Business)

John Barasik (Statistics)

Stephanie O'Donohue (Marketing)

Seth Armitage (Capital Markets)

Jim Hine (Human Resources)

Ashley Lloyd (IT)

Instituto de Empresa

General background The Instituto de Empresa (IE) is one of Spain's leading business schools. Located in the financial district of Madrid, it was founded as an independent business school in 1973 by members of the Spanish business community. IE enjoys a good reputation at home and abroad and is fast establishing itself as a serious player alongside other well known European business schools. The school prides itself on its international orientation, its close links with the business world, and an integrated approach to the role of business within society.

As its name suggests, IE places great emphasis on the development of entrepreneurs. This is integral to the school's philosophy, and sets it apart from some other institutions. The School is also launching an International Centre for Entrepreneurship.

An explicit part of the school's mission is to 'encourage enterprise' and this includes helping graduates to launch their own companies. Some 15 per cent of those on the International MBA go on to start their own business, and there is an annual award of two million pesetas to help MBAs get their companies off the ground. In the last ten years, more than 350 firms have been set up by IE graduates, amounting to about 2.25 million pounds worth of investment.

In all, the school runs 12 full-time and part-time masters programmes, including the International MBA, which was launched in 1984 and was accredited by the UK's Association of MBAs in 1997. (The school also has a number of other programmes including an Executive MBA, an MBA in Spanish and an MBA for Professionals.)

Small in comparison to some other MBA programmes, the International MBA has between 50 and 60 places each year. Highly regarded in the Spanish-speaking world, it attracts a large number of applicants from South America, but is also popular with students from other parts of Europe, many of whom are attracted by the bilingual aspect of the programme.

The composition of its International Advisory Board is also evidence of IE's international orientation. The board is made up of 30 eminent academics, entrepreneurs, and professionals from different countries and includes Luciano Benetton, president of the Benetton Group, Peter Sutherland, chairman of Goldman Sachs International, and Rene Dahan, president of Exxon International.

The International MBA programme takes 15 months to complete, and is designed to help students see business markets from a global point of view. A distinctive component of the programme is the World Reality Seminar, where students make an 'in-depth analysis of world markets'. Alternatively, in place of the World Reality Seminar students can opt to undertake an exchange programme with a US or Latin American business school. In the past these have included Babson, UCLA, Kellogg, and SMU Dallas. (In 1997, 16 out of the 50 students on the programme went on exchanges.)

Teamwork is also an important aspect of the MBA, and at least one hour a day is dedicated to teamwork activities. Students are deliberately divided into small groups which include a diversity of backgrounds, which IE regards as an excellent preparation for the real world of work. In certain subjects, teams are also expected to use role playing to explore the issues.

The International MBA is broken down into six periods. The first period covers basic skills such as case analysis as well as some core subjects. The second period covers management techniques and the third is oriented towards global implementation.

Period four involves a management internship at a company, and period five is the World Reality Seminar. The programme culminates in period six with the remaining core courses and the opportunity to specialize through a choice of elective courses.

IE uses the Case Method extensively. Cases are prepared individually by students, later in a team, and finally discussed in class under the guidance of a professor. A series of introductory conferences are also included on key subjects.

Classes are based on a high level of student participation, which IE believes not only develops analytical ability, but also builds personal aptitudes including confidence, imagination, creativity, pragmatism, competitiveness and decision-making.

Through its Department of Entrepreneurial Studies, the school actively encourages entrepreneurial activity among its students. Each academic year the Department gives students the opportunity to design a business plan as a basis for creating their own entrepreneurial project.

Students on the International MBA are required to produce an entrepreneurial business plan during periods one and two, and can opt to take it further as a project. IE proudly boasts that more than 350 firms have been set up by students in the past 12 years.

The school's other activities include the provision of executive programmes for companies. In 1996, the Colegio de Dirección was established to co-ordinate IE's range of short courses, tailored programmes, seminars and conferences. Some 2 000 managers currently attend short executive programmes at the school each year.

Admission procedures and criteria

Applicants to the International MBA are generally expected to have a good first degree. However, IE places great emphasis on the future potential of applicants as well as their previous academic performance.

Where a candidate has taken the GMAT, a minimum score of 550 is preferred, but the school has its own admissions tests. Numerical and verbal skills are assessed using 45-minute tests developed specifically for the school. Candidates are expected to have good analytical powers and the ability to absorb a lot of information very quickly. Applicants are also expected to take a 90-minute psychometric test or personality questionnaire which is a predictor of how they will perform on the MBA programme.

There are around four applicants for every place on the International MBA, and all candidates are interviewed in person.

Course content

The International MBA programme covers 11 key areas which are developed over a period of 15 months, from October through to December of the following year.

Divided into six teaching periods, the subject matter which covers the core MBA subjects becomes progressively more detailed. Each period is followed up with day-long session with the MBA programme directors.

The programme is bilingual, and students are required to be fluent in both Spanish and English. (The curriculum is currently under review, however, and an English language stream is planned for periods one and two.)

The Pre-programme takes place in the second half of September and consists of an Introduction to Quantitative Analysis (for arts graduates). There is also the option of a Spanish Warm-up Language course for foreign and non-Spanish speaking students.

Period one (October – December): The objective of the first period is to bring together students from a wide variety of backgrounds and to equip them with the necessary tools to complete the course.

Areas covered include: Action Learning; Case Analysis; Financial Accounting for Management; Marketing 1; Quantitative Methods; Organisational Behaviour; Economic Environment; Computer Studies 1; Entrepreneurial Studies.

Period two (December – February): The second period analyses what are known as the basic areas using advanced management techniques. It covers: Management Control 1, Cost Systems; Operations And Technological Management 1; Marketing II; Financial Management I; Strategic Management I; Computer Studies II; Entrepreneurial Studies.

Conference cycle: Public Sector Environment and Private Sector Environment.

Period three (March – May): The third period focuses on implementation and considers organisations' actions and strategies in a global context. Areas covered are: Legal Environment; Tax Environment; Human Resources Management; Marketing III; Management Control II: Advanced Control; Financial Management II; Operations And Technological Management II; Strategic Management II.

Conference cycle: Public Sector Environment and Private Sector Environment.

There is also an Intermediate Oral Exam.

Period four (June – August): In this period students are placed with companies where they take on a management internship, which is also assessed towards their final mark.

Period five (September)

In September, after the highly practical management internship, the World Reality Seminar takes place. Held at the school, this event which is unique among MBA programmes, aims to provide students with a knowledge of key world markets. Business leaders from multinational companies also participate, as lecturers.

Period six (October – December)

The final part of the programme combines a series of mandatory courses with the opportunity for students to specialize in areas that have aroused their interest through a series of elective courses. It includes: Strategic Management II; Integral Vision of the Business Organisation; Operations and Technological Management II; Elective Courses; Company Presentations; Final Oral Examination.

Throughout the programme, students are continuously assessed. Each completed period is followed by approximately one week of examination on the subject matter covered. Having completed the exams on the topics covered in the third period, students take an intermediate oral exam in the presence of an examination panel made up of professors. The exam is based on their understanding of a case prepared beforehand.

To qualify for the MBA students must carry out all requirements successfully and have attended at least 90 per cent of the classes for each subject.

What it's like — IE enjoys a pleasant, if slightly cramped, building close to the financial heart of Madrid. It has all the benefits of a major European capital city. Of special interest are the Prado, which houses one of Europe's most impressive art collections, and the recently refurbished opera house.

Students, however, report that the workload is heavy in the first few months with little time to get to know the city. The International MBA programme, they say, deliberately promotes a competitive environment which challenges them as individuals. (This, the school says, is balanced by the emphasis on teamwork which is another important element of the programme.) The aim is to prepare MBAs for the real world of work.

Unlike some other Spanish business schools, IE has no overt religious connections, something it claims gives its students a greater independence of thought.

The International MBA has a good student mix. Just over half of those on the programme are from Spain, with another 21% from other parts of Europe, and four per cent from North America. In recent years, the proportion of students from South America has risen from nine per cent in 1993/94 to 20% in 1997/98. Compared to some other business schools, the balance of women to men is also quite high at 40%.

Students are highly enthusiastic about the entrepreneurial focus and the 'World Reality Seminar', which attracts many of those on the International MBA. They also speak highly of a learning environment that is a combination of a collaborative and competitive culture.

Because of its appeal to the Spanish-speaking business communities, the school attracts students from Latin American countries, making for a fascinating cultural mix. It also has specialist knowledge and links with a number of countries in the region, including: Argentina, Bolivia, Chile, Colombia, Costa Rica, Cuba, Dominican Republic, Ecuador, El Salvador, Equatorial Guinea, Guatemala, Honduras, Mexico, Nicaragua, Panama, Paraguay, Peru, Puerto Rico, Uruguay and Venezuela.

Class schedules in the first three periods are from 09.00 to 15.00 Monday to Friday. There are three and a half hour sessions each day, including an hour where students meet in teams in work rooms designed for this purpose, to discuss case studies to be analysed in subsequent sessions.

Late afternoons and evenings are usually used for further work-team meetings, or for preparing work in the computer rooms or library. During the World Reality seminar in September, the schedule is different, with classes held during the evening as well as in the morning.

A day in the life...

0900–1030	Lecture/ class discussion of prepared case study
1030–1130	Work group
1130–1200	Coffee
1200–1330	Class discussion of prepared case study
1330–1430	Lunch
1430–1500	Class discussion of prepared case study
1500–onwards	End of sessions – More group meetings/ individual preparation of case studies, Self-managed learning/ preparation for next day's classes, and dinner

Through its Career Placement Department, IE works to bring students into contact with the professional job market, and to facilitate job placements. Each year, the school contacts major companies to ask them to come in and talk directly to students. **Career management aspects**

The school reports that its careers department received more than 2 000 offers of jobs from employers in 1997, of which 65% were for postgraduate students and 35% for experienced professionals. The career department also organises company presentations on-campus (some 39 companies came to the school in 1997).

IE's close proximity to the main financial area of Madrid and close ties with the business community also make it a natural recruiting ground for both Spanish and foreign companies. Marks & Spencer and Andersen Consulting are among the companies that have made recruitment presentations at the IE campus in recent years.

The Entrepreneurship Department also plays an active role in creating jobs for MBA graduates by helping them set up their own companies. In particular it offers assistance with business plans and offers a full range of business, legal and tax advice for IE students.

In addition, all IE graduates become members of the 19 000 strong Alumni Association. Through the Career Placement Department, association members are eligible for career planning services.

Professor Fernando Bartolome' Pardo (Organisational Behaviour) **Faculty highly rated by students**

Professor William L. Carney (International Marketing)

Professor Gonzalo Garland (Economics)

Professor Bryan W. Husted (Business Ethics)

Kingston Business School: The Open Learning MBA

Kingston University, of which the business school is a part, has the reputation of being in the top flight of the former polytechnics which were upgraded to university status in the late 1980s. The quality of its teaching was rated 'excellent' by the Higher Education Funding Council in 1994, which spoke in glowing terms of the course, the students and the faculty. In 1997 its Business and Management faculty was ranked 17th out of 85 institutions surveyed in the unofficial *Times* Good University Guide. Over the last year the buildings and facilities at the school have been vastly improved with the help of a £15m government funded package and further improvements are under way. **General background**

The business school, which is also home to a wide range of master's programmes and is a 'Centre of Excellence' for the Institute of Personnel and Development (IPD), has been offering an MBA since 1984. It is some way distant from the main campus in Kingston and is closer to the London suburbs of Roehampton and

Putney. Though there are good bus services you would probably need a car to get to it, but the people the open learning MBA programme is aimed at – senior to middle managers with five years' experience – would generally have their own transport. The school claims that its location puts it within reach of the highest concentration in the country of managers of this kind. The faculty also point out that the location, equidistant between Gatwick and Heathrow, makes it possible for participants in the programme to fly in from mainland Europe, though internationalisation of the student body is, for obvious reasons, not a big feature on part-time programmes. However, there is an active exchange programme with the Haarlem Business School in the Netherlands and it does not take much more time to fly in from Europe than to get to the school from the other side of London. A part-time Kingston MBA is also offered in Greece and has just been started in conjunction with the Academy of National Economy in Moscow.

The Kingston programme which goes under the name of Open Learning has two start dates – February or September – and takes a minimum of two years. It calls for weekend attendance once a month: Friday evening (6pm–10.30pm) and all day Saturday in the first stage and Saturday and all day Sunday (9am–5pm) in the second. This makes Kingston the only business school within the London area to provide a part-time programme which can be followed by weekend attendance. An evening MBA is another part-time option that is available.

The programme falls into two year-long stages, though it is possible to stretch it out longer. The idea, however, is that it is realistically geared to the schedules of hard pressed managers, and this concept includes not just people in business, but managers from a wide variety of other organisations as well, including the public sector and professional firms.

Currently the programme has some 120 participants in each year, of whom over 25% are women. Fees are £9 000, a sum which covers the cost of learning materials specially written for the course, and regularly updated and revised. About 70% of the students are sponsored by their employer for whom the attraction of the arrangement is that participants can combine their job with study, bring the lessons they are learning to bear immediately on their work and, in the final stages, deliver a project which can be a consultancy assignment directly related to their organisation. Indeed 'selling' a project to your employer before you start can be a way of getting them to sponsor you on the programme. From both the employer's and the individual's point of view, the profile of the participants is reassuring: most are middle to senior management, with an average in the mid-thirties and several years of working experience.

Admission procedures and criteria The response time on applications is described by students as good. The school gets a lot of enquiries, which means that Kingston is able to insist on rigorous admission procedures, the centrepiece of which – once your application is accepted in principle – is an all-day session of diagnostic tests of verbal, numerical and reasoning ability, an interview to discuss issues of motivation and commitment and a group exercise to look at whether you can function well in a group situation. A GMAT score of at least 550 can take the place of the tests, though the suitability of individuals remains the overriding factor. If the feeling is that you are not up to doing the MBA, you may be directed to one of the numerous other master's or diploma courses offered at the school. 'It's better not to start than to fail,' says one faculty member, a view which ensures a completion/success rate in excess of 90%.

Each stage starts with an introductory week of full-time attendance, though this may be preceded by some pre-course reading suggestions, notably in maths – a typical area of concern for some students. In the introductory week you meet the others on the programme and particularly fellow-members of your study group. As is customary in business schools, most learning takes place in the group, rather in lectures. The group discusses assignments, analyses case studies and works together on group projects. The introductory week also surveys the content of the first stage of the programme, made up of modules covering and integrating the basic building blocks of management, added to which a good deal of attention is paid to issues of personal development – the soft skills which knit the technical content together. Assessment is partly based on the outcome of personal and group assignments, but at the end of Stage 1 there are also conventional examinations to test subject knowledge.

Course content

Stage 2 is more concerned with strategic management issues such as globalisation and it is also here that you move on to the electives. There is a choice of three from a number of options that changes slightly each year, according to popular demand. The electives, some of which are taught by outside consultants and guest lecturers, give you the chance to follow some interest of your own, possibly related to career objectives. You should choose in the first year which electives you plan to do in the second.

The final part of the programme – though it is also one that you need to think about and start to plan for well ahead of time – is a project, culminating in a dissertation of around 15,000 words. Like the electives, the project which you have to agree with a supervisor on the basis of a detailed proposal, may be chosen to further a career objective or to tackle a business problem within a sponsoring organisation. Its aim is to test your project management skills and the extent to which you are able to apply the lessons of the programme to a live problem.

About 5% of each cohort is awarded distinctions at the end of the course, though unlike first degrees, there are no classes of qualifications.

Open Evenings are held several times a year, at which you can talk to students and faculty to get a feel for the place and the programme. Though it's a part-time MBA, it also has some of the characteristics of a distance learning course, inasmuch as each module has an extensive suite of self-learning materials, specially written for the programme and regularly revised by the tutors. In addition to the weekends of full-time attendance, you should allow for a heavy load of private study – the estimates range between 15–20 hours a week. This implies that you need to get support from your employer while you are studying, because inevitably there will be occasions when work and study conflict. If you run into real difficulty over this, you can defer parts of the programme for up to a year. The important thing is to advise your course tutor

What it's like

directly if and when you feel you are likely to be running into a problem of this kind. There is also a helpline to the faculty if you run into a specific problem.

It is essential to bring your employer on side before you start and one student cautioned that for this reason it is unwise to change jobs during the duration of the programme and that even internal transfers or promotions can cause problems if you don't have the full backing of your new superiors. You will also need to ensure the support of your family or partner. 'Don't underestimate the commitment' is the universal comment and graduates even complain that once they have finished the programme they feel at something of a loose end. One interesting piece of advice is that you should then take on something else which involves your partner as well, like learning a language.

The work of groups is tremendously important. They are made up of five to six students from different functional backgrounds, so that if an assignment or project has a particular dimension, for instance involving a knowledge of marketing or accounting, there is probably someone in the group who has worked in that area. Apart from the direct benefit of that, it also teaches the members of the group to work as a team, though it does also imply that everyone has to keep up with the work in order to make their contribution. Group work is less of a feature in the electives, though the bonding process is so strong that many groups continue to meet informally.

There is a brief summer vacation, which students use to catch up on whatever reading they have missed out on. It's important not to lose momentum, even though some find that work gets easier as the programme goes on. This is not because it actually is so, but because you gradually develop the appropriate study techniques, for instance by learning to focus on essential information in a case study or by assigning detailed study of parts of it to the expert in your group.

Career management aspects Since many students are sponsored, specific career management material related to job changes does not figure as part of the programme, though the personal development content does have some indirect career management bearing, inasmuch as it helps you to become more aware of your strengths and weaknesses. Furthermore, recent graduates report that the business skills they acquire, plus greater confidence to handle a wide range of issues within their organisation, do actually improve their prospects. About 40% say that they were promoted either during the programme or shortly after completing it. Others, who have opted for self employment, say that they found the programme of real practical value, while those who wanted to change jobs say that the MBA has opened up opportunities in areas which used to be the preserve of Oxbridge graduates.

Faculty highly rated by students Students spoke highly of the amount of practical experience that many faculty members brought to their teaching.

Phillip Samouel (Statistics and Quantitative Methods)

David Browne (Business Forecasting)

Robin Matthews (Managerial Economics and Business Strategy)

Robin Jarvis (Finance)

John Forgan (Accountancy)

Annik Hogg (Marketing)

Stephen Goodchild (Financial Management)

Ann Rinsler (Finance)

Pat Thurbin (Strategic Management)

Lancaster University: The Management School

Part of Lancaster University, the Management School is one of the UK's most **General** comprehensive providers of management education. The school has a large **background** undergraduate population, and a range of postgraduate courses including masters and doctoral programmes. Through its Management Development Centre, it is also active in the short executive course market where it specializes in tailored programmes.

Lancaster is a rising star among Europe's business schools, with a large and impressive faculty of over 80 full-time teaching staff. Its one-year full-time MBA programme is relatively small, with between 65 and 70 places. Expansion of the programme much beyond that would require students to be split into two groups, requiring investment in additional lecture rooms. The strategy at present is to stay at around 70.

The school has a strong reputation overseas, especially in parts of Asia. With about ten applicants for every place, the small size of the programme means Lancaster can afford to be choosy about which students it takes. The school also runs a part-time consortial MBA for managers sponsored by consortium members, with a small number of places available to self-sponsored students.

Lancaster attracts applicants from a wide range of backgrounds, which leads to more diversity on its programme than some other schools. It is also unusual in the fact that its MBA programme has almost equal numbers of men and women. According to the school, there is no such thing as a typical Lancaster MBA student. The average age of the 1998 intake was 30, with the average work experience seven years – which is about par for the Lancaster course.

While the MBA is general in its scope, the school is also known for its specialized masters programmes, including the two-year M. Phil in Critical Management and MA in Management Learning.

It has a strong research base, and makes much of the fact that it is one of only three business schools in the UK to receive a 5* (five star) research rating in a recent government assessment (an honour it shares with London Business School and UMIST).

However, the research culture is combined with an innovative approach to teaching, which benefits from the work of the Management Learning Department, which specializes in this field and keeps Lancaster at the leading edge of teaching techniques. (The MBA syllabus is currently under review and some innovations can be expected in the next few years.) The School also places great emphasis on the practical aspects of management.

The summer project is an integral part of the course and accounts for some 30 per cent of the final mark. The projects run from June to September, and are usually conducted by small teams of between two and four students, with supervision from a member of faculty. It's an approach that emphasizes team work – a theme of the Lancaster MBA – and also allows projects of greater scope to be tackled, and a broader range of skills, experience and imagination to be brought to bear.

Students do not receive a fee for their project work although all expenses are covered. The companies that benefit from this valuable form of consultancy pay a nominal fee to the School to offset the cost of administrating and supervising the project.

The school is international in outlook and the current intake includes students from 25 different nationalities, from as far afield as China and parts of Africa. However, the majority of participants are from Europe and Asia. North American participants are rare.

Of those on the 1998 MBA programme, for example, 35 per cent of students were European, with just over a third of them coming from the UK. Of the remainder, another 54 per cent were from Asia, with just over four per cent from the Middle East and Africa and just over six per cent from North and South America.

In recent years Lancaster has made a conscious effort to build an international network, and is one of the five business schools which participate in the prestigious International Masters Programme in Management (IMPM), in which Professor Henry Mintzberg of McGill University and INSEAD fame plays a major part.

It is also one of the few UK schools to offer MBA students the opportunity to spend one term of a twelve-month programme on exchange at one of 12 partner schools overseas (students from some partner schools also spend up to a year at Lancaster, adding to the student mix). Language classes are also offered.

At £10 500 for the full-time programme (£11 200 for the consortial programme) the Lancaster MBA is deliberately priced at the lower end of the premier courses, and represents excellent value for money. Around 20 per cent of MBAs are sponsored (most of them through British Council scholarships) with the remaining 80 per cent paying for themselves.

Admission procedures and criteria

Lancaster says applicants should have:

- a good first degree from a recognized university or an equivalent professional qualification
- at least three years' professional work experience. (Five years' for the part-time MBA)
- two good references, usually from the current employer and from someone who knows the candidate's academic ability.

GMAT is not required for UK applicants with a good first degree, but is required for overseas students and UK applicants without a first degree.

Non-UK entrants should also have:

● a well balanced GMAT score, normally 600 overall. The School is particularly interested in how candidates perform on the analytical writing test (AWA)
● IELTS score of 7.0, or TOEFL score of 600 or more.

All UK-based applicants who meet the admissions criteria are required to attend one of the School's Selection Days, which includes a personal interview. Applicants from outside the UK may be required to attend an interview in their country of residence by one of Lancaster's staff or alumni.

Bursaries and scholarships: the MBA programme has allocated a sum of about £50 000 for scholarships and bursaries in 1998/99. This includes the *Sunday Times*/Lancaster University Scholarship for Women.

Course content

The Lancaster one-year, full-time MBA consists of three terms and a summer project. The design of the MBA programme reflects the School's extensive experience in the field of management learning processes.

Active (and self-directed) learning is fundamental to the Lancaster approach, and a significant proportion of time is spent on project work of various kinds. These include the Business Planning Project in the first term, the Learning Cell in the third term, but the largest by far is the summer project.

The School uses a range of techniques, including case studies, lectures, syndicate work and class discussion. The core MBA subjects are covered in the first two terms, with the third term devoted to electives and project work.

Immediately before the start of the first term there is a compulsory induction week to introduce students to Lancaster University and provide an opportunity to meet one another.

The first term contains compulsory foundation courses. These provide a grounding and framework for what follows. They include methods and techniques which can be used to improve business performance. Courses are: Marketing; Accounting; Organisational Behaviour; Business Economics; Management Science; Business Planning Project – a group based exercise; Managerial Roles and Capabilities.

A number of optional support courses are also offered in the first term. These include: Personal Computing; Quantitative Methods; European Languages (depending on demand).

Students who are already proficient in the foundation subjects can choose to spend the first term in either Copenhagen or Rotterdam. Early application, though, is essential for this.

Three more core courses run through the Spring term: Strategic Management; Financial Management; Human Resource Management. Students are also assessed on two Spring term electives, chosen from: Marketing Strategy and Management; International Business; Management Control Systems; Operations Management; Managing the Information Resource; Problems of Managing Complexity; Small Business and Entrepreneurship.

In the Summer Term all students must take one core course: Managing organisational change. Students also choose either three electives, or two electives plus a learning cell. (A Learning Cell allows students to develop their own topic).

The list of electives changes slightly from year to year, but typical electives include: Market research; Marketing communications; Social and environmental responsibility in business; Employment relations; International HRM; Business in Europe: the legal framework; The European Union; International finance; Logistics management; Exchange rate economics and international investment; Organisational learning and the learning company.

The Summer project period starts in early June and runs through until mid-September. During this three-month period, students work in a small team, supervised by a staff member. In recent years, students have carried out project work for multinationals such as: Shell, BT, McKinsey and GE Capital, as well as a wide range of UK-based companies and not-for-profit organisations. Lancaster's links with overseas companies also mean that some international projects are available for those who are proficient in the appropriate language.

Most core subjects are assessed by a combination of coursework and formal examinations. Electives tend to be assessed by coursework.

The degree is awarded on the basis of a number of methods of assessment, including 8 days of examinations split between the Spring and Summer terms. The projects normally conclude with a presentation to the client and to the faculty (the latter is assessed), and a written dissertation.

What it's like Lancaster is one of Britain's historic cities and has many fine old buildings, including Lancaster Castle which dates back to the 12th Century. The city also has a thriving theatre, the Duke's Playhouse, which is known for its outdoor productions in the summer. There are also a number of excellent pubs in the area.

MBA students talk about the friendly atmosphere at the School, and the high quality of the faculty. Students are also attracted to Lancaster by a down-to-earth, practical approach to management, which pervades every aspect of the programme.

The opportunity to participate in the international exchange programme is another major attraction. Participating schools are in Austria, Denmark, France, Germany, Italy, The Netherlands, Norway, Spain, Sweden, Switzerland and Canada. The two-way nature of the arrangement also provides an opportunity to share experiences with students on other MBA programmes.

Students are also attracted by the standing of the main University. Founded in 1964, Lancaster University has established an excellent reputation both in the UK and further afield. In total it has over 9 000 students – 2 400 of whom are postgraduate. The self-contained campus has its own restaurants and bars, which contribute to a lively social atmosphere.

The School of Management is located near the south end of the main University campus, and a new building for the Graduate Management School was added in 1995. Teaching space is somewhat limited, with only one large lecture theatre for

MBAs, but there are additional seminar areas, a common room and computer facilities (plans are currently being developed for a dedicated MBA computer room). The University has a large and well-stocked library.

Despite its remoteness from London, which lies about 240 miles to the South, Lancaster has good road (M6) and rail links to other parts of Britain. Scotland is just 90 minutes by car, for example, and Manchester International Airport is about 50 minutes by road.

Lancaster also benefits from being just half an hour from the Lake District, one of the UK's most beautiful national parks. The Yorkshire Dales, famous for caves and pot-holes, are also within easy reach. Students also benefit from other main university facilities, including sports and recreational amenities. These include an Outdoors Pursuits Centre near to Ingleton in the heart of the pot-holing area.

A criticism made by some students is that the School doesn't attract enough high profile speakers from industry and other walks of public life. In part, this is the price the School pays for being so far from London. The flip side of this is that being off the beaten track there are fewer distractions. Lancaster is also fast gaining a reputation for innovative approaches to teaching the MBA syllabus, and is more open to experimentation than other more 'stuffy' business schools.

A day in the life...

0830–0930	Unstructured time to prepare for class
0930–1030	Lecture
1030–1045	Coffee
1045–1230	Case study and small group discussion linked to morning's lecture
1230–1400	Lunch and free time
1400–1530	Business planning project tutorial
1530–1700	Coffee followed by project group meeting
1730–1900	Guest speaker from industry
1900 onwards	Unstructured time to eat, relax, prepare assignments, and prepare for the following day's classes.

Career management aspects

Because of its geographic position in the North of England and the relatively small size of its MBA intake, Lancaster finds it difficult to persuade large numbers of headhunters and major recruiters to interview on campus. However, the School has recently appointed a full-time careers adviser for MBA students who is able to provide a high degree of personal attention. Lancaster reports that this is already showing tangible results, and at the time of writing companies from Japan and India had just agreed to interview MBA students.

The School also offers good library facilities to help students research prospective employers. The careers adviser organizes a programme of career workshops to help MBA students realize their career goals. These include help with preparing CVs, job seeking strategies, and interviewing techniques.

A growing number of students take advantage of the opportunity to market themselves via the School's web site, posting their CVs and areas of specialist interest for recruiters all over the world to browse.

The summer project also offers an excellent opportunity to get to know a prospective employer, and Lancaster makes good use of the constant flow of prospective employers attending executive courses at its Development Centre.

Faculty highly rated by students

Professor V N Balasubramanyam (Economics)

David Brown (Strategy)

Professor Peter Checkland (Management Science)

Professor Geoff Easton (Marketing)

London Business School: The Sloan Fellowship Masters Programme

General background

The Sloan Fellowship Masters Programme is not an MBA. The degree it awards is an MSc in management and some maintain that its status is higher than that of the MBA itself, a fact which is reinforced by the limitation put on numbers.

It originated at MIT back in 1931 as an initiative by Alfred P. Sloan, chairman of General Motors, and one of the giants of 20th century business, to provide a management development programme for his company's most talented executives. It was then also offered at Stanford. Thirty years ago the first European Sloan Fellowship was started at LBS under Professor Charles Handy. MIT, Stanford and LBS remain the only business schools in the world that run the programme. Only 60 students a year are admitted by LBS, a few of whom already have an MBA.

Most of them are self-sponsored but a number of blue chip companies do send high flyers on the programme, which costs £25 000 for the ten month course, lasting from September to June. That sum includes the cost of field trips and assignments and projects abroad, which occur during the programme, but not living costs in London. These are estimated to add between £10 000-£20 000 to that figure, depending on family status and required level of living standard. This, however, is less than it would cost in the USA and though the programme is not an MBA, it is eligible for the Association of MBA's loan scheme.

The majority, both of sponsored students and others, have been high earners, a few spectacularly so. The average age is around 36–37 and they come from a wide variety of backgrounds and nationalities. Interestingly, though finance and consulting are well represented among the students' previous experience, these areas are not as dominant as they are on many MBA programmes.

The Sloan programme is taught by the school's regular – and famously multinational – faculty, though the core programme is quite separate from that of the MBA. The electives, however, are those offered generally at LBS.

Sloan students use the excellent library and other LBS facilities, though they also have their own dedicated area with computers and other equipment. At present this looks rather cramped, but LBS is in the process of a major new building programme more or less across the road which should relieve the obvious shortages of space that are beginning to develop.

The deadline for applications is 1 July for the year starting in September. As with the MBA, there is a detailed admission form to be filled in, which covers such things as motivation, academic and work qualification, and references. You also need to have a good GMAT score. **Admission procedures and criteria**

All applicants are interviewed, either at LBS or at some major centre outside the UK. Interviewers looks for commitment, fit and the ability to make a contribution to the programme which, again like the MBA, is largely based on syndicate and group work. The ratio of acceptances to applications is roughly 1:3 but the rigour of the admissions criteria means that there is a considerable degree of self-selection before people send in their forms.

The programme proper starts in late September with a three-day team building exercise made up of ten groups of six students, which is how you will be working during the programme. The group is determined by the programme management team. It changes each term and the composition is based on maximising diversity and achieving a range of complementary skills between the members. **Course content**

That however is preceded by a pre-programme accounting module which has to be taken unless you already have an accepted finance or accounting qualification. There is also a pre-programme maths revision course, which is advisable unless you are really sure you are up to speed on your maths.

The programme takes place over three terms. They are all very tough and intensive, but the first term – known as 'the boot camp' at MIT – is generally considered the toughest. It covers five and half of the ten core courses on the basic disciplines of management at a senior and sophisticated level. A further two and a half follow in the second term, at which point you also take two electives. At the beginning of this term, there is the European field trip, a deep immersion experience in an important region – the Veneto and Catalonia have been the two most recent sites. At the end of the term, there is an integrative exam which links two core subjects together, for instance, strategy and finance. Between terms two and three comes the international strategy consultancy assignment, when a team of three to five participants travel abroad, to sites which may be as far away as the Pacific Rim, to carry out a two-week live assignment without faculty supervision, on which a report is made to the client organisation.

In the third term you take a further two core subjects and one elective. The most important feature of the third term is the individual project, a substantial piece of work based on what you have been learning. Sponsored students usually do something related to their company. Others are likely to want to explore some topic connected with a particular change in career direction, since many self-sponsored students go on the Sloan Masters with that object in mind.

Throughout the year there are top management briefings, some carried out by global business leaders. However assessment is on the main work of the programme and is based on class and written work, both individually and in groups, and on the exam and the individual project.

What it's like The general consensus is that it's a wonderful learning experience that also brings a network of valuable future contacts, but that the warnings given by the Sloan Programme Office at LBS about the amount of work involved are, if anything, an understatement. That raises serious questions of stamina in the context of family circumstances. Students talk of getting as little as 5 hours sleep a night at times and that it is much harder work on a much steeper learning curve than anything they had encountered before. Only at weekends does the pressure let up, though not all that much. If you miss anything due to illness you can swiftly fall seriously behind, though the support system from other members of your team works well in these circumstances. The school can also provide tapes of any lectures you miss.

The loss of earnings for a year are an obvious consideration, especially for those who, in their mid-thirties may have been on quite high packages. However, the feeling is that the value of the programme offsets that, especially in terms of its potential career impact. As one participant puts it 'we're poor adults, but rich students.'

A day in the life...

0830–0915	Early meetings with the group to discuss preparation carried out the previous night
0915–1230	Lectures and group work
1230–1415	Lunch break. Sometimes company presentations on campus or lunchtimes lectures
1415–1730	Lectures and group work
1730–1900	Group meetings
1900–2100	Relaxation and dinner
2100–0000	Preparation for the following day

Career management aspects The possession of a Sloan Masters itself has a premium value from a career point of view, though for non-sponsored students, one of the disadvantages of such an intensive and relatively short programme is that it doesn't leave much time for jobhunting while it is going on. It can take several months to find a job after completing it, since Sloan graduates naturally set their sights high. However, the School recognises this by having a career service dedicated to Sloan Fellows. The Sloan Career Service works with the School's Career Management Centre but is a distinct entity. Its activities range from career workshops on jobhunting techniques at senior levels and individual counselling to events which bring students together with alumni for networking purposes.

One way in which career aims can be fostered is through the choice of electives. Students warn, however, that experience has shown that LBS's high standards mean that electives can be very difficult unless you either know a lot about the subject already, or choice is related to the content of core courses.

Students talk in glowing terms of overall teaching standards, but the following were often mentioned: **Faculty highly rated by students**

Professor Sumantra Goshal (Strategy)

Assistant Professor Don Sull (Strategy)

Professor Terry Hill (Operations Management)

Visiting Professor George Day (Marketing)

Manchester Metropolitan University: The Part-Time MBA

Manchester Metropolitan University (MMU) launched its MBA in 1990 and has obviously had the challenge of establishing a position distinct from that of the better known Manchester Business School. Both MBS and MMU make a point of their closeness to the business community, but the MMU has a competitive advantage in terms of cost. Its 30 month part-time programme fee is £9 000, including books, which represents good value for money for an MBA from an Association of MBAs accredited school. Furthermore the campus, in an award-winning modern building in the centre of the city, is well resourced in its library and computer facilities. In fact the library has established link-ups with other university libraries in and around Manchester which means that computer literate students can tap into a good many of the data-rich resources of bigger schools. However, MMU is also much larger than many people think. The Faculty of Management and Business alone has a full-time staff of 150 and nearly 5 000 students, including over 1 000 at postgraduate level doing various masters' degrees. Its HEFC research rating was a fairly modest 3b, but the fact that it is one of only two new universities in the country to receive Economic and Science Research Council (ESRC) recognition for research training suggests that improvements are already on the way. MMU is home to a number of business research institutes, such as the centres for Business History and Policy Modelling, which contribute the of content of the MBA, especially in the electives. **General background**

Students on the part-time MBA come from a wide variety of organisations in and around the Manchester area. About one-third are from the public sector, and a further one-third are from manufacturing. Most students are sponsored by their employer in a variety of ways from total financial support to simply time off for study, especially just before exams. The intake into the programme, which starts in May, is about 40 a year.

The basic requirement is the usual one of a good honours degree or equivalent professional qualification, plus at least three years of work experience at an appropriate level. All applicants have to fill an application form. Those considered suitable – about 50% – are interviewed by the faculty who look for further evidence of commitment, intellectual ability and support from family and employers during the duration of the programme. **Admission procedures and criteria**

MMU is slightly unusual in having a more liberal policy than some accredited schools in the matter of exemptions. Those who have started a programme at another accredited school may get exemptions from relevant modules completed there. Also, those who completed a DMS at MMV can claim exemptions from some modules in the first year.

Course content There is an induction day before the start of the programme, which begins with a residential 'getting to know you' weekend, where you meet the faculty and fellow students, explore your own learning style and get introduced to the learning process – working in small study groups on and off campus is an important part of that – and the underlying ideas behind the way the programme is conducted; principally the way that it enables you to apply what you are learning to your daytime job and vice versa. After that the taught part of the course runs every week from 4pm–8.30pm on Tuesdays in the first year, and on Wednesdays in the second year.

In the first year you cover the core subjects – the basic functions of management, such as finance, marketing, HR etc. With each module you have to complete a 3000-5000 word written assignment on the topic – something which demonstrates your ability to grasp both its content and its practical relevance. Often the assignment is tailored directly to something happening at work. At the end of the year each of these modules is also examined in a series of three, 3-hour exams.

In the second year you take three further modules on the strategic aspects of management. These modules, which are heavily geared to case studies, integrate what you have learned earlier into an overall context. Again there are further assignments related to them. After that you have a choice of three electives out of some 20 topics. These enable you to pursue some subject of personal interest to you, probably because of career objectives inside or outside your organisation. Again there are assignments related to every elective, though the electives are not formally examined.

Interwoven with the evening taught sessions there are a number of workshops and some residential weekends – four in the first year, and three in the second year. In the first year the emphasis is on personal development and on developing some of the 'soft' skills of management. In the second year there is a residential week at a business school abroad – most recently this was a trip to Hungary to study some of the problems of managing in a different cultural and economic environment. The three weekends deal more with some of the skills and techniques involved in the dissertation which concludes the programme in the final six months.

Preparation for this starts in May at the end of the second year at which time the taught programme comes to an end. The dissertation is around 15–20 000 words long and usually relates to some issue related to your job or some topic suggested by your employer and agreed by the school.

What it's like Students agree that the workload, including contact time on the taught part of the programme, comes to about 20 hours a week. 'You have to put your personal life on hold for the duration of the course,' one said. In every module it inevitably covers a lot of ground with which some students are more familiar than others, by virtue of their qualifications and experience. This is where the study groups come into their own because participants with more knowledge give back up and even on occasion informal tuition to those with less. Members of the study groups of five to six students also help each other when someone misses a lecture or two, due to illness or pressure of work. However, the pace of the course is such that to miss out on too much of it is likely to be disastrous. In fact, it turns out that the drop-out rate is quite high: about 30%.

One problem that inevitably crops up with part-time students is that of participants who have to relocate as a result of job changes or promotions. The school says that though it does not run a distance learning programme as such, it is possible to complete a course by a form of 'virtual' distance learning. Lecture notes can be faxed or e-mailed and assignments can be dealt with in the same way. However, this would only be feasible in the latter parts of the programme.

Students speak highly of the teaching. They like the challenging atmosphere and interactive style of classroom teaching and also valued the contribution of 'adjunct faculty': senior managers from local big name companies such as BAe and Eagle Star who teach on parts of the programme.

Career management aspects

Since most students on the part-time MBA are sponsored by their organisations, there is no formal career management content in the programme as such, though students feel it is extremely useful in career terms. Partly this is because of the networking opportunities and relationships that are developed in the course of the programme, which are then furthered through the school's developing alumni association. But it is also because having an MBA widens business experience and builds confidence. 'It's something no one can take away from you, no matter what happens in your organisation,' was the comment of one student who had also noted the growing tendency for job ads to list the possession of an MBA as a very positive factor. There was also the feeling that, as another participant put it, 'it puts firm floor under your salary expectations.'

Faculty highly rated by students

Richard Thorpe (Business Organisation and Strategy)

Stuart Horsburgh (Finance and Strategy)

David Murphy (Finance)

Jim Khan (Economics)

The Modular MBA (Arthur Andersen Initiative): Arthur Andersen in collaboration with Warwick and Manchester Business Schools

General background

The Arthur Andersen Initiative at Warwick and Manchester was launched as an additional stream of entry to the Schools' open Modular MBA programmes in September 1997, to take its place alongside several other longer-established relationships with leading organisations. Arthur Andersen have funded an initial intake of 50 senior managers and partners from the audit parts of their UK practices on this four-year variant, though the intention is rapidly to extend the scheme to other divisions, to increase the number of students to around 100 a year, and to recruit across Europe, and ultimately perhaps further afield.

Students complete the first two years of the programme at either Warwick or Manchester. The syllabus follows the standard core of the MBA but in an adapted delivery format which allows more flexibility for dealing with workload peaks. Thereafter, Arthur Andersen Initiative students join open programme participants, including those from other local full and part-time MBA variants, on electives which may be selected from those offered by either of the partner institutions. The degree is awarded from the university at which they complete the core element. Roughly half the students are going to each school.

Admission procedures and criteria Applicants are assessed first by Arthur Andersen's own selection panel and through the school's standard admissions procedures, involving an in-depth interview and optionally an observed case study. The final acceptance decision is made by the school of their choice.

Course content The contents are the same as for the open modular MBA, though the core has been extended to include a compulsory Management of Change module, as agreed with the school. Also the finance and accounting core module is slightly 'tweaked' to take account of the fact that Arthur Andersen students will already be familiar with the basics of this part of the course.

To minimise disruption with work, the residential element of the core is delivered in four-day blocks and students have to give up their Saturdays, so the residential period is from Wednesday to Saturday. Also there is no teaching from January to March, because that is a peak audit period for the practice. It is too early yet to assess the results, but Arthur Andersen's commitment to the MBA is certainly sending out the right signals to its professional staff about the firm's attitude to employability. Accountants notoriously often feel their careers are blocked by their lack of knowledge of wider business issues. The MBA fills that gap.

The Open University Business School

General background The Open University Business School (OUBS) justly claims to be one of Europe's largest business schools. Part of the Open University, a world leader in distance learning courses, since the inception of the OUBS in 1983, more than 190 000 managers have studied at Certificate, Diploma and MBA level making it one of the Europe's most important management development providers.

The OUBS introduced its MBA programme in 1989, and about 5 500 students have successfully completed the course since then. In 1994 it was the first wholly distance taught MBA to be accredited by the Association of MBAs (although other distance-learning MBAs were also accredited at the same time). Its great appeal to students is that it enables them to remain in their jobs while studying for the prestigious qualification.

The programme is modular in design, and provides building blocks in what the school describes as an 'integrated system of management development'. Students can work through the Professional Certificate of Management, the Professional Diploma in Management and then the Master of Business Administration (MBA). Alternatively, they can opt to take an accelerated one-year course, followed by Stage 2 of the MBA programme.

In keeping with the overall philosophy of the Open University, the OUBS aims to provide courses and programmes of the highest academic and professional quality to a wide audience. All OUBS courses are studied by individuals in their own time and at a location that suits them best.

Because the school deals only with distance learning courses, it can justifiably claim a depth of expertise in this area that is virtually unrivalled in the MBA market. Along with high quality learning materials, the OUBS places great emphasis on the fact that its MBA offers 'supported distance learning'. This involves a combination of written materials, BBC-produced video and audio cassettes, written assignments, tutorial support, residential schools, and increasingly a computer component, using groupware over the Internet.

As well as computer disks and CD-ROMs, the OUBS has also developed its own on-line conferencing system. This enables all MBA students to 'meet' their tutors, their course team and each other via their computers keyboards. This provides a vital support tool, and goes some way to compensating for the lack of interaction and peer learning that is part of the traditional MBA experience.

However, nothing can substitute for face-to-face contact, and the OUBS regards residential schools as an important and integral part of the MBA. These vary between two to five days in length, and unlike tutorials which are optional, are a compulsory part of the programme. Residential schools are held in a number of locations in the UK and throughout Europe. Accommodation is in hotels and purpose-built management training centres. Students can choose from a selection of dates and locations.

The OUBS says it now accounts for around 20 per cent of all enrolments on MBA courses in the UK – and around 40 per cent of all enrolments on distance-learning MBAs. (With some of those taking the Certificate and Diploma qualifications likely to go on to take an MBA, it is difficult to say for certain how many students are studying towards the MBA at any one time.)

The school has a permanent staff of around 200 plus some 800 part-time associate lecturers. It puts a great deal of effort and time into the development of its courses and course materials, and it has an excellent reputation for the quality of its distance learning materials.

The school's students come from a wide range of organisations – private, public and voluntary sector. Each year, around 3 000 organisations sponsor or in some way support their employees on OUBS courses. About half (47 per cent) of those on the MBA programme are currently sponsored.

In recent years, the OUBS has successfully expanded beyond the UK not only into Ireland and Western Europe, but also into Central and Eastern Europe and parts of Africa and Asia. (In 1997, it received the Queen's Award for Export Achievement.) The school has established additional offices in Brussels and

Dublin, and through its European network allows managers studying for qualifications to move fairly easily between countries.

In the 1994 Quality Assessment Review carried out by the Higher Education Funding Council for England (HEFCE) it was judged 'excellent' for the quality of its teaching. In 1996, the OUBS received a 3a (good) assessment from the HEFCE for its research.

Admission procedures and criteria

There are two routes into an MBA with OUBS:

1. Aged over 27-years, with an honours degree and at least 3 to 5 years management experience, *or*

2. A Certificate and Diploma qualification.

Credit transfer is also sometimes possible. There is no interview requirement.

Course content

The opportunity to study in their own time and at their own pace is what attracts students to the OUBS. The MBA course is modular in design, with periods of distance learning and some residential sessions.

Modules are designed like building blocks and students have the option of working their way through the Certificate in Management, followed by the Diploma in Management, which then qualifies them for Stage 2 of the MBA course. Alternatively, students with a first degree can opt for an accelerated route.

The MBA programme is in two stages:

Stage 1: there are two routes for Stage 1; students can either opt for the Fast Track or Open Access. (Open Access is where students qualify by achieving Certificate and Diploma). The Fast Track route is via a twelve-month accelerated course called 'The Foundations of Senior Management'. (To gain entry to the Fast Track route candidates must be at least 27-years-old, have an honours degree or equivalent professional qualification and have at least 3 to 5 years management experience).

Stage 2: This involves studying one compulsory course 'Strategy' and three electives. The six-month compulsory course is followed by the first elective, and electives two and three are studied consecutively. All electives are chosen from the following:

- Financial Strategy
- Managing Human Resources
- Performance Measurement and Evaluation
- Creative Management
- The Challenge of the External Environment
- International Enterprise
- Managing Knowledge (available 1999)
- The Management project.

Stage 2 courses are studied for six months.

The way the programme is structured means that it is possible to complete an MBA in three years:

Year 1 Stage 1 fast-track course 'Foundations of Senior Management'

Year 2 compulsory Stage 2 course 'Strategy' (six months), followed by one elective (six months)

Year 3 two Stage 2 electives studied consecutively.

Students with an OUBS Professional Diploma can complete it in two years.

What it's like

The OUBS has its headquarters at Milton Keynes, which enjoys excellent communications with the rest of the UK. However, as the school is entirely distance learning based there are no students on campus most of the time. A downside of this is that students inevitably miss out on the comradery of the traditional class room learning experience. However, the OUBS is one of the world's leading exponents of distance learning and does all within its power (and budget) to overcome this problem.

The advent of CD-ROM and video mean that distance learning materials have come a long way in recent years. As new techniques are developed to deliver learning via the Internet, too, distance learning will become both more widespread and more interactive.

The level of support for students – both from tutors and from other students– helps differentiate the OUBS programme from some other distance learning MBAs. Residential schools, in particular, are a valuable part of the OUBS approach and are likely to remain so for the foreseeable future. Participants say that the opportunity to meet fellow students is especially useful, and can put relationships on a much more solid footing.

A day in the life...

There really is no such thing as a typical day in the life of a distance learning MBA student. Rather, there are a great many evenings and weekends that go towards the final result. Most students choose to study this way so that they don't have to give up their jobs. This means that most studying has to be fitted into their spare time, something that requires a great deal of personal discipline (and a very supportive family).

Career management aspects

The OUBS does not have a career placement office for MBA students, but does offer post-degree support via Alumni Association Business Clubs, which are discussion groups held on a regional basis. These provide opportunities for networking and continuous professional development.

Faculty highly rated by students

Professor Leslie de Chernatony (Brand Management)

Professor Janette Ruttersford (Financial Management)

Professor John Storey (Human Resource Management)

Professor Keith Bradley (International Management)

Warwick Business School: The Modular MBA

General background Warwick Business School is universally recognised as being in the first division of European Business Schools, a fact that is reinforced by its 5a rating for research by the Higher Education Funding Council and its 'excellent' rating for teaching from the same body. All its delivery modes for the MBA – full-time, evening, modular and distance learning – are accredited by the Association of MBAs.

A distinctive feature of the Warwick MBA is the amount of flexibility between these various modes. People can and do switch between the part-time programmes to fit in with their work demands and can even transfer to a full-time MBA in the third year of their course to accelerate their progress in its final stages. The modular MBA normally takes three years, though up to eight is allowed to complete it.

The Modular version consists of 13 courses, plus the final dissertation/project. These intensive one-week (Monday–Friday) periods of residential study and shorter workshops take place on campus, and are plotted on a three-year forward schedule to enable students to plan their work and course commitments to minimize disruption. The first year core component is the most intensive, with six modules scheduled at roughly six-week intervals. Usually people stay at the Executive Centres on the University campus during the residential periods, but there is plenty of accommodation available in the neighbourhood as well.

Students also study course material and prepare written assessments at home, but the idea of the modular MBA is that you should be able to combine it with your daytime job. Students say that home study takes up to 10–15 hours a week, which they mostly do at weekends. The fact that you can do your job while taking your degree makes the modular MBA popular with employers and the great majority of students are sponsored by them. The school, incidentally gives guidance to potential students on how to get employer sponsorship.

Modular MBA students tend to be somewhat older than those on the full-time programme – the average age is around 34 – with a slightly higher than usual percentage of women participants. The nature of the course means that students can attend from a widely dispersed geographical area, two on current cohorts jet in from Asia and another from South Africa; 15% of the most recent intake now live and work in continental Europe – but in spite of this there is a great deal of co-operation within the groups which, as at most business schools, are the foundation on which learning is built. In fact the school is actively expanding the international flavour of the programme, not only among the participants but in the range of learning experiences it offers. It plans to increase the number of one-week elective modules offered in partnership with several European B-schools on management issues or themes with a strong regional focus and the School itself runs other modules in the Far East, led by Warwick faculty but again taking advantage of local inputs.

The cost of the Modular MBA is approximately £14 000 overall, split into annual instalments, to which has to be added residential costs of £6 000 for acommodation and meals if you choose to stay at the school during these periods.

Numbers are kept down to around 55 a year. The course starts in December, but demand means that you have to get your application in by early August. The basic requirement is for at least four years of work experience – most students have a great deal more – a good first degree or equivalent professional qualification, and the usual references. Applicants who don't have a degree but have impressive business experience will also be considered, but may be asked to do the GMAT or Warwick's own admission test, which is somewhat similar. An important evaluation is through a one-to-one interview, to which all well-qualified candidates are invited. Warwick University has something of a reputation for being tough on numeracy standards, but in fact the business school says that maths up to GCSE/O levels may be all you need.

Admission procedures and criteria

You are given a preliminary reading list of books on study techniques, basic quantitative methods and the work of a few influential management writers, such as Charles Handy. The course itself starts with an induction weekend at which you are introduced to members of your study group, and which also includes a psychometric test to establish your learning style. This is put together by the Programme staff to produce a stimulating mix of complementary skills, background and previous experience.

Course content

Five core modules covering the building blocks of management skills are taken in the earlier part of the programme. These are followed by an integrative module which ties together what you have learned; two further core courses and five out of a wide choice of electives, some of which can be taken abroad, complete the taught course requirement.

Midway through the second year there is a workshop on research methods. This is a valuable preliminary to the project/dissertation in the final part of the course. The project is a live consultancy exercise undertaken for a client, normally your sponsor. The more academic part of this is the dissertation which you develop from it. In other words it combines a practical outcome with an underpinning of academic rigour.

All modular MBA courses are examined primarily by individual assessments, often with a strong in-company focus. Syndicate presentations and group projects are also part of the overall examination scheme, as is the dissertation. Only the core courses on market analysis and financial accounting have a formal examination component alongside the usual individual assessment, but if you take part of the programme by other modes you may be examined on those. The distance learning MBA, for instance, is awarded largely by formal examination.

The 13 residential modules are very intensive – students report that they involve a 60 hour week of all day lectures and evening preparation, but this, they say, provides the experience of total immersion in the content of the module. During the non-residential periods in between, you will be doing preparatory reading as well as working on a written assessment – strict deadlines apply to this.

What it's like

There is a lot of informal collaboration between group members in the form of communication by phone, email and personal meetings where this is feasible – one group sometimes holds these at a convenient motorway service station. Participants support each other with aspects of the work, when one member of the group may, by virtue of work experience or academic qualification, be more familiar with some topic than others. This kind of interactive support within the group is very important, which is why no exemptions are given to those who might feel they know the topic already.

You can also communicate with the faculty and programme staff by email and increasing numbers are doing so; the school actively encourages this and provides guidelines on hardware selection and on remote access.

A day in the life...

During residential weeks

0900–1030 Preparation for a lecture or a lecture accompanied by a presentation in class

1030–1115 Working on a case

1115–1145 Presentation in class

1145–1230 Lecture

1400–1800 Lectures or discussions, exercises, simulations, presentations and casework, as above

1830–1930 Dinner

2000–2130 Evening speaker and discussion

Thereafter, until midnight (or later!) Preparation for the next day's work/case study or a business simulation.

Career management aspects

Since virtually all students on the modular MBA are sponsored by their employers there are no formal career management elements in the programme. Students say, however, that the career advantages are implicit. One participant, for instance, with responsibility for public affairs and PR for a leading PLC, says that his studies are enabling him to speak more knowledgeably to journalists, who themselves are becoming more knowledgeable, and to do presentations to City analysts. Function specialists in other areas see the MBA as a qualification that broadens career options, while everyone values the networking opportunities that come through contact with alumni and with fellow students who themselves might go on to more senior jobs when they graduate. The fact that Warwick Business School Full-time MBA graduates came fourth in Europe in a recent survey in the *Financial Times* of the effects on salaries[1] is an indication of the financial advantages.

Faculty highly rated by students

Professor P. Doyle (Marketing and Strategic Management)

Professor A. Pettigrew (Strategic Management and Organisational Behaviour)

Professor R. Wensley (Strategic Management and Marketing)

Professor David Wilson (Strategy)

Professor I. Davidson (International Finance)

Professor Nigel Slack (Operations Management and Strategy)

Dr Elena Antonacopoulou (Management of Change)

Nigel Sykes (Entrepreneurship and New Venture Creation)

[1] *Financial Times*, 19 January 1998.

Where does it all get you?
The MBA and your career

8

According to estimates by the Association of MBAs there are now over 45 000 MBAs living in the UK. That makes it, by a wide margin, Britain's most popular postgraduate qualification, and evidence is gathering that the rest of Europe is moving the same way, in spite of differences in the educational system between continental countries and the Anglo-American world. Several schools on the continent are now of acknowledged global standing and this process is likely to accelerate as transnational accreditation and standard-setting steps gather momentum. As David Wilson, chief executive of GMAC, told the *Financial Times*, 'I think the MBA has become a currency. It's the currency of intellectual capital.'

Employers across a wide spectrum of enterprises and organisations also now recognise the value of the MBA. One reason is that in a global economy, with a wide diversity of national qualifications whose meaning and value is often difficult to establish outside the country where they were earned, an MBA from an accredited schools does provide a degree, literally, of quality and content assurance. Students at a French school interviewed in the course of the Association's assessment procedures for accreditation confirmed this in saying 'they wanted to have a degree which has Europe-wide recognition, so that they can easily move jobs.'[1]

Level of employer support

(Base: all those employed while studying for MBA)

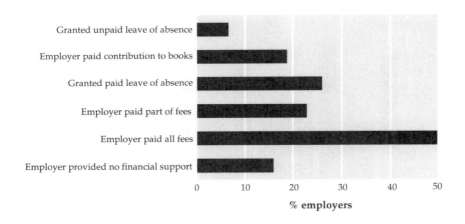

% employers

[1] *Financial Times*, 3 March 1998.

Another is that more and more senior managers have the degree themselves. The latest board of directors survey from the headhunters Korn/Ferry International, based on a sample of 345 companies, showed that 41% of UK firms and 36% of mainland European ones have an MBA on the board.

A further sign of recognition is the extent to which employers are supporting MBA students. In the words of the Association's survey, 'Over 80% of respondents who were employed while studying for their MBA received some form of financial support from their employer.' Fifty per cent of them paid all fees and only about 15% provided no support at all.

There is, of course, no such thing as a free lunch, and 22% of those who were to some extent funded by their employer were also under some contractual obligation. The report does not spell this out, though in some cases students have apparently been funded on the provision that they would repay their employers if they left within a certain time of completing their studies. Mainly, though, the obligation is more a moral one, which seems to be broadly observed. At any rate 61% of respondents stayed with their employer for at least a year after graduating, though another 31% left within that time.

That response may have had something to do with how employers treated them when they had gained their qualification. One student who had been fully sponsored by a bank reports, for instance, that it did not seem to be able to make use of what she had learned on her programme. 'The banks have their own exams, and they couldn't figure out where the MBA fitted in'. She left when she realised that, though she adds that since that time, her previous employers have become much more aware of the all-round business skills the MBA confers. This is then being reflected in their career pattern, which shows a significant number of promotions on graduating, continuing thereafter.

Role within the organisation

(Base: all who move to new employing organisation post MBA)

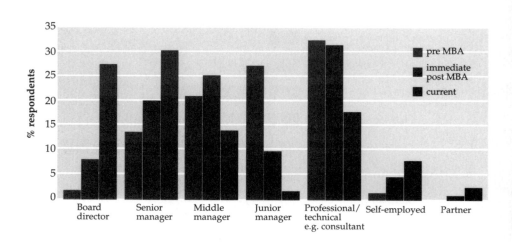

Promotions between 1970 and 1997

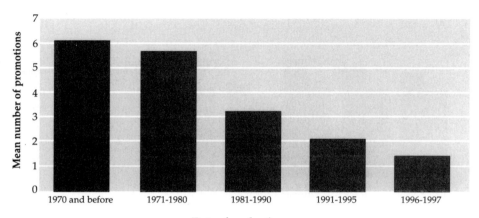

What is behind this encouraging trend is that the core parts of an MBA Programme – marketing, finance, human resource management, information systems and so forth – are now seen as essential managerial competencies instead of being left to the relevant experts. Furthermore, completing an MBA extends the competencies of functional or sector specialists themselves beyond the limited life of their specific, technical expertise and into that of general management. It is often noted that as you move up in an organisation, technical competence becomes less important and general management competencies become more so.

The all-round working knowledge of business processes that an MBA gives you is also very valuable, irrespective of your particular skills, knowledge or expertise. Many young managers who feel that colleagues in areas of which their own knowledge is limited – finance is a typical example for those without a financial training – can pull the wool over their eyes. They hope the MBA will give them enough insight into what their colleagues, subordinates and indeed bosses are doing to enable them at least to know what is going on.

To what extent does the MBA programme deliver these expectations? Apparently satisfaction is very high. According to the 1997 survey of salaries and careers, over 60% of those who had taken an MBA by whatever method said that they found the content of their course 'extremely relevant' or 'very relevant' to their eventual jobs and to the development of their careers in general. In informal discussions between the writer and MBA graduates and students, the fact that they were acquiring enough understanding of the basic management discipline to understand what was going on in every key function was a theme which emerged repeatedly. 'I wouldn't have my present job without it', was a typical comment from one recent graduate.

Relevance of MBA to job and career

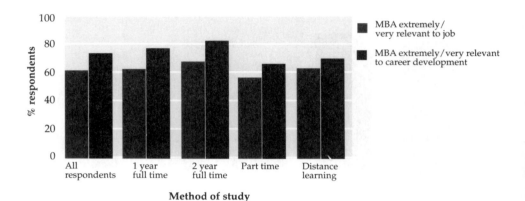

A graduate perspective

'Though I had a degree in economics, I'd reached the point in my mid-thirties, where I was beginning to realise that it was of limited value in the financial services sector', says banker Chris Wheeler, who has an MBA from the OUBS. 'The programme gave me the opportunity to explore ideas in a safe environment, but also to apply them to the job I was doing. For instance, I wrote a report for the board on the strategic direction of the company, which put facts and figures on some of the options that were being considered. It also enabled me to think creatively about some of the issues that were facing us, and that fed immediately into a training project I was undertaking in the company at the time'.

As happens with all MBA students, he found that the amount of material he had to absorb over the four years it took him to complete the programme was formidable – 'a tremendous drain on one's social life' – but he said it was not inherently difficult, and that the experience of working in a group was immensely useful from both a learning and personal development point of view. He adds also that he learned to pick and choose the elements in the programme which were most useful to him.

He has recently changed jobs, and though the letters after his name did not seem to make a great deal of difference in themselves, the technical and interpersonal skills he acquired on the course did. 'It's enabled me to talk on equal terms with people across a wide variety of functions and businesses, some of them at a higher level than my own'. However, he also adds that the funding of an MBA is an excellent investment for an organisation – provided it is able to make full use of what graduates have learned.

Some MBAs use what they have learned to set their career in a new direction. Edinburgh University MBA graduate John Newlands was a naval officer with a background in electrical/electronic engineering. He had alswways been interested in the financial sector, so Edinburgh with its strong connections in that sphere, was a natural destination for him when he left the navy and decided to do an MBA. He chose a somewhat arcane subject for his dissertation – the potential effects of change in the taxation of certain investment instruments – and that led to a job offer from a senior investment trust analyst in a London firm. His career was progressing nicely when his employer was involved with a merger, followed by the inevitable rationalisation in which his job was one of the ones that disappeared. However, his MBA training stood him in good stead. Research for his dissertation had shown him that there was a gap in public knowledge about the workings of the investment trust industry which was affecting its capacity to market itself to the public – despite the vast amount of money it spends on advertising. He developed a proposal for publication on this topic, costed it and looked for a sponsor. Within a very short time he found a major backer. 'The MBA enabled me to unlock – and commercialise – potential I knew that I had and that I couldn't have developed otherwise,' he sums up.

Another person who used an MBA to facilitate a career change in Elaine Bailey, head of the Prison Service Construction Unit – a huge operation with an annual construction budget of £250m. Before taking a one year full-time MBA at Imperial College, she had worked for 17 years for a construction company. Her employer was involved in a merger and though her job was secure she decided that the right career move for her was to boost her business knowledge before looking at other opportunities. At first she found the course terrifying and was afraid her ignorance of some of the material would reveal her as a 'fraud', as she put it in an interview with *Ambassador*[2] but she found the group work and the mutual support the members gave each other enormously reassuring and helpful. The course has given her "a framework for looking at problems and making sense of them" and the tools to develop the more market-oriented approach which the public sector is working towards. Equally valuable were the contacts she made. If she wants to make another career move, her address

Recruiter John Courtis agrees with these sentiments, but he says that MBAs also have to learn how to sell themselves in a highly competitive market, where the degree certainly has status as a good, numerate qualification but does not in itself confer decisive advantage. One aspect of this is that MBAs need to learn some of the basic lessons of job-hunting, and, in particular, how to frame applications and interview replies in ways that show that what they have learned on the programme is relevant to the job in question. In most schools these topics are now offered as part of a full-time programme, though they are less in evidence in the part-time options, where the assumption is that students are being sponsored by their employers. But what are the generic virtues of an MBA, divorced from the relevance of its content to a particular organisation? Here are some ideas.

● *Evidence of Dedication and Commitment.* As previous chapters have shown, the MBA requires a willingness to invest time, and often money, in acquiring a

[2] 'Stonewalling Does Not a Prison Make,' *Ambassador*, December 1997.

wider range of management skills – and a readiness to forego what might be more pleasurable things in the short-term.

Commitment to the task in hand is a quality which employers are increasingly seeking, on top of a variety of experience, plus training (preferably paid for by someone else!) rather than years of loyal service.

- *Training Across a Broad Range of 'Hard' Business Skills.* MBAs are sometimes criticised because they are short of experience 'at the sharp end', but they can show that they have gone through an intensive training course across a variety of the hard disciplines of management, embodied in the core subjects of an MBA programme. At good schools, as we have shown, the interconnection between these topics is the underlying theme of all teaching, just as it is in business practice.

MBA graduates, in conversation with the writer, agree that this does not make you a great manager in itself, but it certainly enables you to understand what is going on around you, whereas many general managers, even good ones, have very little understanding of what functional specialists in these areas are talking about.

- *Development of 'Soft' Management Skills.* The way courses are taught, with a great emphasis on group work, develops the soft skills that are becoming increasingly important in the context of flat-hierarchy, knowledge organisations: motivation, teamwork, presentation, and negotiating skills.

It also enables MBAs to understand much more about themselves. Knowing one's own strengths and weaknesses is an essential part of learning to function as a team player. For this reason placement officers wisely advise students not to start targeting jobs until they have been through the self-assessment phase of the programme. In some cases, this is becoming a part of an actual module, but in most cases it is a realisation that begins to gell about halfway through the course.

- *An International Orientation.* MBA courses are now increasingly international in the content of teaching – for instance, in extending the use of case studies from international business, in encouraging foreign students, in recruiting foreign members of faculty and visiting speakers from abroad, in focusing on projects with an international content, in running language courses, and in exchange and collaboration arrangements with business schools in other countries. Most valuable perhaps, is the increasingly multinational nature of students taking an MBA, both in the UK and in Continental Europe. Most full-time programmes have a foreign national participation of at least 50%, and distance learning programmes are also moving in the direction of participation from abroad, using advances in information technology. Learning to work in a multinational team is now part of the MBA experience, though some take the view that if your career aim is to work globally, your best plan is to do your MBA outside your own country. That was the reason given to the writer, when interviewing students from the UK, Australasia and the USA at schools such as IESE in Spain and Bocconi in Italy. Equally, headhunters argue that the best preparation for a career in the USA is to do your MBA at one of the blue chip US schools.

- *The Ability to Work Under Pressure.* By whichever mode the MBA is taken, it involves working under pressure. That is not just a question of having to learn to turn out quality work with the little time in which to do it; it means acquiring time management skills and the ability to prioritise tasks. Many graduates mentioned that at first they felt they were given a greater workload than they could possibly handle, until they realised that being able to focus on essentials was part of the training.

The anti-climax effect

All the MBAs the writer talked to mentioned 'greater confidence' as one of the gains of the course, but in career terms, that has a downside. MBAs on sponsored courses come away with a feeling summed up by one who said: 'You feel you've changed, but the organisation hasn't'. Many people on sponsored MBAs move on following a decent interval because, although their salary has increased, they feel that their experience and hard-won skills are not being used properly by their employers. Even at Ashridge, whose course consists of a mix of in-company and residential modules, 40% of company-sponsored students reported that few of the recommendations arising out of their main project had been accepted. For non-sponsored ones, the situation was worse. The great advantage of part-time and distance learning programmes, is that you can immediately apply what you are learning to your normal work. However, that does not necessarily happen on its own. MBAs need to be proactive in ensuring that what they do presents opportunities for the practical application of learning, even though the pressures of simply doing the course make it hard to focus on longer term objectives.

Another way that MBAs can hit the ground running when they return to their employers or re-enter the job market, is to link the project and/or dissertation which forms the later part of most courses to their career aims. Part-timers often choose a project which is virtually an internal consultancy assignment. Indeed, this can be a way of 'selling' the idea of sponsorship to their employers. Full-timers who are taking an MBA with a view to changing career tracks, can focus the project in an appropriate career sector or discipline.

Students have also reported feeling at a loose end when the work pressure of the MBA suddenly eases off at the end of the programme. If you do feel the need to go on to learn something else, some suggest, it should be an activity that involves your partner, such as learning a language. For others, the prospect of a DBA, the doctorate in business administration, beckons.

Impact on salary

What about salary prospects, though? While the survey shows a variety of motives for doing an MBA in which more money comes behind improving job opportunities, the idea of an eventual pay-off must linger in most of their minds somewhere.

Even those who have been sponsored by their employer will have made a considerable sacrifice in terms of time, while self-funded MBAs will have made a direct and substantial financial investment, often funded through the Association loan scheme. There are also opportunity costs to consider. Full-timers will have lost at least a year's income and even part-timers might have had to put a promotion on hold because of the additional pressure of work that it might have entailed.

Respondents citing a particular objective

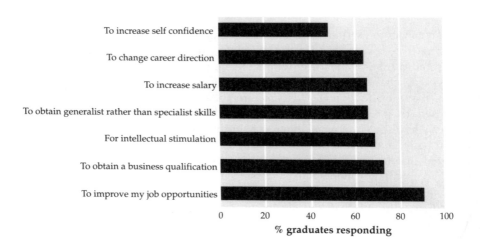

The Association's research into the salaries of its members, based on 1591 replies from 6085 questionnaires, does show that having an MBA is worthwhile from a financial point of view. After a slowdown in the early 1990s, the trend has been significantly upwards. At the time the report was published in November 1997 graduates from an accredited MBA programme were earning an average of £53 700, an increase of almost 15% on the 1995 figure of £46 800. That, however, is the base salary. If you add on performance related pay which, in some form or other was received by 57% of the respondents, the average cash remuneration moves up to £65 000.

The picture gets even better at the top end of the market. The Survey shows that 11% of the sample earned over £100 000 and 3% over £200 000. This reflects the booming demand for MBAs in consultancy and finance, and a trend towards global rather than national benchmarks in remuneration in these sectors. According to the *Financial Times*,[3] the big consultancies alone are looking to recruit 2000 new graduates each year, at salaries which are increasingly benchmarked globally and which often now include signing on bonuses so large as to substantially cover course fees. 'Starting salaries offered this year at the established business schools for a 28 or 29 year old MBA average £55 000 to £60 000 a year but on top of that there is a one-off sign on bonus of £15 000,' the paper reports, though anecdotal evidence suggests that major consultancies do a fair amount of cherry picking among the graduate crop.

MBAs from the top schools are equally in demand by the big banks – Deutsche Morgan Grenfell, again according to the FT, alone recruits 75 MBAs a year, about 30 of whom come from Europe. Benchmarking against US banks is reported to mean a total starting package of $120 000 a year and the trend is still upwards.

[3] 'A Boom For Graduates', 19 January 1998.

Industrial companies are not quite so generous but they too are having to raise their sights in recruiting MBAs. They are also tending to look beyond the big names of the premier league and at graduates from the first division of accredited schools.

A closer analysis of the Association's statistics produces some fascinating information on the realtionships between careers strategies, reward outcomes and the various modes of study.

- Two year full-time MBAs do best. Their average total cash salary was £100 200. This may be because LBS, Manchester, and some big European schools who offer a two-year programme, are also happy hunting grounds for recruiters and headhunters working for and with global companies.
- One year full-time graduates come next with an average of £67 500.
- They are followed by part-times and distance learners: £58 900 and £51 200 respectively.
- Sixty-three per cent of respondents changed employers within a year of graduating. In terms of income they did significantly better out of their qualification than the stay-puts.

If you want to gear your MBA towards a primarily financial objective the highest rewards are reported by MBAs currently working in the following sectors.

Changing places

Base salaries by industrial sector
note: sectors with a base of less than 30 respondents have been excluded

Industrial sector	Mean	Median
All resps	53 700	44 000
Commerce/retailing	70 400	45 000
Banking, finance and insurance	65 200	52 800
Management consultancy	60 700	50 000
Energy – electricity, oil, gas, coal	57 700	45 000
Printing, publishing and media	56 200	50 500
Food, drink and tobacco	54 500	46 600
Mechanical engineering products	53 100	45 000
Pharms and healthcare products	52 800	47 000
Computer services/IT	51 700	43 500
Electrical engineering and electronics	51 200	47 000
Other consultancy	50 800	41 000
Travel, transport and tourism	50 500	42 000
Chemical, plastic and rubber	49 400	45 000
Telecommunications	48 800	44 000
Other services	45 100	41 000
Building and construction	45 100	40 000
Healthcare	42 300	37 500
Public services, government etc	37 100	35 000
Education	28 800	28 000

Comment: those working in the private sector command higher salaries than those in the public sector and the differential between them is significant.

Looking at the picture from a further point of view – that of function – general management, finance, corporate strategy and planning and personnel come out best, whereas MBAs in production and administration do least well. There are also geographic variations. Salaries are highest in inner London, which is probably also a reflection of the concentration of consultancy and finance-related jobs there. They are significantly lower in the North-East, Wales and the Midlands.

This raises an important question: to what extent can having an MBA facilitate a change of career direction in search of more money or better prospects? Reports indicate that this can be very difficult, except in the case of those who want to move into consultancy or some of the more analytical areas of financial services, and that is confirmed by the sharp rise in the numbers employed in consultancy and corporate planning, following graduation. 'The MBA gives a sound grounding in strategic thinking, aside from providing a theoretical framework from which to operate and provides exposure to ideas and situations which would not be confronted by someone other than working at senior management CEO level,' is a characteristic comment from a recent MBA. In other words, it adds value to experience by giving it an intellectual framework, a strategic view of the business you are in. But it is of limited, immediately bankable value if you move out of that sector into a line management role elsewhere and find yourself competing for jobs against others who can point to practical experience in it – though the schools claim that the answer to the problem lies in the skilful choice of electives and, above all, of the final dissertation.

In addition, as recruiter John Courtis points out, you have to be able to analyse job advertisements, and show exactly how what you learned relates to the job specification. More and more, schools have become aware of the need to make job hunting techniques part of the MBA programme. However, one disadvantage of a cross-sector move is that this may, at least initially, limit the extent of the salary increase you would expect on completing an MBA.

Where moves across sectors do occur, research confirms that they are mostly into finance, strategy and consultancy and out of, mainly engineering, construction, the public sector and some branches of engineering.

There is a continuing trend for MBAs to move from larger to smaller organisations when they change employers. 'In many respects MBA graduates are becoming big fish in smaller ponds,' notes the Survey. 'This could reflect a desire to be able to use the full breadth of managerial skills gained through the MBA.' It also, perhaps, indicates that new and more dynamic companies value them more highly than the established ones. But there are hopeful signs among the latter too. There has been much criticism of the way MBAs were used by large employers – often subjected to trial by some kind of management ordeal rather than being put into roles where they could best apply what they had learned. The suggestion was that this might best be in internal consultancy-related roles. The growing number of MBAs going into the corporate strategy and planning function indicates that this might actually be happening (see fiure 8).

In spite of the disclaimers about a financial motive for doing an MBA, the conflict many face on graduating is between short-term financial gains, driven possibly by the need to repay a loan, and long-term career development. The former can push you in the direction of the highest bidder, rather than the best career move. Schools are increasingly devoting attention to career strategies, as well as 'how to get job' basics, as significant adjuncts in MBA programmes. Students are warned against the dangers of making a false first move for financial reasons. It has happened, and executive search and selection consultants say that an MBA who has suffered a career crash in his or her first postgraduate job is in a worse position than someone without an MBA. Employers will think they should have known better!

Functional area within the organisation

(Base: all who move to new employing organisation post MBA)

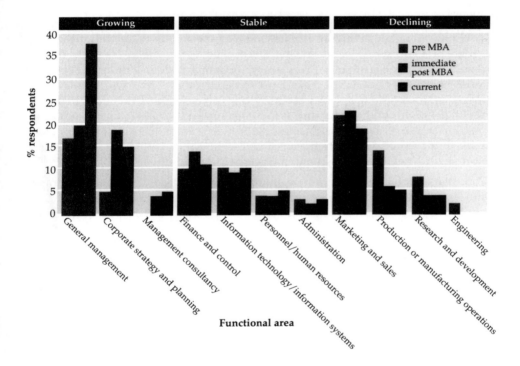

Functional area

For many MBA students considering a change in career direction first thoughts turn to management consultancy. This is not only because the content of the course teaches you in many respects to look at business problems in the analytical way that consultants do, but because the financial rewards being offered by management consultancy firms will probably be the highest you encounter as a new minted MBA. A study of the consulting industry produced by ADD-Resources, a firm which specialises in headhunting in this sector, shows a minimum 35% earnings differential, pre- and post-MBA.[4]

The charms of consultancy

[4] Mutual Attraction. Management Consultancy, September 1997.

The highest earnings are to be found in the three big strategy firms, McKinsey, Boston Consulting Group and Bain, who between them are currently looking for 900 MBAs – more than the annual output of Europe's five leading business schools, though of course their main recruitment grounds are in the big US schools, where top students can expect to have several competing job offers before they graduate. According to ADD-Resources, they may also receive a golden hello which could be as high as the course fees they paid to get the qualification.

Apart from the big name consultancies, there are numerous boutique firms which are looking for MBAs – not to mention the big five accounting firms who also recruit MBAs in large numbers every year. ADD-Resources tracked 7000 graduates last year and found that 30% of them went into some form of consultancy.

If the starting salaries are substantial, the rewards of partnership can be astronomical – high, six figure rewards can be expected by those who make it in a good firm. It usually takes four–ten years. The down side is that only one in four do, and that consultancy firms tend to operate a ruthless "up or out" policy. Furthermore, they work you very hard for your money. You will regularly be putting in a 60 hour week and be living out of a suitcase, admittedly in a first class hotel. Often you will be abroad for weeks on end – these days consultancies look for language as well as business skills. Some young consultants who have worked out their hourly rate have claimed to find they would have been better off doing a 9–5 day as an assistant manager with Sainsbury.

Consultancy used to be seen as something of a career dead end; not a way to get into line management. 'Consultants arrange the pictures on the wall, but they can't paint them,' as one American tycoon put it. There are, however, signs that this is changing. ADD-Resources say that a spell with a big name consultancy adds lustre to your CV and says that a growing number of CEOs have spent time in the early part of their career in consultancy. A prominent example is Archie Norman, a Harvard MBA who worked for McKinsey and went on to become the highly regarded chairman of Asda. The experience may even be useful in other spheres, as the career of William Hague, an INSEAD graduate and a member of the Association of MBAs, shows. He, too, used to work for McKinsey.

Doing your doctorate
For those who are considering an academic career or work in some of the more esoteric areas of management consultancy, the DBA is the next level up in postgraduate qualifications in business. A number of schools already offer one – Henley (by far the largest provider), Manchester, Strathclyde and Newcastle, as well as some others which are not accredited. Others are known to be considering it.

The big difference between a DBA differs and a PhD is that the object of the latter is to advance knowledge, whereas a DBA, while equally rigorous academically, has a more practical slant and is about the application of existing theories and research to a business problem. It is not a solitary research study but one that involves a good deal of interaction with other participants and with the faculty. Its practical orientation also implies a high degree of organisational support over a period of time. Whether this will be forthcoming is one of the factors schools look for in considering applications from people wanting to do a DBA. One of the difficulties about this is that over the time span it takes to complete a DBA, the nature and extent of a sponsor's interest in a particular corporate issue may have changed.

Like the PhD, the DBA eventually involves the preparation of a doctoral dissertation and a school will want a detailed and clearly though out proposal for it when you apply. It is much longer than the MBA dissertation: 50 000–60 000 words, as compared to 15 000–20 000. The DBA is an expensive course for schools to manage and supervise, a fact which is reflected in the relatively high fee structure. A special survey produced by the Association of MBAs[5] says that costs vary between £2 500 – £4 100 full-time and £1 250 – £6 300 part-time.

Interest in the DBA is not large, but is said to be increasing. However, some schools report that though MBAs who have gone into finance or management consultancy do sense a need for further and more specialised qualifications later in their career, the demand is for taught master's (MSc) programmes rather than for the more self-directed doctorate.

Follow your passion

A stimulating article by Tom Peters, unpublished in the UK, is entitled *Hey MBAs, Follow Your Passion.*[6] It offers some of the best career advice to MBAs that the writer has seen. Peters writes: 'MBAs often ask me how to assess companies that recruit at their schools. My response: If the interviewer turns you on, move ahead. If he or she is a stiff you wouldn't be caught dead hanging out with, forget it. Don't assume that he's the rare jerk in a company of gems'.

Basing his words on his own experience, Peters advises his readers to go for the person, not the assignment. 'A lousy boss can make the best assignment hell. A super boss can make the dullest assignment sparkle'.

Above all he advises MBAs to follow their 'passion' – the things which really interest them. 'If necessary, apprentice yourself for bread and board to someone who can teach you to excel at doing something you already love', he writes, and adds: 'Tough advice for top school MBAs, I admit. Many have borrowed $50 000 or more to finance their education. No wonder they're suckers for big, dull companies who overpay entry-level MBAs. . . . In smaller firms talented people have a good chance of making a huge difference, fast'. Some people, of course, feel happier in large companies, dull or otherwise. The whole business of career management is all about aligning your own skills and values with the appropriate tasks and organisational culture. Learning about yourself and where you fit into the corporate world is becoming an express part of an increasing number of programmes, under a variety of headings. At Cranfield, for instance, there is a core course in presentation and communication skills; in other places, it comes in the form of workshops and outdoor exercises. However, it emerges as an underlying theme from your studies, the work you do with fellow students, and the company-related project you undertake, is one of the most valuable things, in career terms, that the MBA provides.

[5] 'DBA or not DBA? That Is The Question,' Association of MBAs Special Report, 1997.
[6] Privately circulated by Tom Peters, 2 December 1991.

9 Business schools and executive education

Executive education – not to be confused with the Executive MBA – is an increasingly important revenue earner for business schools. Some go so far as to admit privately that their MBA programmes only break even, and that the profits which fund their very high level of plant and other facilities – much higher than you would find in the tertiary education sector both in the UK and abroad – is derived from short courses. Exact breakdowns are hard to get, but Warwick Business School's turnover from non-degree courses in 1997 was £1.76 million, while Cranfield, another major player in this market, has funded a £6m state of the art management development centre from its revenues in this sector.[1]

Like the MBA itself, these may be full-time residential, lasting for anything from a few days to three or four weeks, or part-time programmes running in the evenings or over weekends. The two latter stretch out over longer periods – in some cases as much as six months or a year, though the one-week model is the most popular, according to Ashridge, a long established provider of short courses. On the European continent, six of the leading schools have followed the new vogue for partnerships by getting together to deliver an executive programme which runs over 10 months and is delivered in 5-day modules in five different countries. The name, PRIME, also expresses the theme: Programme For International Managers in Europe.

At a total cost of 16,000 ECUs it is priced at the top end of the market, but fees generally run well into four figures, even for the shorter courses, so it is not surprising that business schools attract many competitors. Some of them are external consultants, who include business school gurus retained independently by large firms to give a short course to senior managers on their particular field of expertise (or the flavour of the month fad!), some are specialist training firms, and others are suppliers, for instance in the IT area, who train actual or potential customers in the use of some new product or technique.

A potentially significant training and development phenomenon is that of the 'company university', of which the best known examples are Unipart in the UK and Motorola in the USA. These train staff at all levels, though mostly in middle and junior management. They also pull in outside consultants on a temporary basis, including business school faculty, to run some programme modules. Some commentators think this might be the wave of the future. For instance, Henley is 'working closely with organisations such as Cable & Wireless and IDV to develop and deliver programmes in conjunction with their own learning centres',[2] while NatWest, BT, Cable & Wireless and GEC have established

---

[1] Short Cuts To Management Know-How, the *Times*, 13 March 1998.
[2] Here Endeth The Lesson, *People Management*, 19 February 1998.

executive development centres to train their own people.[3] City University Business School has also got into the game with an on-line training system called Direct-It.

A further new variant on the company university theme, is the Academy of Business, launched by Anita Roddick, founder of the Body Shop. It has teamed up with Bath University's accredited School of Management to offer a master's degree in various areas of the social responsibilities of business, as well as to provide modules on this subject for executive education courses at a number of business schools. This recognises the fact that by and large it is the business schools themselves who are undoubtedly the best equipped to provide the general context for executive education to help managers deal with big issues of the late 90s.

The word 'equipped' has a quite literal meaning here. There are some private providers who can offer accommodation of a higher standard than some business schools – though standards in the latter can come as a pleasant surprise for those expecting the rigours of academic study bedrooms – but probably none can match the technology or the library facilities of Association-accredited schools. What matters most, however, is that in the normal course of their work, faculty teaching MBA students constantly address and come into daily contact with the themes that are also much in demand in the field of management education: globalisation; the integration of functional areas of business; teamworking; the management of change; and the development of core competencies. All these themes spill over to a greater or lesser extent into shorter executive courses.

- *Globalisation* is a reality for business schools in the UK and increasingly in the rest of Europe, as the growth in cross-border alliances and in MBA programmes that are taught at least partly in English schools. The mix between students is usually around 50:50 between home country and foreign nationals, of whom typically 20–25% are from outside the EU. This means that as in the work of syndicate groups of 5-7 students that are an essential part of the learning process on the MBA, the faculty are constantly concerned with observing and reconciling differences in national attitude in the context of business decisions. As one professor observed, 'Putting together a team of individuals from Europe, Asia, Africa and America, with all the different assumptions they bring from their cultures and education, may not be the fastest way of getting a project done, but it's the way that business is increasingly being conducted'. The reality of that comes into a good number of executive education courses.
  The faculty members themselves are also increasingly global. If you look at the provenance of the teaching staff, you will find academic qualifications and teaching experience across a wide range of subjects. One leading school, for instance, now insists that new appointees should have had at least five years' experience abroad, while the amount of foreign travel on academic or consultancy assignments undertaken by faculty members in most of them, easily matches that of senior executives in multinational companies.
- *The integration of functional areas of business.* An important object of executive education is to get managers to think out of their box of functional

---

[3] *Times, op. cit* 13 March 1998.

responsibilities – to consider, for instance, how a decision in marketing will impinge on operations management, or how financial factors might affect human resources policy. This is actually the way the core subjects of the MBA, which form the basic building block of management skills, are taught in MBA programmes. An interesting development in executive education, in fact, is the appearance of what might be called 'chopped down' MBA programmes which focus on core subjects only. They are aimed at managers who are too busy to do the full programme, but do need an overview of how the core disciplines of management fit together. INSEAD and IMD are offering programmes of this kind.[4]

● *Teamworking*. This is also an integral part of MBA programmes from the very beginning, when the faculty forms students into syndicate groups of 5–7 who, under supervision, learn to work together on cases and projects. The experience of business school faculty as facilitators of teamworking is unrivalled.

● *The management of change*. Many students come on MBA programmes because they either want to effect changes in their careers, or because they want to develop adequate responses to changes taking place within their organisations. A classic example of the latter is the public sector or civil service MBA that has been developed at a number of schools in response to the huge changes in culture and practice that have taken place there. The management of change is usually either an integral part of the core programme of the MBA, or is implied in the way subjects are taught. Indeed, the nature of change in an organisation itself often has to do with thinking and working in a more integrated way.

● *The development of core competencies*. Business schools recognise that this is not a matter of developing strengths on a purely technical axis; it also has to do with fostering the 'soft' transactional and interpersonal skills, for instance in areas such as negotiation, without which core competencies cannot be translated into implementation. Management development courses dealing with these aspects are often preceded by a development centre at which the main needs of the individual are identified before he or she is sent on the appropriate programme.

Tailored vs open programmes

The major choice facing clients of executive education is not only between various kinds of providers, but also between open and tailored programmes. The latter are most popular with organisations, since they address their specific needs in the context of an organisational culture which is familiar to all participants. Tailored programmes are most suitable therefore, for the development of large groups of managers who have to effect or learn to live with changes within their own organisation. Furthermore, because they are rooted in the organisation and can be related to the particular circumstances that managers encounter in their everyday work, the huge step between learning and implementation becomes less of an obstacle. Companies reckon that the pay-off from tailored programmes is high in terms of quick results. There are, however, two problems. One is that tailored programmes, being company-specific, do not add the value of

[4] *Financial Times*, 16 February 1998.

transferability and employability that managers, especially the younger ones, often look for as a benefit of training. The other is simply cost and critical mass. Smaller organisations may not have enough people to run tailored programmes, and even large organisations may not have enough specialists in a particular field to justify setting up a tailored programme on it.

Open programmes are, as the name implies, open to all comers. As well as being suitable for management education needs in smaller firms, they are also appropriate for large ones who want to develop individuals in a specific area – such as some new financial technique, where the need to know is confined to one or two people, or even a single individual. However, they have another value which is also present in MBA programmes: they allow participants to mingle with others from a wide variety of backgrounds and disciplines, and to imbibe new ideas from their contributions in the class and from the socialisation which accompanies such courses. A further benefit is the morale boosting one. If a company invests money in sending a manager on a course at a leading business school, either here or abroad, it sends them the appropriate signal: we have plans for you. That can be an important tool to retain the people it most wants to keep.

The criteria for selecting providers of executive education are not dissimilar to those used by individuals in choosing a school at which to take an MBA: **Selecting providers**

- the standing of the provider in the business community – which can be judged on the basis of who regularly sends managers on courses there, or who has recently done so, and can be contacted to discuss the outcome
- the reputation of the provider in his peer group – which is often somewhat easier to establish in the case of a business school; Association-accreditation, for instance, is a very positive factor
- the qualifications and experience of the faculty – especially in relation to the business world; consultancy assignments carried out with major clients provide a clue here
- the quality of the presentation provided by the supplier and of the people they send along for this purpose – it is usual to look at a number of presentations before making a choice, certainly with tailored courses
- who will actually be giving the course – if you are hoping that it will be one of the school's stars, make sure that they will actually be on the case
- the look of the place where the training is being given – on the campus, in the case of business schools; there are quite marked differences in the facilities and general appearance of the top (but therefore) pricey schools and those who are not in the premier league. However, these may do a perfectly adequate job; ask previous clients
- how proactive they are in helping clients identify their training needs – whether they can demonstrate that they have the staff, the experience and the facilities to meet them
- whether they give any sort of credit for doing the programme. The idea that an individual's development should be credited to the continuous professional development requirements of bodies such as the IPD, to the school's own certificate or to diplomas and MBAs increasingly makes sense,' writes Michael Pitfield of Henley Management College. He says that many

business schools are now offering a 'stepladder' of qualifications at various levels for managers at differing stages of their careers.[5]

The final test, as in any client-supplier relationship, is, however, personal chemistry. Training relationships with external suppliers should ideally be long-term, and sensitive to the changing needs of individuals and organisations, rather than one-night (or one-fad) stands.

---

[5] *People Management, op.cit* above, 19 February 1998.

Part 2

SCHOOL
DIRECTORY

Accreditation of MBA programmes

Since the time of its inception in 1967, The Association of MBAs has encouraged management education at postgraduate level to help create professional managers. At the time, the Association had two objectives:

- to promote the MBA to academic institutions, prospective students and employers and to increase the supply of, and demand for, MBA programmes
- to check that the quality of MBA programmes was of a high enough standard to produce professional managers.

An accreditation process was established to secure the latter of these objectives and to assess the characteristics of the business school and its programme(s) against specific criteria. The criteria which the Association established have been progressively refined over the years and business schools and employers have made major contributions to this process. The Association continues to promote quality management education at postgraduate level and it now seeks to meet the challenges of an increasingly international MBA market. A new international accreditation scheme was launched in April 1997. The scheme has been designed as an independent validation for MBA programmes offered at institutions throughout the world.

An International Accreditation Advisory Board has been set up to ensure that the strategic issues within the international MBA arena are reflected within the accreditation criteria and process. The Board consists of senior academics and representatives of corporate and international bodies and meets twice a year.

Accreditation panels conduct the accreditation visits and they are drawn from a pool of academics who are closely involved with MBA programmes across a variety of international business schools and practitioners who are familiar with both business school academia and corporate management development. This combination ensures that each accreditation panel is well equipped to assess the quality of nominated MBA programmes. The composition of the panel is crucial to the public standing of the whole process. It must be accepted as well-informed both in academic and in commercial matters, fully independent, and having no financial or other interest in the outcome of the accreditation under discussion.

The accreditation system focuses on the quality standard of a particular MBA programme and is not a *de facto* accreditation of the school, although the context within which an MBA programme is delivered is obviously considered.

Process As a first step the Association welcomes an initial discussion with a business school seeking first time accreditation, in order to establish whether there is a reasonable consistency of outlook. If appropriate, the school will then be asked to complete a self-audit. This documentation will be used as the basis for assessing the likelihood that, if undertaken, an accreditation visit would have a successful outcome and therefore, whether or not an on-site visit should be carried out. The self-audit helps to ensure that, where carried out, during any team visit time is used in the most productive way possible.

The visiting panel will comprise:

- two academics from schools offering accredited MBA programmes and a practitioner
- representatives of the Association, namely, the Director General and the Manager, Accreditation Services who is also responsible for the administrative aspects of the process.

A report is subsequently prepared for the National Committee of the Association which will recommend: accreditation; accreditation subject to qualification; or, non-accreditation. Accreditation is valid for a maximum of five years after which the school would be invited to submit an application for re-accreditation.

Criteria for the accreditation of MBA programmes

The criteria are rigorous and offer consumer protection for the prospective student as well as a measure of quality for future employers. While setting the norms which an accredited programme will be expected to meet, the criteria are not intended to be so prescriptive as to stifle innovation or to preclude other measures by which quality may be assessed.

The salient features of the criteria are detailed below.

The business school

The assessment of MBA programmes will take account of the business school offering the programme. The business school shall have a clear sense of mission, explicitly expressed and regularly updated. It will have identified its target population and have a developed sense of the market for its products. This will include a means of regular access to employer opinion. The school should have its own discrete identity and an adequate degree of independence within the institution of which it is part.

A school offering an accredited programme must be able to provide relevant evidence of the quality of teaching on the MBA programme from within its faculty. High levels of quality in the MBA teaching team will be demonstrated by management research, scholarship and consultancy. The majority of the MBA teaching team should be actively involved in research contracts, indicating effectiveness in the business and/or public sector communities.

A school should be able to demonstrate satisfactory outcomes from its own internal or national audit processes. The school should provide evidence that it has implemented successfully any recommendations resulting from these processes. Mechanisms must exist to ensure adequate feedback and response to student reactions to course delivery and content.

There shall be clearly defined roles relating to the academic leadership and administrative responsibilities for the programme with individuals identified for each. A school should be able to demonstrate a level and quality of administrative support appropriate to the size of the MBA provision.

Institutions should demonstrate that the level of overall resourcing is appropriate for postgraduate/post-experience students. Library, computing and research facilities must be of a high standard and should be accessible out of normal working hours and at weekends. Access to industry standard hardware and software is important, as is the availability of literature search facilities and business databases. Facilities should exist to assist in employment for full-time students at the conclusion of their studies.

Faculty

Staff teaching at MBA level must be appropriately qualified and credible. At least 75 per cent of the teaching staff should have a relevant postgraduate degree and it is expected that the majority of faculty will hold a doctorate. The staff team should be aware of debates at the forefront of knowledge in the relevant management field and be able to relate their subject to other subjects in the MBA. They should have an up-to-date understanding of business practice gained through, for example, recent managerial experience, consultancy or research organisations so that teaching can be linked to good practice as well as to theory. The institution should have a well-founded staff development policy to ensure that staff continue to meet high standards.

The MBA teaching faculty should be of a size which can, with regard to the number of participants, fully resource the programme(s) for which accreditation is being sought. It is expected that the pool from which staff are drawn will normally consist of at least 40 full-time academic staff. Due regard will be given to the need for a critical mass of core staff to administer, deliver and manage the MBA programme effectively. Also taken into account are new technological approaches to delivery and learning which transcend the traditional concept of the school and tutor/participant interaction.

Students

The MBA is designed for those who may be expected, in time, to make a significant contribution to managing at the strategic level in their organisation. It should offer both a rigorous and intellectually demanding programme of study and the opportunity for personal development. Evidence will be required to show rigour in standards for admission, which must include managerial experience as well as academic criteria. Typically, an MBA student would have an honours degree or a professional qualification, in addition to at least three years managerial experience.

The student body must be large and varied enough to form an intellectually critical mass and emphasis is placed on the value of peer group exposure. Students should be selected on the basis of the contribution they may be expected to make as well as the benefit they may gain. Given the important role members of the cohort play in the learning process, a broad mix of disciplines, job functions, cultures etc. is seen to enrich the learning process. In order to achieve adequate group interaction, the minimum intake on an accredited programme would be a cohort size of least 40. Due regard will be given to the need for a critical mass of participants and geographical factors which may serve to constrain a local market.

Curriculum

Each individual MBA programme should have clearly stated aims, objectives and learning outcomes. Learning outcomes should be clear and explicit in describing what participants are expected to know and be able to do as a result of the programme. They should make clear the ways in which the school recognises and assesses intellectual, analytical, personal and enterprise qualities as well as the specific knowledge being developed by the programme.

The design and content of the programme should embrace a range of relevant theory firmly linked to the practical world of management; where possible employing organisations should contribute to the development of the course. The MBA is a postgraduate general management degree and care should be taken to ensure that the academic programme is properly related to the practical world of management. All programmes should ensure that candidates acquire a firm understanding of the major areas of knowledge which underpin general management, including:

- the concepts, processes and institutions in the production and marketing of goods and/or services and the financing of business enterprise or other forms of organisation
- the impact of environmental forces on organisations, including: legal systems; ethical, social, economic, and technological change issues; and the effect of international developments
- the ability to respond to and manage change should be covered explicitly
- the concepts and applications of accounting, of quantitative methods, and management information systems including IT applications
- organisation theory, behaviour, HRM issues and interpersonal communications
- the processes and problems of general management at the operational and strategic level
- business policy or strategy should be a core integrative course.

Normally, an MBA should contain substantial evidence of individual work undertaken as a project or projects, providing evidence of ability to integrate the individual core subjects.

While all programmes should reflect the general character of the MBA, individual courses may be designed to meet the needs of a specific functional sector. The general educational aims of the programme should be to develop transferable intellectual skills at Master's level; to develop students' ability to communicate clearly in various media; to argue rationally and draw conclusions based on a rigorous, analytical and critical approach to data; to demonstrate an awareness of the wider context of the programme of study; and to develop interpersonal and teamworking skills; to accelerate careers; to develop entrepreneurial ability and to create more effective managers. The programme should offer the means of self-evaluation and renewal for the participants. It is important that participants are able to apply the concepts learned during the programme.

Programmes may be full-time, part-time, distance/open learning or multi-mode. Innovative approaches to design and delivery are welcomed if they enhance learning opportunities and can maintain the coherence and integrity of the course. The Association has developed supplementary criteria for the assessment of distance/open learning MBAs which address issues such as resources, materials, infrastructure, quality control of agents, student/student interaction and student/faculty interaction.

Programme structure, duration and delivery

The duration of an MBA programme shall meet the general Master's requirement that it should be equivalent to at least one year's full-time study. For what might be regarded as a standard course for a normal entrant, the minimum duration is likely to be one calendar year full-time or two to three years part-time. An MBA programme will correspond to the equivalent of at least 1,200 hours of candidate learning effort. Additionally, the total number of contact hours is expected to be not less than 400 hours for a full-time programme.

The applied nature of much of the MBA demands a range of teaching and learning methods. These methods include lectures, seminars, workshops, action learning, reading, individual and group projects, distance learning, computer-based training and in-company training (whether formal courses or on-the-job learning with a mentor). It is expected that much of the learning will be practically-based. Co-operation of employers is to be encouraged. Much of the learning in an MBA can be expected to take place between members of the learning group, and opportunities for this to occur should be provided.

Assessment
The key purpose of student assessment is to enable students to demonstrate that they have met the objectives and achieved the learning outcomes of the programme at the standard required for the award of an MBA degree. The assessment scheme should have detailed criteria and clarify the range and relative values of the various assessment methods used.

The assessment scheme should reflect the particular aims and characteristics of the course. Individual examinations should play a significant role in any such scheme since they are seen as testing intellectual rigour under controlled conditions. While innovation in assessment methods is welcomed, particularly where new teaching and learning methods are being used, detailed evaluation by the school of such innovations will also be looked for.

Outcomes
When assessing the overall quality of the programme, consideration will be given to the value added by the MBA programme to work experience and career development. The views and experiences of appropriate alumni, employers and sponsors will also be sought. Where possible the transfer of learning from the programme to the place of work will be evaluated.

The international demand for The Association's accreditation service is growing as the need for an unbiased arbiter is recognised both by students and employers.

United Kingdom

Department of Management Studies, University of Aberdeen

Address: Edward Wright Building, Dunbar Street, Old Aberdeen, Aberdeen AB24 3QY
Tel: 01224 272712   Fax: 01224 273843
EMail: s.allen@abdn.ac.uk

Co-ordinator: Nicky Gunson

MBA Admissions Officer: Department Secretary

MBA Programmes
Executive MBA (Part-time)

Programme Details	Part-time
Duration	2½ years
Class Contact	300 hours
Commencement	September
Which evening/day	Varies
Application deadline	September
GMAT Yes/No	No
Fees EC/Overseas	£6,435
Annual student intake	20
Average student age	36
Min. required	6 years
%EC/Overseas:	100/0
%Men/Women	80/20
Number of Professors	6
Number of Academic Staff	20
Number of elective	10
Assessment: Exams/Assignments	Both
Dissertation/Project	D

Additional Information
Library hours: 7 days per week during term time
IT facilities: Available 24 hours per day
Electives not readily available elsewhere: Petroleum Economics

School Description
The MBA programme at Aberdeen University draws from staff in numerous departments, not only the Centre for Management Studies. These include Economics (research rating 4, teaching quality assessment 'excellent'), Accounting and Finance, Law and Philosophy. The part-time course is particularly attractive to those working in the oil industry, and there is a specific Petroleum Economics elective.

Aberystwyth Business School, University Of Wales, Aberystwyth

Address: Sir George Stapledon Building, Penglais, Aberystwyth SY23 3DY
Tel: 01970 622523   Fax: 01970 622524
EMail: nnf@aber.ac.uk
Director & MBA Admissions Officer: Mrs N Fullerlove

MBA Programmes
Full-time MBA; Full-time MBA (Agribusiness); Full-time MBA (Environmental Management)

Programme Details	Full-time
Duration	1 year
Class Contact	20 hours per week
Commencement	September
Application deadline	July
GMAT Yes/No	No
Fees EC/Overseas	£3,950/£6,200
Annual student intake	50
Average student age	28
%EC/Overseas	50
%Men/Women	50/50
Number of Professors	5
Number of Academic Staff	25
Number of elective courses	5
Assessment: Exams/Assignments	Both
Dissertation/Project	D

Additional Information
Library hours: 0830-1830

IT facilities: Yes

School Description
The Aberystwyth MBA, an intensive one-year programme of study comprising 12 taught modules followed by a three-month Dissertation, is designed both for students wishing to convert to management from other disciplines, and for people already embarked on managerial careers wishing to acquire the necessary skills to progress to higher levels.

The Aberystwyth MBA is based on a core of general management modules in Accounting, Economics, Law and Marketing. The specialist MBA (Agribusiness) however, is designed for graduates qualified in agriculture and related disciplines wishing to broaden their business knowledge whilst gaining a deeper knowledge of elective modules such as Agribusiness Management, Agricultural Production Economics, and Agrifood Marketing Systems.

The MBA (Environmental Management) is specifically aimed at graduates wishing to increase their understanding of environmental management from both the management and environmental angles. Subjects studied can include Environmental Auditing, Environmental Resource Management, and Environmental Impact Assessment.

The MBA programme has the fullest possible flexibility to meet students' individual needs. Students with no previous business qualifications study the seven core modules, mainly in the first semester, with their own choice of five elective modules in the second. Students are encouraged to interact and the emphasis is on team work, so opportunities are provided for residential weekends where personal skills can be developed in a social and friendly environment. These opportunities have opened doors for many past students, who otherwise would have been unaware of others' views.

Case studies also play an important part of the Aberystwyth MBA; visiting speakers from industries in the UK are invited to talk to the students, who then have the opportunity to ask questions regarding the marketing and financial aspects of the businesses relevant to the various speakers.

Previous Aberystwyth MBA graduates have stated that studying for the MBA helped them to understand some of the complexities of the business world and also changed their lives for the better.

The MBA at Aberystwyth was recently commended by The University of Wales Quality Review.

UNIVERSITY OF WALES, ABERYSTWYTH

MBA
(Master of Business Administration)

- One-year full-time programme
- Core modules: marketing, accounting, economics, organisation behaviour, quantitative methods, law, strategic management
- Electives available in marketing, accounting, agribusiness, economics, law
- Team building residential courses
- Specialist MBA programmes in Agribusiness and Environment Management

Further information and application forms:
Centre for Business Studies
University of Wales, Aberystwyth,
Dyfed, SY23 3DB, UK
Tel: 01970 622208. Fax: 01970 622524

Anglia Business School, Danbury Park Campus

Address: Anglia Polytechnic University, Main Road, Chelmsford, Essex CM3 4AT
Tel: 01245 225511/903692   Fax: 01245 224331
EMail: jknowles@bridge.anglia.ac.uk
Internet: www.ABS.anglia.ac.uk

Dean: Professor Hugh Jenkins

MBA Co-ordinator: Jonathan Knowles

MBA Admissions Officer: Ms Alice Gregson (Danbury)

MBA Admissions Officer: Annabel Hunt (Danbury)

MBA Admissions Officer: Ms Linda Lawrence (Cambridge)

MBA Programmes
Part-time Executive MBA; Business and Systems Management MBA; Financial Management MBA; Marketing Management MBA (all offered at Danbury & Cambridge sites); Full-time International MBA; Business and Systems Management MBA; Financial Management MBA; Marketing Management MBA; joint Executive MBA programmes in Spain, Germany, Belgium. Executive MBA also available at Norwich City College.

Programme Details	Full-time	Part-time
Duration	1 year	2½ years
Class Contact	18 hours	w/e blocks
Commencement	September/ February	September
Application deadline	September/ January	September

GMAT Yes/No	No	No
Fees EC/Overseas	£6,200	£7,200
Annual student intake	40	90
Average student age	29	33
Min. required experience	2 years preferred	
%EC/Overseas	75	100
%Men/Women	2/1	2/1
Number of Professors	5	5
Number of Academic Staff	85	85
Number of elective courses	13	13
Assessment: Exams/Assignments	A	A
Dissertation/Project	D	D

Additional Information

International Links   Berlin (Germany); Valencia (Spain); Belgium; Israel

Library hours: Libraries open extensively on 3 campuses, Cambridge, Danbury and Chelmsford

IT facilities: Internet links for all academic staff, open access PCs at Danbury and Cambridge for MBA students

Electives not readily available elsewhere: Innovation Management; Project Management; Total Quality Management; HRM Strategy in a Competitive Environment

Other information: An accommodation reservation service is offered to international students upon request. The accommodation office at the University is fully staffed throughout the year to assist with accommodation needs. Full-time MBAs offered industry visits, career advice and personal tutor system

School Description

Anglia Business School is one of the largest business schools in the United Kingdom with an international reputation as a Centre of Excellence in the field of Business and Management Development. There are 85 academic staff based in three divisions, located on three sites: Cambridge, Chelmsford and Danbury. The Business School has widespread and well established partnership agreements with higher education institutions across Europe, in North America and Malaysia, and these support the School's distinctive international mission. Anglia Business School is particularly proud of its association with the Ford Motor Company. Currently there are approximately 1,500 full-time and 1,500 part-time students registered within the School at both undergraduate and postgraduate levels. The School prides itself on being close to its customers and continually strives to understand and respond to their needs. Its programmes are practical and relevant, built on sound applied research and close involvement with industry and commerce.

The School is engaged in three major areas of inter-related activities:

- Teaching on Award programmes at undergraduate and postgraduate levels.
- Applied Research to underpin the Award programmes and consultancy activities.
- Services to Industry including the provision of tailor-made short courses and consultancy.

The School offers a comprehensive range of MBAs. The decision to offer specialist MBAs that build on the success of the established Executive MBA represents a significant step in the development of the regions' managers. Hundreds of managers have graduated with our Executive MBA over the last nine years. We hope these will be joined by new MBA colleagues who have taken an Anglia Business School MBA with a strong specialist element.

The MBA programme is intensive and highly interdisciplinary; it is internationally-oriented, and takes a very practical view of industry and organisations. Corporate policy is to have small class sizes, which is considered one of the school's strengths.

There are no formal examinations; each module has a work/industry/case study based assignment.

Ashridge

Address: Berkhamsted, Hertfordshire HP4 1NS
Tel: 01442 841143   Fax: 01442 841144
EMail: doris.boyle@ashridge.org.uk
Internet: www.ashridge.org.uk

Dean: Stephen Robinson

MBA Admissions Officer: Doris Boyle

MBA Programmes

Full-time (Modular); Part-time (Modular); Consortium (Modular-Deutsche Bank, Lufthansa, Merck)

Programme Details	Full-time ✔	Part-time ✔
Duration	1 year	2 years
Class Contact	620	620
Commencement	January	October
Which evening/day		Modular
Application deadline	December	September
GMAT Yes/No	Yes	Yes
Fees EC/Overseas	£16,000	£16,000
Annual student intake	30 max	30 max
Average student age	34	33
Min. required	5 years	5 years
%EC/Overseas	39	21
%Men/Women	4/1	6/1
Number of Academic Staff	51	51
Assessment: Exams/Assignments	Both	Both
Dissertation/Project	P	P

School Description

The Ashridge Executive MBA provides the opportunity to study and develop whilst achieving tangible benefits for a business sponsor who may be an existing employer or, if the candidate is self-funding, provide the opportunity to work in a different industry sector. Integral to the programme is a consultancy project where taught elements are applied to real world situations. Ashridge works with candidates to ensure a suitable project is found.

The programme brings together practising managers who offer experience of working internationally, tackling radical change or managing in different organisational cultures.

The small group size (maximum 30) provides a degree of personal development unmatched by other MBA Programmes. The executive education environment combined with the high quality facilities make Ashridge a good choice for practising managers.

The teaching approach at Ashridge is practical. In addition to their academic qualifications, tutors have management experience and many are active consultants. This is evident in the programme teaching and is reflected in the assignments which are focused on the functional areas of the business. Our emphasis is on developing the soft skills of individuals. Opportunities are created in the small group environment and via the project and assignments to enable these skills to be utilised and improved.

The Programme encourages participants to experiment with new ways of learning in a supportive environment. Ashridge has created in its Learning Resource Centre, a facility designed to optimise potential for self-managed learning. One of the most advanced Centres of its kind in Europe, this Centre houses our library, information services, personal computing and media training facilities.

It's no accident that the most practical MBA is also the most powerful

Ashridge Executive MBA

Ashridge's one and two year MBA programmes are designed for experienced managers and based on real-life assignments and a major strategic consultancy project. Small class sizes, faculty who are all experienced businesspeople, an international participant mix and a strong focus on personal development add up to a powerful preparation for the challenge of leadership.

Don't leave your career development to chance – talk to Ashridge.

Doris Boyle or Jane Tobin **Telephone:** *+44 (0)1442 841143* **Facsimile:** *+44 (0)1442 841144*
e-mail: *doris.boyle@ashridge.org.uk* **Internet:** *http://www.ashridge.org.uk* *Quoting Reference: GBS29/5/98*

Ashridge Ashridge Management College Berkhamsted Hertfordshire HP4 1NS England
the international centre for management and organization development
Ashridge is a charity registered as Ashridge (Bonar Law Memorial) Trust – charity number 311096

MBA candidates need to balance the intensive workload with relaxation and exercise. Our Physical Fitness Centre includes a swimming pool, squash courts, gymnasium, sauna and jacuzzi, with a Health and Fitness expert on hand to tailor your exercise programme.

Aston Business School

Address: Aston University, Birmingham B4 7ET
Tel: 0121 359 3611   Fax: 0121 333 4731
EMail: l.croker@aston.ac.uk
Dean: Dr M H Oakley
MBA Admissions Officer: Ms L Croker

MBA Programmes
Full-time MBA; Part-time Evening MBA; Part-time Day Release MBA; Part-time Distance Learning MBA (UK only); MBA in Public Services Management

Programme Details	Full-time ✔	Part-time ✔
Duration	1 year	2-3 years
Class Contact	18 hours (per week)	6 hours (per week)
Commencement	October	January/April/ October
Which evening/day		Day release and evening
Application deadline	No specific date	No specific date
GMAT Yes/No	Not compulsory	Not compulsory
Fees EC/Overseas	£8,750/£10,500	£8,750/£10,500
Annual student intake	60 approx	100 approx
Average student age	29	32

Min. required experience	3 years	3 years
%EC/Overseas	50/50	100
%Men/Women	3/2	3/2
Number of Professors	7	7
Number of Academic Staff	73	73
Number of elective courses	choose 4 from 30	choose 4 from 30
Assessment: Exams/Assignments	Both	Both
Dissertation/Project	P	P

Additional Information

Library hours: 0900-2200 (Mon-Thurs); 0900-1700 (Fri); 1000-1700 (Sat)

IT facilities: Extensive IT facilities are available on campus with dedicated computing equipment for postgraduate course members

School Description

Aston Business School is one of the largest and best regarded centres for business education in Europe, having provided Masters and Diploma courses in business and management for over 25 years.

The School has an excellent academic profile including 7 Professors and over 100 teaching and research staff. The expertise offered by such staff ensure that Aston Business school makes an outstanding contribution to the quality of practical management through its teaching, consultancy and research activities.

In addition to the full-time MBA and both day-release and evening modes of study for the part-time MBA, Aston leads the way in innovative distance learning. We offer one of the UK's most flexible MBA programmes allowing you to control how, when and where you learn. We provide unique video-based lectures which are produced directly from the MBA course taught on campus. The videos are not edited after recording and include interactive discussions and question and answer sessions. The distance learning programme is supported by tutor notes and study weekends as well as first rate academic and administrative staff.

All part-time students have the flexibility to decide their mode of study each term. On-campus and off-campus learning can be combined throughout the programme ensuring that the pace and location of studies can be tailored to suit individual study patterns and work commitments. Project-based learning is also an important feature of the Aston MBA as it allows students to apply theory in a practical context. Most of the projects are 'live' and involve students working with major employers on real business problems. This ensures that Aston MBA graduates are equipped with the practical skills required for a successful career in management.

Aston Business School shows a long term commitment to its students through the provision of the Aston MBA Alumni Network. At the heart of the Network is a body of Aston MBA graduates, many of whom now hold senior management positions around the world. Services provided for members of the Alumni Network include a regular Newsletter, Up-date Seminars, an MBA Alumni Network Directory and access to the Professional Development Programme provided within the Business School.

University of Bath

Address: School of Management, Claverton Down, Bath BA2 7AY
Tel: 01225 826152/826211   Fax: 01225 826210
EMail: mba-info@management
Internet: www.bath.ac.uk/Departments/Management
Director: Professor Brian Bayliss

MBA Programmes
Full-time MBA; Executive MBA (Part-time); Modular MBA

Programme Details	Full-time ✔	Part-time ✔	Modular ✔
Duration	1 years	2 years	3-8 years
Class Contact	14 week	8 week	35 hrs per module
Commencement	September	October	April/July/Sept/Jan
Which evening/day		Friday/Saturday	
Application deadline	August	September	Rolling procedure
GMAT Yes/No	Yes	No	in individual cases
Fees EC/Overseas	£11,000	£14,000	approx £11,000
Annual student intake	65	40	40
Average student age	31	36	36
Min. required experience	3 years	5 years	3 years
%EC/Overseas	51/49	100	95/5
%Men/Women	60/40	80/20	75/25
Number of Professors	12	12	12
Number of Academic Staff	80	80	80
Number of elective courses	12	12	12
Assessment: Exams/Assignments	Both	Both	Both
Dissertation/Project	Both	Both	Both

Additional Information
International Links: Joint MBA with the Malaysian Institute of Management (Association of MBAs-accredited course); agreements with 21 highly ranked overseas business schools

Library hours: 24 hour opening during term time

IT facilities: Over 300 PCs available in library and learning centre; dedicated IT facilities in School of Management

Electives not readily available elsewhere: Technology Management in supply chains; diversity and management; business ethics and social responsibility; management in the regulated sector

Other information: Purpose built MBA teaching centre; photocopying and information search service for part-time MBA students provided by the library; optional, free of charge foreign language classes; pre-MBA English course; world class sports facilities; thriving arts centre

School Description
Bath's internationally renowned School of Management is one of only five British MBA schools awarded top ratings for teaching and research in the latest Funding Council assessments and is amongst the most successful in Britain in terms of research income. There are 600 postgraduates on a wide range of taught and postgraduate degrees and 650 students following the highly regarded undergraduate programmes.

All three Bath MBA programmes are accredited by the Association of MBAs. All are general

THE BATH

MBA...

...TELLS THE WORLD YOU MEAN BUSINESS.

From this exceptional academic environment comes an exceptional business qualification: the Bath MBA.

The University of Bath School of Management is one of only five British MBA Schools to receive top Funding Council ratings for both teaching and research. So you can be sure of excellent teaching, programme content and academic support.

Our rigorous entry standards are designed not to promote elitism but to eliminate the "production line" approach. This enables a more personalised, interactive style of tuition to a quality mix of experienced and mature participants from all over the world.

All 3 variants of the Bath MBA, FULL-TIME, EXECUTIVE and MODULAR are accredited by The Association of MBAs.

For full details, including our regular Open Days/Evenings, contact us quoting Ref. AB98. Tel: +44 (0) 1225 826152 (F/T) 826211(EXEC) 323871(MOD)

Fax: +44 (0) 1225 826210

Email: mba-info@management.bath.ac.uk

http://www.bath.ac.uk/Departments/Management

School of Management, Dept. A101, University of Bath, Claverton Down, Bath BA2 7AY.

UNIVERSITY OF BATH
SCHOOL OF MANAGEMENT

OVER 20 YEARS' EXPERIENCE IN MBA PROVISION • ESTABLISHED, INTERNATIONALLY RESPECTED MANAGEMENT SCHOOL • A HIGHLY RANKED UNIVERSITY.
Advancing Learning and Knowledge in Association with Business and Industry.

management programmes designed for mature and experienced individuals. Bath's small group, high contact approach fosters teamwork, leadership and interpersonal skills while teaching is enriched through research of international excellence. The Full-time MBA has a strong integrative and international perspective with some 12-15 nationalities represented. Entrepreneurial and teamwork skills are developed through an eight-month business start-up exercise. Business Strategy and Change Management cover the key areas of strategic planning and organisational development. A Career Development Manager provides weekly individual counselling sessions and regular career workshops specifically for Full-time MBA students. Graduates have an excellent record of finding employment in their chosen field.

The Executive MBA is designed for participants with substantial managerial experience who wish to enhance their career prospects while staying with their present companies. Core courses in key management areas are complemented by a strong focus on the role of the manager as part of a senior team and on the nature of strategy and its implementation.

The Modular MBA is designed for individuals who require maximum flexibility in programme content, format and duration to suit their professional and personal commitments. The one-week modules, held on dates scheduled around 18 months ahead, are self-contained and can be taken at the student's chosen pace in virtually any sequence. Most students take four modules per year thus completing the MBA in 3-4 years.

The Birmingham Business School

Address: The University of Birmingham, Priorsfield, 46 Edgbaston Park Road, Birmingham B15 2RU
Tel: 0121 414 6693   Fax: 0121 414 3553
EMail: mba@bham.ac.uk
Internet: www.bham.ac.uk

Dean: Mr J R Slater

MBA Admissions Officer: Mr D M Perman

MBA Programmes
Full-time International Business MBA; Part-time Executive MBA by evening or modular study; International Banking and Finance MBA (F/T); European Birmingham/Montpellier MBA (F/T); Executive MBA (P/T modular, Singapore); other Executive MBAs available

Programme Details	Full-time ✔	Part-time ✔ Evening	Part-time ✔ Executive
Duration	12-24 months	24-48 months	24-48 months
Commencement	September	September/ January	January/April/ June/Sept
Which evening/day		Mon/Thurs	Mon-Mon (8 day block)
Application deadline	May/June	Continuous	Continuous
GMAT Yes/No	Recommended	Recommended	Recommended
Fees EC/Overseas	£7,500/£8,900	£7,700	£7,700
Annual student intake	70	25	25
Average student age	30	34	35
Min. required experience	3-5 years	5 years	5 years
%EC/Overseas	40/60	100	80/20
%Men/Women	58/42	80/20	70/30

**THE UNIVERSITY
OF BIRMINGHAM**

THE BIRMINGHAM BUSINESS SCHOOL

The MBA Programmes

FULL-TIME PROGRAMMES of 12, 18 OR 24 months duration

*MBA International Business   *MBA International Banking and Finance
*The European MBA (with Sup de Co, Montpellier)
*Diploma in Business Administration

PART-TIME PROGRAMMES of 24 to 48 months duration
taken by Evening or Modular Study
*Modular courses comprise of 8 modules each of 8 days duration.
Candidates return to work between each module and have up to 4 years
to complete the programme.*

*Executive MBA   *Executive MBA (Singapore)
*MBA (Strategic Procurement Management)

THE PROGRAMMES FEATURE:

*Flexible entry points depending on qualifications, age and experience
*International student body and faculty

The Birmingham Business School has been providing international
management education for almost a century. The research expertise of the
school, especially in International Finance, Trade and Industrial Strategy, Marketing
and Consumer Behaviour, is assimilated into the taught programmes, and
complements the practical bias, to give an in-depth knowledge of the
operational and strategic aspects of managing organizations.

The Birmingham Business School
The University of Birmingham
Priorsfield
46 Edgbaston Park Road
Birmingham, B15 2RU
ENGLAND

Tel: 0121 414 6693/4   Fax: 0121 414 3553
Email: MBA@bham.ac.uk   Website: http://www.bham.ac.uk

Number of Professors	12		
Number of Academic Staff	37		
Number of elective courses	19	n/a	n/a
Exams/Assignments	Both		
Dissertation/Project	Both		

Additional Information
International Links: Sup de Co, Montpellier, Memphis University
Library hours: 0800-2200 – 2.5 million volumes, CDRom and databases

School Description
The School of Business at the University of Birmingham has been providing international management education longer than any other university in England. We are situated in a prestigious suburb of Birmingham, the United Kingdom's second largest city, which has an international airport and is at the heart of the country's rail and road network. Each year, students representing some 45 nationalities study at the school which is considered to be one of the most international in Europe. The MBA programmes offered by the School are designed to develop a range of competencies encompassing the needs of both general and specialist sector managers and can be completed by full or part-time study in Birmingham or our international learning centres. Research centres in International Finance, Strategic Procurement, Industrial Strategy and EU-South East Asia Trade are assimilated into our taught programmes, ensuring that the latest developments in theory and practice are communciated to the cohort. We teach the programmes in Priorsfield, a dedicated building set in its own grounds, which is just a short walk from the main campus and postgraduate accommodation.

The sports facilities are excellent, with an athletics track, swimming pool and gymnasia, tennis courts and all weather pitches for ball games. A wealth of cultural activities are available in the university and the city. The Symphony Orchestra is renowned worldwide and the Royal Shakespeare Company perform in Stratford on Avon, not twenty miles from Birmingham.

The needs of participants are met by: continuing English language support; university accommodation; cultural and social programmes; industrial visits; mainframe and personal computing facilities.

School of Public Policy, University of Birmingham

Address: Edgbaston, Birmingham B15 2TT
Tel: 0121 414 4962   Fax: 0121 414 4989
EMail: c.k.skelcher@bham.ac.uk
Dean: Professor Ken Spencer
MBA Admissions Officer: Chris Skelcher

MBA Programmes
Full-time MBA (Public Service); Part-time MBA (Public Service)

Programme Details	*Full-time*	*Part-time*
Duration	1 year	2 years
Class Contact	12 hours	6 hours

Commencement	October	October
Which evening/day		Monday 1st yr – Tuesday 2nd year
Application deadline	end of August	end of August
Fees EC/Overseas	£6,700/£7,500	£6,700/£7,500
Annual student intake	3	c20
Average student age	30	35
Min. required experience	5 years	5 years
%EC/Overseas	0	0
%Men/Women	70/30	70/30
Number of Professors	8	8
Number of Academic Staff	120	120
Exams/Assignments	Both	Both
Dissertation/Project	D	D

Bolton Business School

Address: Bolton Institute, Deane Road, Bolton BL3 5AB
Tel: 01204 903612/903692   Fax: 01204 900516
EMail: dm5@bolton.ac.uk

Dean: Professor Alan Kitson

MBA Admissions Officer: David MacGregor

MBA Programmes
Part-time MBA; Part-time MBA in Small Business Management

Programme Details	*Part-time*	*MBA in Small Business Management*
Duration	3 years	2 years
Class Contact	6	one w/e per month
Commencement	September	January and June
Which evening/day	Mon/Wed; Tues/Thurs	Friday and Saturday
Application deadline	August	n/a
GMAT Yes/No	no	no
Fees EC/Overseas	£3,000	£3,600 no overseas
Annual student intake	50	24
Average student age	34	35
Min. required experience	3 years	3 years
%EC/Overseas	n/a	n/a
%Men/Women	60/40	70/30
Number of Professors	3	3

Individual programmes accredited by the Association of MBAs are indicated by a tick

Number of Academic Staff	72	72
Assessment: Exams/Assignments	A	A
Dissertation/Project	P	P

School Description

Bolton Business School, part of Bolton Institute, is located in Eagle Tower, a former textile mill which has been refurbished to a high standard using funds from the Higher Education Funding Council and the European Commission. The location provides an integrated learning resource centre (library, computing services, TV studio) and specialist School facilities (Languages, IT for Managers, Management Learning Centre) as well as teaching and staff accommodation within the same building. There are 70 full-time academic staff, 15 visiting lecturers and 5 visiting professors. The School has very close contacts with local industry and commerce, with senior executives from major companies serving on the School's Advisory Council.

The School has a strong tradition of providing part-time business, computing and management education. With over 2000 students in total, the School has 1000 part-time students (over 250 postgraduate).

The newly established Centre for Enterprise and Management delivers teaching, consultancy and research in small business management and management development.

Bradford Management Centre

Address: Emm Lane, Bradford BD9 4JL
Tel: 01274 234373/234374/234359   Fax: 01274 546866
EMail: g.h.barbour@bradford.ac.uk
Internet: www.brad.ac.uk/acad/mancen/ubmchome.html
Dean: Professor D T H Weir
MBA Admissions Officer: Ms S Avery

MBA Programmes

Full-time MBA; Part-time MBA (evening MBA); Open Learning MBA – from Sept 1998

Programme Details	Full-time ✔	Part-time ✔	Open Learning
Duration	1 year	2-6 years	3-6 years
Class Contact	20 hours per week	4 hours per week	min 15 days a year
Commencement	September	September	Sept/March
Application deadline	July/August	August	August/February
GMAT Yes/No	Yes for O/S students who cannot take admission test		
Fees EC/Overseas	£9,250/£9,750	£8,750	
Annual student intake	100	80	100
Average student age	31	35	
Min. required experience	3 years	3 years	3 years
%EC/Overseas	45/55	95/5	

Schools offering an Association of MBAs-accredited programme are indicated by a roundel

%Men/Women	60/40	70/30	
Number of Professors	14		
Number of Academic Staff	50		
Number of elective courses	30+	approx 20	min 12
Assessment: Exams/Assignments	Both	Both	Both
Dissertation/Project	P	P	P

Additional Information

International Links: Singapore; The Netherlands; Miskolc; Botswana; Erasmus; Israel; India; American and Australian universities

Library hours: Term time: 0845-1900 (Mon-Fri); 1000-1400 (Sat) Vacation time: 0845-1730

IT facilities: HP9000 business server; 200 fully networked PCs; Connection to University main campus. Email and Internet facilities for all students

Other information: Sony Language library; a multi-media system; a library on site with 35,000 books and 250 journal subscriptions

School Description

The Centre's buildings, a pleasant blend of old and new properties, are set in 13 acres of parkland forming a self-contained site situated two and a half miles from the centre of Bradford. Recreational facilities are in close proximity and there is a sports centre on the main University campus. This is a general management course which also allows for functional specialisation. The first (foundation) stage focuses on key business functions and includes: Economics; Productions and Operations Management; Finance and Accounting; Marketing; Human Resource Management; Information Management. The second (elective) stage enables students to tailor-make their own degree, choosing six electives from a selection of up to 50 which includes such diverse subjects as The Management of Change, International Business, Services Operations Management, and Credit Risk Management. Running throughout both these stages is an 'Integrative Core' focusing on Cross-functional Management and Strategic Planning, essential disciplines in modern management. The final (project) stage allows students to apply their knowledge and understanding either by an in-company project or a research-based review.

To ensure that individuals' personal needs are catered for, the Management Centre offers a variety of learning experiences including individual support on the development of a portfolio, interpersonal skills workshops, guidance on presentation skills, language training, European exchange programmes, and seminars by visiting speakers. Bradford Management Centre is fully committed to helping MBA students get the right job at the end of the course, and provides career services dedicated specifically to the MBA Programme. The Career and Projects Manager works with MBA participants on both a group and an individual basis, providing advice and support on career decisions, job search techniques and skills, and project placements. Close contact is maintained with local, national, and international employers to provide MBA students with appropriate opportunities.

The Claire Jarvis Bursary, established in memory of a past student, is awarded annually. Its objective is to enlarge the opportunities for female graduates to fulfil their potential and obtain senior management positions in British Industry. In addition, the Bob Gardner Bursary is offered to a student with no other sources of finance and who is considered the most deserving.

All students automatically become members of the Alumni Association on graduating.

University of Brighton Business School, Centre for Management Development

Address: Mithras House, Lewes Road, Brighton BN2 4AT
Tel: 01273 642341   Fax: 01273 642980
EMail: s.tonkin@bton.ac.uk
Internet: www.bus.bton.ac.uk

Dean: Professor John Bareham

MBA Admissions Officer: Mr Peter Bell

MBA Programmes
Full-time MBA; European MBA; Part-time MBA

Programme Details	Full-time	Part-time	Action Learning
Duration	12/16 months	3 years	3 years
Class Contact	30 hours	6 hours	variable
Commencement	September	September	October
Which evening/day	n/a	Weds all day, Tues aft/eve and Mon/Weds eves	variable
Application deadline	August	n/a	n/a
GMAT Yes/No	Yes	No	No
Fees EC/Overseas	12 months: £6,360/7,350 16 months: £7,875/8,925	to be confirmed	to be confirmed
Annual student intake	35/40	100	25
Average student age	27	29	29
Min. required experience	3 years	3 years	3 years
%EC/Overseas	35/65		
%Men/Women	60/40	50/50	50/50
Number of Professors	3	3	3
Number of Academic Staff	135	135	135
Number of elective courses	8-10	8-10	8-10
Assessment: Exams/Assignments	Both	Both	Both
Dissertation/Project	D	D	D

Additional Information
International Links: ESC Grenoble (France); FH Pforzheim (Germany); SAA University of Turin; University of Madrid (Spain)

Library hours: 0900-2100 (Mon-Fri), 1230-1700 Weekends

IT facilities: One workroom with PCs and printers for MBA students exclusively, 100+ PCs in computer pool rooms

School Description
The Business School was founded in 1986 but the institution and its precurors have been teaching business studies in the town since the beginning of the century. In recent years it has been one of the pioneers of student exchanges and joint European courses. The work of the School is supported by 135 teaching and research staff, five libraries with the largest collection of business and management books in the region, plus a wide range of specialist journals, commercial databases and other media materials.

The Business School is located about two kilometres from the town centre and the sea. For more than 150 years Brighton has been one of England's leading resort towns less than one hour by train from London and within easy reach of the Channel Tunnel and the ports connecting Britain to mainland Europe. The town has been described 'as a unique blend of history, eccentricity and elegance'; the Royal Pavilion, 'Europe's most fantastic palace', 'the Lanes', the sea front Regency terraces, the flourishing Theatre Royal, an international Festival of Music and the Arts, an international conference centre and probably one of the widest ranges of restaurants, pubs, clubs and wine bars outside London.

Most core modules are assessed by a combination of individual and group coursework. Formal examinations and computer simulation games are used where appropriate. A particular feature of the Brighton MBA is the high level of classroom contact. This is a taught programme. A Course Handbook detailing the aims and objectives for each module, the syllabus, teaching and assessment methods, and a reading list is given to all candidates at the start of the course.

The Business School consists of 38 senior academics with wide ranging research, publication and consultancy expertise on most aspects of UK and European business. The Department of Finance and Accountancy, and the Language Centre are particularly strong. Where appropriate, specialists in a particular field, for example European integration, and the impact of EC legislation, are brought in to teach on the programme.

Individual programmes accredited by the Association of MBAs are indicated by a tick

Bristol Business School, UWE

Address: Frenchay Campus, Coldharbour Lane, Frenchay, Bristol BS16 1QY
Tel: 0117 976 3848   Fax: 0117 976 2718
EMail: business@uwe.ac.uk
Internet: www.uwe.ac.uk
Dean: Professor J M Rees
MBA Admissions Officer: Sharon Bohin

MBA Programmes
Full-time MBA (not yet accredited); Part-time MBA (accredited)

Programme Details	Full-time	Part-time ✔
Duration	1 year	2½ years
Class Contact	390	6 hours per week
Commencement	September	September
Which evening/day	n/a	Part 1 Tues, Thurs; Part 2 Weds
Application deadline	July	July
GMAT Yes/No	Yes	Yes
Fees EC/Overseas	£5,950/£7,749	£8,211
Annual student intake	30/60	50/70
Average student age	27	35
Min. required experience	2 years	3 years
%EC/Overseas	85/15	100
%Men/Women	70/30	65/35
Number of Professors	3	3
Number of Academic Staff	150	150
Number of elective courses	8	8
Assessment: Exams/Assignments	Both	Both
Dissertation/Project	D	D

Additional Information
International Links: ICN Nancy (France); Georg-Simon-Ohm Fachhochschule Nürnberg (Germany)
Library hours: 0900-2100 (Mon-Thurs); 0900-1800 (Fri); 0930-1300 (Sat)
IT facilities: 6 computer rooms; 24 hour access

School Description
Bristol Business School is one of the largest business schools in the UK, with over 3,000 students following full-time, sandwich and part-time courses. The quality of business and management studies at the School has been assessed as 'excellent' by the Higher Education Funding Council for England. The School has 150 academic and support staff with experience and expertise in a wide range of disciplines.

The established Part-time MBA is Association of MBAs-accredited; the Full-time MBA commenced in September 1997; and is thus not yet eligible for accreditation by the Association. The new Full- time MBA programme can be followed in three parts in the UK, France and Germany by those wishing to develop skills and competencies with a strong European emphasis. Managers interested in a more general management perspective can complete the entire programme in the UK. Programme delivery for both routes is in English.

BBS is an approved provider institution for the NHS Executive Management Education Bursary Scheme. A bursary may be available for this year's part-time MBA programme. Please contact Bristol Business School's Admissions Office for further details.

University of Bristol, Graduate School of International Business

Address: 10 Woodland Road, Clifton, Bristol BS8 1UQ
Tel: 0117 973 7683   Fax: 0117 973 7687
EMail: gsintbus@bristol.ac.uk
Internet: www.bris.ac.uk/Depts/MBA/

MBA Admissions Officer: Judy Denham

MBA Programmes
Full-time MBA; Part-time MBA

Programme Details	Full-time ✔	Part-time ✔
Duration	13-15 months	2-3 years
Class Contact	620 hours	620 hours
Commencement	September/January	September/January
Which evening/day	Modular	Modular
Application deadline	15 August/1 December	15 August/1 December
GMAT Yes/No	Yes	Yes
Fees EC/Overseas	£12,500	£14,000
Annual student intake	60	12
Average student age	28	28
Min. required experience	2 years	5 years
%EC/Overseas	20/80	80/20
%Men/Women	60/40	80/20
Number of Professors	10	
Number of Academic Staff	38	
Number of elective courses	40	
Assessment: Exams/Assignments	Both	
Dissertation/Project	Both	

Additional Information
International Links: Ecole Nationale des Ponts et Chaussées, Paris (France); University of Hong Kong; University of Ljubljana (Slovenia)

Library hours: 0845-2300 (Mon-Thurs); 0845-1800 (Fri-Sat); 1400-2200 (Sun)

IT facilities: 24 hour access

Other information: Language tuition; Personal development and team-building skills; Mathematics and IT skills

School Description
The MBA in International Business is international, multicultural and practical. Both the student body and teaching faculty are international, drawn from all over the world, and study options are available outside the UK. Students work in a very intensive and interactive way in multicultural teams, managing diversity. The programme has a high regard for the individual and encourages students to test their personal and professional strengths, and to achieve their own objectives.

This is a modular programme and can be studied on a full-time or part-time basis. Students are required to obtain 15 credits of taught modules, to study at least one option overseas, to undertake a four to six month professional placement in an international company, and to present a 10,000 word dissertation based on the placement project.

Brunel Graduate Business School

Address: Brunel University, Uxbridge, Middlesex UB8 3PH
Tel: 01895 203064   Fax: 01895 203149
EMail: Pauline.Seston@brunel.ac.uk
Internet: www.brunel.ac.uk.depts/cbms/mba

Dean: Professor David Sims

MBA Admissions Officer: Mrs Pauline Seston

MBA Programmes
Multi-modal MBA (Full-time, Part-time and Distance Learning modes interchangeable)

Programme Details	Full-time	Part-time	Distance Learning
Duration	1 year	2 years	2-5 years
Class Contact	696 hours	420 hours	Approx 96 residential hours
Commencement	September	September	September/ March
Which evening/day		One day per week	
Application deadline	No formal deadline	No formal deadline	No formal deadline
GMAT Yes/No	Normally	Normally	Normally
Fees EC/Overseas	£10,250	£10,250	£10,250
Min. required experience	3-5 years	3-5 years	3-5 years
Number of Professors	6	6	6
Number of Academic Staff	18	18	18
Number of elective courses	3	3	3
Assessment: Exams/Assignments	Both	Both	Both
Dissertation/Project	D	D	D

Additional Information
International Links: Includes State University of New York (USA); Cleveland State University (USA); Ecole Central de Lille (France); Technical University of Wroclaw (Poland); University of Stuttgart (Germany); Ecole Polytechnique Federale de Zurich (Switzerland); University of West Bohemia (Czech Republic)

Library hours: 1000-2100 (Mon); 0900-2100 (Tues-Thurs); 0900-1800 (Fri); 0930-1300 (Sat); 1400-1900 (Sun)

IT facilities: Computer terminals available in the library and computer centre

School Description
Brunel has been a university since 1966, and is now recognised as a major force in the UK higher education scene. Through both its high-quality degree courses and research activity, the University has developed extensive and rewarding links with industry and commerce. It is within easy reach of London, Heathrow and the national motorway system.

The Graduate Business School, responsible for the Brunel MBA, is part of the School of

Business and Management. As well as the MBA, the School offers a range of undergraduate single and joint Honours degrees, including the unique distance-learning BSc in Business Administration, a variety of Certificate, Diploma and Professional Development courses, and Masters and Doctoral programmes on a part- or full-time basis for graduates wishing to specialise in particular management areas.

The Brunel MBA is practically oriented and is structured to give students an in-depth understanding of a specific business area, alongside a generic study of core subjects. The emphasis is on employable knowledge. Alongside a core section on Foundations of Business Management, students are able to pursue specialist pathways in Information Management or Managing for the Future. New specialisms will be added progressively, drawing specialist teaching support from across the whole of the University's broad spectrum of expertise. The final part of the course is an option-related research project conducted within an organisation.

A particular feature of the course is that students are able to switch from one delivery mode to another if job demands or personal circumstances require. The course fees for all three delivery modes are the same.

Students may use the University Sports Centre and join in with all the social activities of a large University campus.

The Brunel Campus Careers Advisory Service offers advice on interview techniques, self-marketing and career evaluation. Brunel University offers some scholarships for overseas postgraduate students, whilst the Graduate Business School has a few limited bursaries for MBA students.

Buckinghamshire Business School, Buckinghamshire Chilterns University College

Address: Newland Park, Chalfont St Giles, Buckinghamshire HP8 4AD
Tel: 01494 874441   Fax: 01494 874230
EMail: znaji01@buckscol.ac.uk
Internet: www.buckscol.ac.uk/business/courses.html
Dean: Nigel V Cox
MBA Admissions Officer: Dr Zeyad Naji

MBA Programmes
Part-time MBA; Distance Learning MBA; Full-time MBA (subject to validation)

Programme Details	Full-time	Part-time	Distance Learning
Duration	12 months		
Class Contact	12 hours	6 hours	
Commencement	October	October	
Which evening/day		Tuesday	
Application deadline	September	September	September
GMAT Yes/No	No	No	No
Fees EC/Overseas	To be published after validation	Yr 2 £1,110; Yr 3 £2,370	Yr2 £1,110; Yr 3 + Diss £2,370
Annual student intake	n/a	16	n/a
Average student age		32	
Min. required experience	3 years	2 years	2 years

Individual programmes accredited by the Association of MBAs are indicated by a tick

%EC/Overseas	n/a	60	n/a
%Men/Women	n/a	50/50	n/a
Number of Professors	1	1	1
Number of Academic Staff	60	60	60
Number of elective courses	7	7	7
Assessment: Exams/Assignments	Both	Both	Both
Dissertation/Project	D	Both	Both

Additional Information

International Links:
Well established links with educational institutions in Europe (including Eastern Europe) and USA; a distance learning version of the MBA has been launched in Hungary and South Africa, and is to be launched in Germany.

Library hours: 0830-2100 (Mon-Thurs); 0830-1730 (Fri); 1000-1700 (Sat)

IT facilities: Well-equipped computer rooms with current business software and multimedia teaching support systems; very supportive technical staff

Electives not readily available elsewhere: Business and Management in Central and Eastern Europe; Business in the Pacific Rim; Managing in the Public Sector (UK); Business and Professional Ethics; International Logistics (NB Elective modules are offered on a distance learning basis, so can be taken by students registered on MBA programmes at other institutions provided that the MBA-awarding institution will accredit the modules.)

Other information: Modern teaching accommodation in a pleasant rural setting

School Description

Buckinghamshire Business School is the largest faculty of Buckinghamshire Chilterns University College, which has some 8,000 students spread over sites in High Wycombe, Great Missenden and Chalfont St Giles. The Privy Council has granted the college taught course degree-awarding powers, encompassing both undergraduate and postgraduate degrees. The college aims to become a university at the beginning of the new millennium.

The Business School has a long history of collaboration with overseas academic institutions; this is reflected in the development of the MBA and the inclusion of electives on Business and Management in Central and Eastern Europe and Business in the Pacific Rim. The MBA is offered in a distance learning mode to students in Hungary and South Africa.

It is intended to hold a week-long 'international summer school' at which UK students on the part-time course will meet their distance learning counterparts from overseas countries.

The Part-time MBA students are a good mix of private-sector and public sector employees. Students wishing to explore the particular challenges of the sector from a theoretical or practical perspective may take an elective which focuses on these issues.

The MBA is now in its ninth year and is a well-established programme with a high completion rate. A recent survey of MBA graduates showed that a significant number had been promoted within their own organisation, or had obtained desirable positions in other organisations, within two years of completing the MBA.

University of Cambridge

Address: The Judge Institute of Management Studies, Trumpington Street, Cambridge CB2 1AG
Tel: 01223 337051/2/3   Fax: 01223 339581
EMail: mba-enquiries@eng.cam.ac.uk
Internet: www.jims.cam.ac.uk
Director: Professor Sandra Dawson
MBA Admissions Officer: Dr Ian Rudy

MBA Programmes
Full-time MBA

Programme Details	Full-time ✔
Duration	1 or 2 years
Class Contact	25-30 approx
Commencement	October
Application deadline	No set deadline
GMAT Yes/No	Yes
Fees EC/Overseas	£18,000 1 yr; £19,500 2 yrs
Annual student intake	50-80
Average student age	29
Min. required experience	2 years
%EC/Overseas	33/67
%Men/Women	69/31
Number of Professors	6
Number of Academic Staff	50
Number of elective courses	10
Assessment: Exams/Assignments	Both
Dissertation/Project	Both

Additional Information
International Links: No formalities, International faculty and student body

Library hours: Term time: Mon-Fri 0845-1900, Sat 1000-1300, Sun closed. Vacation Mon-Fri 0900-1700

Electives not readily available elsewhere: Financial engineering, manufacturing management, international politics

School Description
The Judge Institute is Cambridge University's business school practical located in a dramatic complex of purpose-built buildings in the heart of Cambridge. It combines the traditional academic strengths of the University with the resources, facilities and practical relevance you would expect from a leading international business school.

The faculty has over 50 full-time teaching and research staff members who all have international reputations in their fields. Their particular strengths are represented in areas such as international and cross-cultural management, the management of technology, corporate finance, marketing and the study of organizations. Both staff and students are drawn from around the world with at least 30 nationalities represented.

The Cambridge MBA has a strong practical orientation with a core programme concentrating on cross-cultural teamworking and international management, backed up by group projects and real-world assignments. The comprehensive core also includes programmes on business strategy, organisations, and marketing and finance, providing students with both the 'hard' and the 'soft' skills needed for success in today's global business environment. Small interactive classes, in the Cambridge tradition, allow everybody to participate fully and collaboration and co-operation are strongly encouraged.

The Institute has a dedicated MBA careers advisor who works alongside the highly regarded and well-resourced University Careers Service to provide a comprehensive service of career counselling, technical support and up-to-date corporate recruiting information. Major companies visit Cambridge to recruit both undergraduate and graduate students. These formal activities are supplemented by informal ones, using the worldwide network of University of Cambridge alumni to introduce students to a wide range of potential employers.

A limited number of bursaries are available for UK applicants working in the not-for-profit sector. There is also an annual scholarship for UK applicants working in the hotel/catering industry.

Canterbury Business School

Address: The University, Canterbury, Kent CT2 TPE
Tel: 01227 827726   Fax: 01227 761187
EMail: cbs_Admissions@ukc.ac.uk
Internet: snipe@ukc.ac.uk/cbs/
Dean: Professor Brian Rutherford
MBA Admissions Officer: Mr Bernard Kemp

MBA Programmes
Full-time MBA; Part-time MBA; Strategic Health Services Management MBA full and part-time; Master of European Business Administration (MEBA) full-time (2 years)

Programme Details	Full-time	Part-time
Duration	1 year	2-5 years
Class Contact	450	450
Commencement	October	October
Which evening/day	Tuesday	afternoons and evenings
Application deadline	31 August	31 August
GMAT Yes/No	No	No
Fees EC/Overseas	£7,000/£9,000	£7,000/£9,000
Annual student intake	60	40
Average student age	28	36
Min. required experience	3 years	3 years
%EC/Overseas	45/55	100/0
%Men/Women	54/46	67/33
Number of Professors	6	6
Number of Academic Staff	34	34
Number of elective courses	4	4
Assessment: Exams/Assignments	Both	Both
Dissertation/Project	D	D

Additional Information

International Links: ESC Reims (France), ESTE San Sebastian (Spain)

Library hours: 0900-2200 (Mon-Thurs), 0900-2000 (Fri), 1200-1900 (Sat), 1400-1900 (Sun)

IT facilities: Dedicated PC Suite – Windows NT giving access to Office 97, email, Internet and CD Roms

School Description

Canterbury Business School is the Postgraduate Management Centre of the University of Kent. The School is located, in a modern, purpose-designed building on the west of the campus, close to the main graduate student village. The building is dedicated to the School's graduate students and is well-equipped with teaching rooms and IT facilities; students have 24 hour access, seven days per week. The relatively small size of the School enables it to provide a more focused and individual approach to student learning, with high levels of personal contact.

The Canterbury Business School MBA provides an international focus on business affairs and recruits students from throughout the world. The Full-time and Part-time MBA programmes are identical in terms of content and structure. The part-time students proceed at a slower pace and are taught together with the full-time students one day per week. This means that the programmes are completely interchangeable, so it is easy for students to change from full-time to part-time or vice versa; this makes for great flexibility in the duration of the programme for part-time students. The programmes are geared to the needs of post-experience students (who have been employed for at least three years in a managerial or professional position and have a minimum age of 25 years). The method of tuition explicitly uses the experience of the students as part of the teaching process, with strong emphasis on small group work.

Cardiff Business School

Address: University of Wales, Aberconway Building, Colum Drive, Cardiff CF1 3EU
Tel: 01222 874417   Fax: 01222 874419
EMail: mansfield@cardiff.ac.uk

Director and MBA Admissions Officer: Professor Roger Mansfield

MBA Programmes
Full-time MBA; Part-time MBA; Modular MBA

Programme Details	Full-time	Part-time	Modular
Duration	1 year	2½ years	2½ years
Class Contact	16	8	0-48
Commencement	late September	late September	any
Which evening/day		1st yr Mon & Tues; 2nd year Tues & Thurs	any
Application deadline	July	July	any
GMAT Yes/No	No	No	No
Fees EC/Overseas	£7,260/£9,000	£6,000	£8,100
Annual student	300-400	50	30
Average student age	27	28	32
Min. required experience	3 years desired	3½ desired	3 years

Individual programmes accredited by the Association of MBAs are indicated by a tick

%EC/Overseas	68%	5%	0%
%Men/Women	72/28	76/24	76/24
Number of Professors	28	28	28
Number of Academic Staff	148	148	148
Number of elective courses	21	21	11
Exams/Assignments	Both	Both	Both
Dissertation/Project	D	D	D

Additional Information

International Links: Links with universities in France, Germany, Italy, Japan and Spain. Major on-site library.

IT facilities: 6 computer links and all networked.

Library hours: 0900-2130 Mon-Fri 1000-1800 Sat

Electives not readily available elsewhere: Integrated facilities on single site covering all aspects of learning process

School Description

A major university business school in a modern purpose-built building with an international approach to management education. A strong research-led faculty with 150 teaching and research staff including 28 professors able to provide world-class education in business and management.

University of Central England Business School

Address: University of Central England in Birmingham, Perry Barr, Birmingham B42 2SU
Tel: 0121 331 5539   Fax: 0121 331 6366
EMail: harinder.bahra@uce.ac.uk

Director and MBA Admissions Officer: Harinder Bahra

MBA Programmes
General Management MBA; Finance MBA; Audit MBA; Manufacturing Management MBA; Economic Development MBA; Marketing MBA

Programme Details	Full-time	Part-time
Duration	1 year	2½ years
Class Contact	varies	varies
Commencement	September	
Which evening/day		Mondays
Application deadline	August (of year of entry)	
GMAT Yes/No	500 (optional)	500 (optional)
Fees EC/Overseas	£6,500	£3,750
Annual student intake	up to 120	100
Average student age	26	30
Min. required experience	2 years (depends on application)	3 years
%EC/Overseas	varies	n/a
%Men/Women	50/50	50/50
Number of Professors	8	4
Number of Academic Staff	180	180
Number of elective courses	subject to intake	subject to intake
Exams/Assignments	Both	Both
Dissertation/Project:	Both	Both

School Description

The Business School is organised into six departments and offers a flexibility in combining disciplines. Research, Consultancy and Training opportunities have resulted from collaborative links with industry and provide evidence of our entrepreneurial and innovative approach. The wealth of specialist expertise available is complemented by the caring environment and modern, well-equipped teaching facilities. The School jointly delivers its programmes with a variety of major local and national organisations and its work is either funded or sponsored by a number of private and public institutions.

The Business School is committed to continuous improvement in the quality of its teaching programmes and student care. Quality is monitored annually and all courses are subject to review and re-validation every five to seven years. We have invested heavily in the provision of student care and there are procedures and systems to regularly gain feedback and comments from our students on all aspects of their learning experience.

The UCE MBA is designed to develop managerial knowledge and skills to meet the challenges faced by new managers in the ever more demanding and dynamic environment of the future. It aims to equip the student to excel within a variety of contexts. UCE has created a stimulating and exciting environment where staff and students enter into a learning partnership with commerce and industry which has relevance for both the public and private sectors.

The UCE MBA encourages innovation, achievement, intellectual rigour and excellence. The programme attracts international students from around the world and core and specialist modules have been designed to prepare students to readily add value to their employer organisations. The programme offers a choice of six pathways, each one tailored to either the traditional management route, or a specialist functional area. MBAs currently offered are: General, Audit, Economic Environment, Finance, Manufacturing Management, Marketing.

Cheltenham and Gloucester College of Higher Education

Address: PO Box 220, Park Campus, Cheltenham GL50 2QF
Tel: 01242 543225   Fax: 01242 544032
EMail: dkendry@chelt.ac.uk
Dean: Paul Taylor
MBA Admissions Officer: Denise Kendry

MBA Programmes
Full-time MBA; Part-time MBA; Operations MBA; Financial Services MBA

Programme Details	Full-time	Part-time
Duration	1 year	3 years
Class Contact	370 hours	370 hours
Commencement	October	October/ February
Which evening/day		Thursday
Application deadline	September	September/January
GMAT Yes/No	No	No
Fees EC/Overseas	£3,100/£5,900	£3,750/£5,900
Annual student intake	20	50
Average student age	27	30
Min. required experience	3 years	
%EC/Overseas	70/30	
%Men/Women	60/40	60/40
Number of Professors	3	3
Number of Academic Staff	50	50
Number of elective courses	10	10
Assessment: Exams/Assignments	A	A
Dissertation/Project	Both	Both

Additional Information
International Links: Hong Kong; Malaysia
Library hours: 0900-2115
IT facilities: Extensive (486 PCs and Apple Macs)

School Description
For full-time students the taught programme runs from October to June, plus the Dissertation due in the December of that year (May of the following year for part-time students).

MBA1/PG Certificate (delivered in Semester 1) introduces students to basic concepts and skills through nine compulsory modules including: Organisational Behaviour and Human Resourcing; Information; Finance; Marketing; Operations; Corporate Environment. MBA 2/3 PG Diploma and Masters delivered in Semester 2. Students take compulsory modules in Finance,

Marketing/Operations, Strategy, Research Methods and Management Ethics, plus two options: one chosen from Services Marketing, Strategic HRM, or Operations Strategy, and one from IT Strategy, Public Services Strategy, or Current Issues in Management. MBA 3 is designed to broaden the strategic perspective and encourage an analytical approach to the solution of problems. The core module is Corporate Strategy, which is followed by a choice of two options from five: Innovation; Global Issues in Business; Marketing for Competitive Advantage; Public Policy Management; Managing People for Effective Performance.

For part-time students delivery is via one evening per week plus one alternate afternoon, or an evening plus five weekend workshops. Students are required to attend two personal development workshops per academic year. Students can gain the intermediate awards of PG certificate after one year or Diploma after two years of part-time study.

City University Business School

Address: Frobisher Crescent, Barbican Centre, London EC2Y 8HB
Tel: 0171 477 8606/7/8 0171 4778988   Fax: 0171 477 8898
EMail: cubs-postgrad@city.ac.uk
Internet: www.city.ac.uk/cubs

Dean: Professor Leslie Hannah

MBA Admissions Officer: Liz Taylor (Full-time)

MBA Admissions Officer: Deidre Hickey (Part-time)

MBA Programmes
Day MBA (Full-time); Evening MBA; Management MBA

Programme Details	Full-time ✔	Part-time ✔	Management ✔
Duration	1 year	2 years	2 years
Class Contact	Varies	890/900	Varies
Commencement	September	mid February/ 1st Sept	October/April
Which evening/day		various eve combs	
Application deadline	31 May	Continuous	
GMAT Yes/No	Yes	Yes (or, own aptitude test)	No
Fees EC/Overseas	£13,000	£18,000	On application
Annual student intake	160	130	35
Average student age	30	32	35
Min. required experience	3 years	3 yrs (2 yrs decision-making)	5 years
%EC/Overseas	59/41	79/21	100
%Men/Women	1.75:1	2.2:1	3.2:1
Number of Professors	22	22	1
Number of Academic Staff	81	81	30
Number of elective courses	Varies	25	
Assessment: Exams/Assignments	Both	Both	A
Dissertation/Project	Both	Both	P

Additional Information
International Links: Member of AMSEC (Alliance of Management Schools in European Capitals) – opportunity for overseas study in Berlin (Technische Universität), Brussels (Ecôle de

Commerce Solvay, Université Libre), Madrid (Universidad Complutense), and other European cities

Library hours: 0900-2100 Mon-Thurs; 0900-1900 Fri; 1000-1600 Sat (term time only)

IT facilities: Two computing labs containing Windows-based networked PCs provide access to the Internet, electronic mail, conferencing facilities, and library, academic and business information worldwide

School Description
Based in the City of London, City University Business School is the only British Business School located in an international financial centre. The school is a leading provider of business and management education at undergraduate, postgraduate and post-experience levels and has one of the highest rates of postgraduate employment in the UK.

The Higher Education Funding Council of England and Wales awarded the Business School's business and management teaching the top rating of 'excellent' and just nine-per-cent of UK business schools have been awarded a 'higher' research rating by the same body.

For the last two years our student numbers have grown at a rate of 10% each year.

Both the full-time and Evening MBA programmes are fully accredited by the Association of MBAs. The Full-time MBA programme, taken over 12 months provides you with a first class management qualification. A unique programme combining a broad management education, with in-depth skills developed in a specialist area, chosen from Finance; Human Resources and Management; Information Technology and Management; International Business and Export Management; Management of Technology or Marketing.

Our City of London location provides participants with unparalleled opportunities to develop contacts in the world of international business and finance.

To support our MBA graduates fulfil their career aspirations, the Business School provides a full career management service – offering extensive support for project and job search throughout the course.

The Evening MBA programme is a part-time course based on 2 evenings per week over two years. A strong focus on flexibility allows working managers to continue their career while developing management techniques and learning new skills.

The Management MBA is a consortium style MBA for company clients providing, managers with a customised programme. Participants apply the theory of management to their own work place, enabling companies to optimise their investment in management development.

Coventry Business School

Address: William Morris Building, Coventry University, Priory Street, Coventry CV1 5FB
Tel: 01203 838461   Fax: 01203 838400
EMail: bsx940@coventry.ac.uk

Dean: Dr David Morris

MBA Admissions Officer: Dr Tom Donnelly

MBA Programmes
Part-time MBA; International MBA; European MBA

Programme Details	*Full-time*	*Part-time*
Duration	1 year	1-3 years
Class Contact	15	6
Commencement	October	
Which evening/day		September

Schools offering an Association of MBAs-accredited programme are indicated by a roundel

GMAT Yes/No	No	No
Fees EC/Overseas	£7,300	£4,700
Annual student intake	80	20-25
Average student age	25	30
Min. required experience	n/a	3 years
%EC/Overseas	90/10	
%Men/Women	55/45	50/50
Number of Professors	0	0
Number of Academic Staff	80	80
Number of elective courses	12	0
Assessment: Exams/Assignments	Both	Both
Dissertation/Project	D	D

Additional Information

International Links: Links with University of Caen (France), Oulu (Finland), Reitaku (Japan), Valencia, Fachhochschule Aachen, Copenhagen

IT facilities: IT facilities available in school.

Electives not readily available elsewhere: IT and Strategic Management; Business and Management in the Pacific Rim

School Description

Coventry Business School (CBS) is one of the UK's largest business schools, with approximately 4,000 students studying a range of courses. The courses available range from broad general business programmes to more specialist programmes, and this spectrum is provided at diploma, undergraduate and postgraduate level.

Study within the School takes place on the central campus and is largely located within the William Morris Building, home of the Business School. The William Morris Building incorporates state-of-the-art computer facilities, lecture theatres and student facilities such as a bistro. The Business School building has five computer laboratories in total, four of these are reserved for Business School students only. All laboratories are equipped with high performance networked PCs providing a wide variety of business software, including access to the Internet and CD-Roms for research purposes. The School also incorporates a new Audio Visual Suite, which is available for developing presentation skills and analysing group interaction.

Coventry Business School has excellent links with major national and multinational companies including The Rover Group and Peugeot, as well as other leading regional organisations such as the South Warwickshire Health Authority. In addition the School has close academic links with universities in Germany, France and Spain. Our network of academic institutions currently numbers over thirty with a widening network in Europe and beyond.

Though CBS is justifiably proud of its academic achievements, it stresses the necessity of preparing people for the real world of work. That requires much more than just knowledge, consequently emphasis is placed on the acquisition of the skills and competencies necessary to cope with the rapidly changing work environment of the 1990s and beyond.

Cranfield School of Management

Address: Cranfield University, Cranfield, Bedford MK43 0AL
Tel: 01234 751122   Fax: 01234 751806
EMail: p.hayes@cranfield.ac.uk
Internet: www.cranfield.ac.uk/som

Dean: Professor Leo Murray

MBA Admissions Officer: Mrs Pat Hayes

MBA Programmes

Full-time MBA; Executive MBA (part-time); Public Sector MBA (full-time and part-time); Full-time MSc in Project Management; Executive MSc in Project Management (part-time)

Programme Details	Full-time ✔	Part-time ✔
Duration	1 year	2 years
Class Contact	675	720
Commencement	October	January
Which evening/day		Alt. Fri & Sat (plus residential weeks)
Application deadline	None	None
GMAT Yes/No	Yes	Yes
Fees EC/Overseas	£15,000	£19,000
Annual student intake	200	100
Average student age	31	32
Min. required experience	3 years	3 years
%EC/Overseas	69/31	92/8
%Men/Women	79/21	82/18
Number of Professors	17	17
Number of Academic Staff	127	127
Number of elective courses	70	35
Assessment: Exams/Assignments	Both	Both
Dissertation/Project	P	P

Additional Information

International Links: Groupe ESC Lyon (double degree); ESADE, Barcelona, Spain; Babson College, Massachusetts USA; Nanyang University, Singapore; University of Cape Town and Witwatersrand University, Johannesburg, South Africa; Macquarie University, Australia

Library hours: 0830-2100 (Mon-Fri); 0930-1800 (Sat)

IT facilities: Dedicated computer studio with 30 networked PCs with laser printers, DTP and scanning facilities, Microsoft windows; access to main university VAX computer via studio. Lotus notes used by all Executive MBA students

Electives not readily available elsewhere: Beyond the Machine Metaphor: Managing in the New Millennium, Psychometrics, Business Check-up, Creative Entrepreneurship, The International Manager in Different Cultures, Managing and Consulting in Developing Countries, Project Design and Implementation

Other information: Fully equipped TV studio with VHS editing facilities. Language lab with satellite TV

School Description

Cranfield School of Management, established in 1967, is a post-graduate management school and a faculty of Cranfield University.

The Cranfield MBA experience is the result of a combination of the personal learning process, the context in which the learning takes place, and the specific content of the programme. Central to the learning process are: the emphasis on personal development; the sharing of experience and skills through the learning teams; and the practical case study approach. The teaching style is highly participative and the approach pragmatic. Participants learn in the context of a stimulating environment with a mature and diverse student body. The faculty have management experience and maintain strong links with organisations from the private and public sectors. They understand the problems of putting theory into practice. The content of the programme is both practical and international. Although the Cranfield MBA is a general management programme, with more than 70 electives on offer participants can customise the programme to their particular requirements. The programme is constantly updated and reviewed to ensure that what is learned at Cranfield will enable participants to meet the challenges of a dynamic global business environment.

Cranfield has an excellent reputation amongst recruiters. The School has its own Career Development Office dedicated to the unsponsored MBA student. The calibre of the student body and the efficiency of the Career Development Service give Cranfield students the edge in their job search. In addition, the Cranfield Management Association, the School's alumni organisation, provides access to a network of nearly 4,000 alumni, and operates a unique Executive Recruitment Service.

The campus offers various sporting facilities including squash, tennis, badminton, a gymnasium and sports fields. Cranfield is only five miles from Milton Keynes with its excellent recreational facilities. There are many cultural and special interest clubs and societies on campus.

Dearne Valley Business School

Address: Old Hall, High Melton, Doncaster DN5 7SZ
Tel: 01302 553666   Fax: 01302 553776
MBA Admissions Officer: Brenda Peach

MBA Programmes
MBA Part-time

Programme Details	Part-time
Duration	1 year
Class Contact	200 hours
Commencement	October
Which evening/day	Wednesday/ weekend
Application deadline	October
GMAT Yes/No	No
Fees EC/Overseas	£2,125
Annual student intake	30
Average student age	33
Min. required	DMA or IM Postgraduate diploma
%EC/Overseas:	100/0
%Men/Women	60/40
Number of Professors	1
Number of Academic Staff	12
Number of elective	2
Exams/Assignments	A
Dissertation/Project	D

School Description

Two progression routes are offered to the MBA. Route one is provided by the Institute of Management suite of programmes and is competency-based, including up to NVQ5. Route two is the developmental route, validated by the University of Hull, including Certificate in Management and Diploma in Management Studies.

The school is recognised as a centre of excellence for operations and personnel management. The site also offers en-suite conference facilities, a TV studio, a language laboratory, computer suites and a refurbished library. Sporting facilities include a 120-acre site for football; rugby; hockey; golf.

There is accommodation for 250 students on site in a pleasant setting, with ample car parking and good access to A1(M) and M18 motorways and to the east coast main line rail links at Doncaster.

De Montfort University, School of Business

Address: The Gateway, Leicester LE1 9BH
Tel: 0116 257 7230   Fax: 0116 250 6329
EMail: stadm@dmu.ac.uk/ onadm@dmu/ac.uk
Internet: www.du.ac.uk

Dean: Professor John Coyne

MBA Admissions Officer: Sue Owen (Postgraduate Programmes Manager)

MBA Programmes

Full-time MBA; Part-time MBA (afternoon/evening mode and evenings only module); Executive MBA (block release) programme to be run at Milton Keynes campus. Programme currently undergoing validation

Programme Details	Full-time	Part-time ✔
Duration	1 year	2-2½ years
Class Contact	18 hours	6 hours
Commencement	October	October
Which evening/day	n/a	various eve combs per year
Application deadline	n/a	n/a
GMAT Yes/No	No	No
Fees EC/Overseas	£6,000/£7,000	£6,000
Annual student intake	60	35
Average student age	27	35
Min. required experience	2 years	4 years
%EC/Overseas	48/52	n/a
%Men/Women	17/11	17/8
Number of Professors	12	12
Number of Academic Staff	120	120
Number of elective courses	24	24
Assessment: Exams/Assignments	Both	Both
Dissertation/Project	D	D

Additional Information

International Links: The Part-time MBA is offered at the School's campuses in Jakarta (Indonesia) and Johannesburg (South Africa). Students on the full-time programme, have the opportunity to participate in an exchange with a number of French institutions.

Library hours: Term time 0845-2200 (Mon-Fri); 0900-1600 (Sat); 1200-1600 (Sun). Vacations: 0900-1730 (Mon-Fri); 0900-1600 (Sat)

IT facilities: Students have access to a dedicated postgraduate lab with a suite of networked PCs (with Internet connections) in addition to the general School and University wide facilities.

School Description

The De Montfort School of Business is one of the largest providers of business education in the UK, with a full-time academic staff of 120 and some 3,600 (FTE) students registered on undergraduate, postgraduate and professional programmes. Staff are actively involved in research and consultancy projects, with over 50 publishing nationally and internationally. In 1994 the School was awarded an 'Excellent' rating by the Higher Education Funding Council in recognition of the high standard of its business and management education. It has also been designated as a Centre of Excellence by the Institute of Personnel and Development and the Market Research Society amongst others.

The De Montfort MBA is a general management programme focusing on the traditional areas of management – Marketing, Financial Reporting, Strategy, Organisational Behaviour, Operations Management, Business Economics, etc. Specialisation is, however, available through a wide-ranging menu of electives which includes TQM, Marketing Communications, Project Management, Logistics and Managing Public Policy. The MBA culminates with a project and dissertation which can be undertaken either within an organisation or independently.

The MBA programme is delivered in the Graduate School of Business which is located in a newly refurbished area of a splendid Victorian building on the University's city campus in the historic heart of Leicester and only a few minutes walk from the many shopping and leisure amenities. Students benefit from a suite of high quality, dedicated teaching and computing rooms and a pleasant working environment. MBA graduates will have the opportunity to continue their studies on to the DBA programme which is scheduled to commence in 1998 (subject to validation).

Dundee Business School, University of Abertay, Dundee

Address: Dudhope Castle, Barrack Road, Dundee DD3 6HF
Tel: 01382 322260   Fax: 01382 322290
EMail: m.e.pretious@abertay-dundee.ac.uk

Dean: Graeme Martin

MBA Admissions Officer: Mike Pretious

MBA Programmes

Full-time MBA; Full-time European MBA; Full-time MBA (Marketing); Part-time linked programme leading to the awards of the Certificate in Management, Diploma in Management Studies and MBA; Part-time MBA (Malaysia)

Programme Details	Full-time	Part-time
Duration	1 year	3 years
Class Contact	15 hours	6 hours
Commencement	September	September
Which evening/day	Mon-Fri	Monday, Tuesday, Thursday

Application deadline	July	July
GMAT Yes/No	No	No
Fees EC/Overseas	£3,500/£6,000	£5,750
Annual student intake	35	40
Average student age	25	29
Min. required experience	2 years preferred	4 years
%EC/Overseas	50/50	100/0
%Men/Women	60/40	60/40
Number of Professors	1	
Number of Academic Staff	30	
Number of elective courses	15	
Assessment: Exams/Assignments	Both	Both
Dissertation/Project	D	D

Additional Information

International Links: European/International residential periods; European MBA partner institutions: EGC Angoulme (France) and University of Karlskrona/Ronneby (Sweden); MBA link with Kemi-Tornio Polytechnic (Finland); University of Toledo

Library hours: 0845-2115 (Mon-Fri); Weekend opening

IT facilities: Computer lab within the Business School

Electives not readily available elsewhere: Business Ethics, Emerging Trends in Information Technology, Supply Chain Management, Entrepreneurship

Other information: New University Library opened in Spring 1998

School Description

Dundee Business School is the postgraduate arm of the School of Management. It is situated within historic Dudhope Castle, which is a ten minute walk from the main University campus and the city centre, and provides a pleasant environment for postgraduate study.

The School has particular strengths in Human Resource Management, Marketing, International Marketing and Quality Management with specialist Masters degrees in these areas. It also has extensive contact with local industry and public sector organizations, often undertaking applied research and consultancy projects with them.

A number of small University bursaries are available to students on the full-time MBA and MBA (Marketing) programmes.

The Business School has 'internationalised' its provision with the European MBA programme and MBA courses in Cyprus, Greece and Malaysia. An MBA programme with Kemi-Tornio Polytechnic (Finland) is also scheduled to commence at the end of 1998.

Dundee Business School launched a Doctorate in Business Administration (DBA) in the 1996-97 session. The course can be studied on a part-time or full-time basis and includes taught modules in Research Methodology and the Research Proposal.

University of Dundee

Address: MBA Office, University of Dundee, Dundee DD1 4HN
Tel: 01382 34 4737/4795/4980   Fax: 01382 228890
EMail: s.i.fitzpatrick@dundee.ac.uk
Internet: www.mba.dundee.ac.uk
Director and MBA Admissions Officer: Ms M B Calder

MBA Programmes

Full-time MBA; Part-time MBA; Diploma in Management; General MBA; Oil & Gas Management MBA; Mineral Resources Management MBA; Water Management MBA; Public Services Management MBA

Programme Details

	Full-time	Part-time	Diploma (FT)	Diploma (PT)
Duration	1	2½	¾ yr	½ yr
Class Contact	288	288	288	288
Commencement	October	October	October	October
Which evening/day	Flexible	Flexible	Flexible	Flexible
Application deadline	None	None	None	None
GMAT Yes/No	No	No	No	No
Fees EC/Overseas	£7,200/ £9,500	£6,000/ £7,500	£5,900	£4,800
Annual student intake	40 max	40 max		
Average student age	31	37	27	32
Min. required experience	3 years	3 years		
%EC/Overseas	21/79	100/0	0/100	100/0
%Men/Women	8/11	9/5		
Number of Professors	7	7	7	7
Number of Academic Staff	30	30	30	30
Number of elective courses	20	20	20	20
Assessment: Exams/Assignments	Both	Both	Both	Both
Dissertation/Project	D	D		

Additional Information

Library hours: 0900-2200 on weekdays, restricted opening at weekends

IT facilities: Wide range of IT facilities available

Electives not readily available elsewhere: Oil & Gas Management, Mineral Resources Management, Public Services Management, Water Management

Other information: Students are normally accommodated in university self-catering flats on campus or within easy walking distance.

School Description

The School of Management and Consumer Studies is responsible for the administrative co-ordination and academic integration of the teaching and dissertation supervision by various specialist departments in the University. The programme consists of nine core modules, three electives and a dissertation of 15,000 words, and may be completed in a minimum of one year full-time or two years part-time. Emphasis is placed on group interaction and problem-solving, and classes are held in suitably furnished executive-style accommodation. MBA students are part of a University community of 6,000 postgraduate and undergraduate students, and have access to a wide range of cultural possibilities and sporting facilities.

University of Dundee
The MBA Office
Dundee DD1 4HN
Scotland

tel•01322 344737 / 344980
fax•01382 228890
e-mail•s.i.fitzpatrick@dundee.ac.uk

The University of Dundee offers the choice of studying for a General MBA or a specialist MBA in Public Services Management, Oil and Gas Management, Mineral Resources Management or Water Management. Each programme consists of nine core modules, three electives and a dissertation. Full-time or part-time study as well as the choice of daytime and/or evening classes.

Course Director • Moira Calder

Durham University Business School

Address: Mill Hill Lane, Durham City DH1 3LB
Tel: 0191 374 2829   Fax: 0191 374 1230
EMail: mba.ft@durham.ac.uk/mba.pt@durham.ac.uk
Internet: www.dur.ac.uk/dubs/
Director: Professor Tony Cockerill
MBA Admissions Officer: Anne-Marie Nevin (Programme Manager)

MBA Programmes
Full-time MBA; Part-time MBA; Distance Learning MBA

Programme Details	Full-time ✔	Part-time ✔	Distance Learning ✔
Duration	1 year	2 years 3 months	3-4 years
Class Contact	550	450	n/a
Commencement	September	January	at any time
Which evening/day		Fri/Sat	
Application deadline	August	December	at any time
GMAT Yes/No	No	No	No
Fees EC/Overseas	£8,750/£9,750	£7,950/£9,500	£6,800/£7,850
Annual student intake	100	100	unlimited
Average student age	30	37	35
Min. required experience	2 years	2 years	2 years
%EC/Overseas	45/55	95/5	55/45
%Men/Women	2/1	1/1	4/1
Number of Professors	5		
Number of Academic Staff	50		
Number of elective courses	choose 10 from 30	choose 8 from 30	
Exams/Assignments	Both	Both	Both
Dissertation/Project	D	D	D

Additional Information
International Links: Business school has its own library and dedicated IT facilities
Library hours: 0845-2000 (Mon-Fri); 0845-1400 (Sat)
Electives not readily available elsewhere: Health management electives (Pt programme)

School Description
Durham University, like Oxford and Cambridge, is a collegiate university, with a first class tradition and reputation. The Business School is one of the longest established and most highly regarded in the UK. It is one of only a handful of schools to have all three of its MBA programmes – Full-Time, Part-Time, and Distance Learning – accredited by the Association of MBAs.

Durham is renowned for the quality of life and support it provides for its MBA participants. The thousand year old historic, cathedral city provides an 'Ivy League' atmosphere, and the postgraduate only Business School gives an excellent staff/student ratio, allowing exceptional levels of support and interaction, especially for overseas students. A purpose-built MBA wing provides high-quality dedicated teaching, IT, library and information facilities.

All applicants are guaranteed high-quality, reasonably priced accommodation, including the choice of an en-suite study bedroom in a new postgraduate block.

From its establishment in 1965 the School has had an international reputation for its supportive style, friendly atmosphere, and for the way it balances theory and knowledge with skills and competencies. The School's Small Business Centre is possibly the leading centre in the world advising on small business start-up, growth, and development and researching into entrepreneurship. Other specialisms include Human Resource Management, Public Sector Management, Crisis Management, Finance and Manufacturing.

The School puts great value on the Durham experience, and provides assistance and support to applicants before the programme, during induction, throughout the programme, and beyond, including an active Alumni Association and an MBA Careers Advisor to help ensure successful job placement. Durham has an explicit aim of making the MBA an enjoyable as well as a rewarding and challenging experience.

University of East Anglia, School of Management

Address: Norwich, Norfolk NR4 7TJ
Tel: 01603 593487   Fax: 01603 583343
Contact name: Andrea Wheatley

MBA Programmes
Evening MBA

Programme Details	Part-time
Duration	2 years
Class Contact	600 hours
Commencement	October
Which evening/day	Tuesday and Thursday
Application deadline	Aug 31
GMAT Yes/No	No
Fees EC/Overseas	£7,700
Annual student	20
Average student age	38
Min. required experience	4 years
%EC/Overseas	90/10
%Men/Women	65/35
Number of Professors	4
Number of Academic Staff	22
Number of elective	5
Assessment: Exams/Assignments	A
Dissertation/Project	D

Additional Information
International Links Yes

Library hours: 0800-2200

IT facilities: Excellent

Other information: Course to be considered by candidates living or working within 1½ hours drive of Norwich.

Individual programmes accredited by the Association of MBAs are indicated by a tick

School Description

The UEA MBA has been designed for ambitious managers who recognise the value of creating a point of difference for themselves and their organisation, through experience and personal and professional development. The MBA provides a high quality learning opportunity which builds on and broadens managers' existing knowledge in a way that is flexible and relevant. While the motivation and commitment needed by participants is high, the delivery method – evening teaching in three ten week terms over two years – has been chosen to minimise the potential conflict of priorities between the MBA and the participant's employment commitments.

The MBA is constructed around themes: Money and Systems (Business Environment, Accounting I and II, Management Information Systems, Business Research); People and Motivation (Business Management, Organisational Behaviour, Human Resource Management, Management Communications, Marketing); Management in Context (choice of two from options such as IT and Marketing, Critical Perspectives on Public Sector Management, Business in Europe, Strategic Management); and a 15,000 word dissertation on a theme of the student's choice.

East London Business School

Address: University of East London, Duncan House, High Street, London E15 2JB
Tel: 0181 349 3454   Fax: 0181 534 4168
EMail: taylor@uel.ac.uk
Director and MBA Admissions Officer: Peter A Taylor

MBA Programmes
MBA (Full-time); MBA (Part-time)

Programme Details	Full-time	Part-time
Duration	1 year	2 years
Class Contact	6 hours	6 hours
Commencement	September/ February	September/ February
Which evening/day		Tues pm & eve or Tues/Weds eve
Application deadline	September 20/February 1	September 20/February 1
GMAT Yes/No	No	No
Fees EC/Overseas	£6,000/£7,000	£2,000 pa
Annual student intake	55	55
Average student age	27	33
Min. required experience	2 years	2 years
%EC/Overseas	63	12
%Men/Women	60/40	55/45
Number of Professors	3	3
Number of Academic Staff	92	
Number of elective courses	21	21
Assessment: Exams/Assignments	E	E
Dissertation/Project	P	P

Additional Information
International Links: MBAs offered in Singapore and Malaysia: further international MBAs planned

School Description

The aim of the East London Business School is to provide comprehensive education programmes which will equip students intellectually and practically for entry into, or further progress in, business or professional areas.

Physically located on the edge of Docklands and the City of London, the School has a key vantage point to view the increasing internationalisation of business. The School's close links with business and commerce has meant that it too has developed a global perspective with firmly established connections in the Far East and a developing network with business, education and professional institutions in Europe and America. Links with Europe have recently been strengthened by success in obtaining ERDF and ESF funding for a Business Development Centre which will provide consultancy and advice services to small and medium enterprises within East London as well as supporting existing academic programmes.

These international dimensions are manifested through the MBA programmes offered – two (full-time and part-time) in London and one block release mode in Singapore. Another block release mode has recently been launched in Malaysia.

All programmes centre around general strategic management issues plus a choice of pathways engaging issues from a variety of functional or sectorial perspectives.

The MBA programmes sit within a wide range of both taught and research-based Masters degrees and Doctorate programmes in areas of interest to management. All programmes are located in a building dedicated to postgraduate and post-experience business and management studies, which has well-equipped computer suites and a Learning Resource Centre. The building is a few minutes walk from an underground railway station wth a 10–15 minutes journey to the City.

Edinburgh Business School, Heriot-Watt University

Address: Edinburgh EH14 4AS
Tel: 0131 451 3090   Fax: 0131 451 3002
EMail: enquires@ebs.hw.ac.uk
Internet: www.ebs.hw.ac.uk

Director: Professor Keith G Lumsden

MBA Programmes

Full-time MBA; Part-time MBA; Distance Learning MBA; Consortium MBA

Programme Details	Full-time	Part-time
Duration	1	2
Class Contact	20	10
Commencement	October	
Which evening/day		Monday/Friday
Application deadline	August	August
GMAT Yes/No	Yes	No
Average student age	29	31
Min. required experience	3 years	3 years

It takes 140 countries to accommodate all our MBA students

The Heriot-Watt University MBA Programme is one of the world's largest with more than 8,000 students studying by distance learning for examinations held at 300 centres in 140 countries.

We have achieved our international success by attracting experienced faculty with leading-edge expertise in their specialist subjects, an excellent reputation for teaching, and a truly international perspective. Their depth of experience is reflected in the high quality study materials which have been developed in association with Financial Times Management, a world leader in management education.

We are also much more flexible than most business schools. You can study full-time or part-time at the new, superbly equipped business school in Edinburgh, Scotland. Or you can study where you live and work through distance learning, and take examinations locally. Or you can combine study methods – some courses with live tuition, some by distance learning.

Those without a Bachelor's degree may enter the programme after passing examinations in two subjects.

For a copy of the 1998 prospectus, including information about 1998 summer schools, please contact, quoting ref. 40:

HERIOT-WATT
UNIVERSITY
MBA PROGRAMME
from
EDINBURGH
BUSINESS SCHOOL

in association with

FINANCIAL TIMES
MANAGEMENT

%EC/Overseas	30	0
%Men/Women	3/1	3/1
Number of Professors	6	
Number of Academic Staff	9	
Number of elective courses	10	
Assessment: Exams/Assignments	E	E
Dissertation/Project	P optional	P optional

Additional Information

International Links: Europe, USA

Library hours: 7 days during term time

IT facilities: Range of IT facilities and networks

Electives not readily available elsewhere: Project management

School Description

Edinburgh Business School is the Graduate School of Business of Heriot-Watt University. Situated on the western side of Edinburgh, the University's 280-acre campus offers a wide range of facilities including accommodation, a sports centre, shops, and restaurants. A new custom-built school in June 1998.

The Heriot-Watt MBA is uniquely flexible, it may be studied anywhere in the world by distance learning, or on-campus by full-time or part-time study, or by a combination of study routes. Each study programme is based on a common core syllabus and examinations, thus course credits are fully transferable from one Heriot-Watt study programmme to another.

With more than 1,300 graduates since the degree was introduced, this is now one of the largest MBA programmes in the world, and students in more than 130 countries are currently studying the Heriot-Watt MBA by distance learning. On campus, individuals from a wide range of countries and professional backgrounds come together on the School's full-time and part-time programmes. The School also offers a series of MBA summer schools.

This is a broad-based programme which aims to provide students with a thorough knowledge and understanding of subjects fundamental to management, and the analytical skills which are indispensable in problem-solving and decision-making. Each course has been designed by a team of academic faculty from Heriot-Watt and other leading international business schools.

The distance learning programme has been carefully constructed to enable individuals to study at times and in locations which suit them. Each course is designed specifically for full distance learning, the materials are self-sufficient, and no tutor contact is required; sophisticated interactive computer software provides feedback and practical work for the compulsory courses. Examinations are held twice per year in more than 350 examination centres around the world.

High quality teaching for permanent and visiting faculty enables on-campus students to develop their understanding of management and to explore the application of management theory to real-world business situations. Class sizes are kept small so that students can reap the full benefits of student/faculty interaction and classroom participation.

The University of Edinburgh Management School

Address: 7 Bristo Square, Edinburgh EH8 9AL
Tel: 0131 650 8066   Fax: 0131 650 8077
EMail: r.kerley@ed.ac.uk
Dean: Professor J Fleck
MBA Admissions Officer: Richard Kerley

MBA Programmes
Full-time MBA; Part-time MBA

Programme Details	Full-time ✔	Part-time ✔
Duration	1 year	2½ years
Class Contact	380 hours	380 hours
Commencement	End September	January
Which evening/day		Monday–Thursday
Application deadline	August/September	October/November
GMAT Yes/No	Preferred	
Fees EC/Overseas	£9,300/£9,900	£8,500 (provisional)
Annual student intake	100	100
Average student age	31	33
Min. required experience	2 years	2 years
%EC/Overseas	54/46	98/2
%Men/Women	65/35	70/30
Number of Professors	15	
Number of Academic Staff	50	
Number of elective courses	50	50
Assessment: Exams/Assignments	Both	Both
Dissertation/Project	D	D

Additional Information
International Links: Extensive

Library hours: 7 days

IT facilities: Full email account for all students open 24 hours per day

Electives not readily available elsewhere: Management Consultancy; Management in Eastern Europe; Entrepreneurship; Management in Japan

School Description
The 12-month programme is divided into three taught terms plus a summer dissertation. Most of the compulsory core course is given in the first term; four electives, either general or grouped into an area of concentration, cover the second and third terms. This allows either a general management course or specialisation in finance, marketing, or operations management. Students also study a Strategic Management course in the second and third terms. This is based on small group analysis and presentation of case studies. There are also business games and group projects, access to language and outdoor education options. During the Spring vacation students carry out consultancy work in small groups for local businesses. Dissertations can be based on research work, projects or business plans. Autumn term: Accounting; Business Law; Business Policy; Economics; Finance; Human Behaviour at Work; Marketing; Operations Management; Statistics. Spring and Summer terms: Strategic Management (core course); four or five electives from 22. Summer term: Dissertation.

University of Exeter, School of Business and Economics

Address: Streatham Court, Rennes Drive, Exeter EX4 4PU
Tel: 01392 263200   Fax: 01392 263242
Director: Mr Martin Timbrell
MBA Admissions Officer: Dr Ashly Pinnington

MBA Programmes
Full-time MBA in General Management and specialist MBAs in: Financial Management, Banking & Financial Management, Finance & Investment, Marketing Management, International Business Management, Public Sector Management. Part-time MBA in General Management and other specialist MBAs (subject to demand) except Finance and Investment.

Programme Details	Full-time	Part-time ✔
Duration	1 year	2-5 years
Class Contact	440	440
Commencement	October	October
Which evening/day		Friday/Saturday
Application deadline	July	July
GMAT Yes/No	Yes	Yes
Fees EC/Overseas	£8,750	£8,750
Annual student intake	100	20+
Average student age	28	33
Min. required experience	3 years	3 years
%EC/Overseas	10/90	90/10
%Men/Women	50/50	50/50
Number of Professors	10	10
Number of Academic Staff	50	50
Number of elective courses	20+	20+
Assessment: Exams/Assignments	Both	Both
Dissertation/Project	Both	Both

Additional Information
International Links: Rennes, Université de Haut Savoie, Chambery, Fachhochschule Reutlingen, Assumption (Thailand)

Library hours: 0900-2215 (Mon-Fri) 0900-1700 (Sat)

IT facilities: Online computer services – Bloomberg and Datastream. Offline facilities – Compustat and Micropal, other IT services totally dedicated to MBA students

Electives not readily available elsewhere: Full range of university clubs, societies, sports; theatre and cinema on campus

School Description
The MBA programme allows for distinctive options to be taken following core courses providing a suite of MBA degrees in general management, financial management, banking and financial management, finance and investment, marketing management, international business management, public sector management. All MBA programmes, with the exception of finance and investment are available on a part-time basis, subject to demand. The school undertakes and supervises extensive research activities covering most areas of business and management but particularly in finance.

The University has excellent library and sports facilities and the campus is one of the most

---

Individual programmes accredited by the Association of MBAs are indicated by a tick

attractively situated of any in the United Kingdom. Exeter has good road, rail and air links, and a thriving city centre. The national parks of Dartmoor and Exmoor and the heritage coastline of Devon and Cornwall are close at hand.

University of Glasgow Business School

Address: 53 Southpark Avenue, Glasgow G12 8LF
Tel: 0141 330 6924/4132   Fax: 0141 330 4939
EMail: s.dobbie@mgt.gla.ac.uk
Dean: Professor Sir Laurie Hunter
MBA Admissions Officer: Sheena Dobbie

MBA Programmes
Part-time MBA; Part-time MBA (Health Care); Part-time MBA (Housing); Full-time MBA

Programme Details	Full-time	Part-time ✔
Duration	13 months	3-5 years
Class Contact	20	5
Commencement	September	September
Which evening/day	Monday to Thursday	Friday/Saturdays
Application deadline	July	August
GMAT Yes/No	Yes	No
Fees EC/Overseas	£9,750	£2,600
Annual student intake	40+	60+
Average student age	27	34
Min. required experience	2	6
%EC/Overseas	50/50	95/5
%Men/Women	50/50	50/50
Number of Professors	20	20
Number of Academic Staff	60	60
Number of elective courses	5/6	5/6
Assessment: Exams/Assignments	Both	Both
Dissertation/Project	D	D

Additional Information
International Links: International Advanced Management Schools – as standard

Library hours: Extensive resources

IT facilities: Extensive resources

Electives not readily available elsewhere: Advanced Management Schools

Other information: Work/Project placements on full-time route

School Description
The University of Glasgow was founded in 1451 and is the fourth oldest university in the United Kingdom. Although younger, the University of Glasgow Business School has an international reputation based on 40 years of business and management education. It has been at the forefront of many innovative developments including the inauguration of a series of intensive modular courses for MBA participants, now supported by Business Schools throughout the world.

The ultimate objective for all of our MBA programmes is, of course, to provide that 'added value' which comes with a better job and salary for our graduates. We aim to do this by creating a culture and environment which focus on individual personal development – hence the small class sizes. In addition full-time participants are offered the opportunity to undertake research and assignments within locally-based enterprises. We know that an MBA is a badge for life and we try our best to ensure that we prepare our graduates for the road ahead. To this end we are also in constant touch with our active alumni group.

Glasgow Caledonian University, Faculty of Business

Address: Cowcaddens Road, Glasgow G4 0BA
Tel: 0141 331 3411   Fax: 0141 331 3296
EMail: JMcCallum@gcal.ac.uk
Dean: Professor John Taylor
MBA Admissions Officer: Julia McCallum

MBA Programmes
Part-time MBA, Full-time MBA

Programme Details	Full-time	Part-time
Duration	1 year	3 years
Class Contact	15	6
Commencement	September	September
Which evening/day		Year 1 Wed; Year 2 Thurs; Year 3 Tues

Application deadline	September	September
GMAT Yes/No	No	No
Fees EC/Overseas	£5,500/£7,000	£5,350
Annual student intake	25	90
Average student age	29	34
Min. required experience	2 years	3 years
%EC/Overseas	50/50	100/0
%Men/Women	4/1	55/45
Number of Professors	10	10
Number of Academic Staff	216	216
Number of elective courses	25	25
Assessment: Exams/Assignments	Both	Both
Dissertation/Project	D	Both

Additional Information

International Links: The full-time course includes a study visit to Europe

Library hours: 0830-2100 (Mon-Thurs), 0830-1700 (Friday), 1000-1600 (Sat and Sun)

IT facilities: Dedicated multimedia PCs

Electives not readily available elsewhere: Management in the Family Enterprise, Risk Management, Managing Voluntary and Non-profit Organisations

School Description

The Business Faculty has close links with Scottish Enterprise, the London Stock Exchange, and many other local organisations. Recent specialist units which have been formed include the Centre for Family Enterprise and the Voluntary Sector Management Development Unit.

The Faculty recognises the value of practical, accelerated learning opportunities offered by residential workshops, and MBA graduates need the skills, capabilities, and knowledge to operate in international markets. To underpin this, Caledonian Part-time MBA students have the opportunity to visit Amsterdam and Utrecht to compete in an international business simulation with students on the NIMBAS (Netherlands Institute for MBA Studies) programme, and spend a weekend in Dublin for an extensive international case study workshop. The full-time MBA students participate in a study visit to Europe; this year the students went to Prague and Vienna, where they visited multinational companies such as Skoda, Coca-Cola, ABB, IBM, and the Czech Finance Ministry. Other residential weekends take place nearer to home at Stirling and Dunblane; these include indoor and outdoor teambuilding activities.

The MBA programmes at Caledonian continue its tradition of innovative teaching and learning approaches. Feedback from the Faculty's customers (employers, current and former students) is highly appreciative of the balance between academic theory and practical application, and of the approachability and accessibility of members of staff.

The Caledonian MBA programmes recognise that the majority of jobs today require people with the skills to drive teams to achieve outstanding performance whilst maintaining the ability to work well as a team player. Personal and team development are therefore central themes running throughout the programme.

The University of Greenwich, School of Business and Management

Address: Riverside House, Beresford Street, Woolwich, London SE18 6BU
Tel: 0181 331 7700   Fax: 0181 331 9005
EMail: r.j.mayor@gre.ac.uk
Director: Robert Mayor
MBA Admissions Officer: Angela Winnie

MBA Programmes
International MBA; International Marketing MBA; International Finance MBA; Evening MBA

Programme Details

	Full-time	Part-time
Duration	12 months	2½ years
Class Contact	24/25 hours/week	6 hours/week
Commencement	September	September
Which evening/day		Monday/Wednesday
Application deadline	August	August
GMAT Yes/No	No	No
Fees EC/Overseas	£9,450	£8,800
Annual student intake	30	30
Average student age	27	32
Min. required experience	2 years	3 Years
%EC/Overseas	90/10	10/90
%Men/Women	30/70	40/60
Number of Academic Staff	50	
Number of elective courses	9	2
Assessment: Exams/Assignments	Both	Both
Dissertation/Project	P	P

Additional Information
International Links: Links with universities in: France, Spain, Slovenia

IT facilities: Specialist business library with CD-ROM and Internet facilities; dedicated IT suite of 60 computers with Microsoft Office, Access, and other specialist software

Electives not readily available elsewhere: Marketing Communications; Staff Management in Multi-nationals; International Financial Markets; Multilingual Communications

School Description
The School of Business and Management has over 25 years of experience in running Masters programmes. Greenwich was one of the first universities to develop a part-time MBA qualification, and now also offers a full-time MBA. The course focuses on the practical use of business techniques in real-life situations. A number of companies are involved in the programme, providing real business problems to which students can apply their developing skills.

Towards the end of the programme, participants undertake a two-week consultancy assignment with one of the companies attached to the programme. This may be conducted in the UK or at one of the linked European business schools.

In addition to excellent academic facilities, the University of Greenwich provides services and activities to enhance the programme of study. Excellent sports facilities are offered, including a swimming pool, sports halls, tennis and squash courts, and football, hockey, and cricket pitches.

Henley Management College

Address: Greenlands, Henley-on-Thames, Oxford RG9 3AU
Tel: 01491 571454   Fax: 01491 418861
EMail: mba@henleymc.ac.uk
Internet: www.henleymc.ac.uk
Dean: Professor Ray Wild
MBA Admissions Officer: Julia Bennett (Distance Learning)
MBA Admissions Officer: Anita Foster (Modular)

MBA Programmes
The Full-time MBA; The Modular MBA one year programme; The Modular MBA two year programme; Distance Learning MBA; MBA in Project management

Programme Details	Full-time ✔	Part-time Modular 1 year ✔	Modular 2 year ✔	Distance Learning ✔
Duration	1 year	1 year	2 years	3 years
Class Contact	1,088	480	640	240
Commencement	September	May	May and September	Jan/April/ July/ October
Which evening/day	Varies	Varies	Varies	
Application deadline	no formal deadline	no formal deadline	no formal deadline	
GMAT Yes/No	No	No	No	No
Fees EC/Overseas	£14,000	£15,500	£15,500	£8,995
Annual student intake	48	20	90	703
Average student age	31	32	33	33
Min. required experience	3/5 years	3/5 years	3/5 years	3 years
%EC/Overseas:		75/25	100/0	50/50
Number of Professors	11			
Number of Academic Staff	53 (56 associate)	56		
Number of elective courses	5	5	5	7
Assessment: Exams/Assignments	Both			
Dissertation/Project	D	D	D	

Additional Information
Library hours: Henley: (Mon-Fri) 0845-2130; (Sat) 0900-1700; (Sun) 1300-1700; Regents Coll: (Mon-Thurs) 0855-2300; (Fri) 0930-2100; (Sat) 1000-1800, (Sun) 1000-2300

IT facilities: Henley Computer terminals also available; Regents College Computer facilities also available in information technology centre

School Description
Henley Management College is situated in 30 acres of parkland on the banks of the River Thames between Henley and Marlow. It is easily accessible on the rail network and from the M4 and M40 motorways.

The Full-time MBA is held at Regents College in Central London. The Henley programme is practically-oriented and relies on the application of work experience within the assessment scheme. It concentrates on developing skills needed for general and strategic management. Course members study eight core subjects, covering all the general management areas and are encouraged to consider issues from a strategic and international perspective. The final part of

If you're launching into an MBA, we make sure of one thing.

Full time, Modular and Distance Learning

A Henley MBA is in a class of its own. All the study is designed to be relevant and in most cases immediately applicable.

Where possible we use live case studies, we won't just swamp you with theory. So when you return to work you will be able to put the experience and knowledge gained to immediate use.

You hit the ground running.

Being an international business school means that a Henley MBA is recognised and respected throughout the world.

If you want to study for a first class MBA and hit the ground running, don't take off for anywhere else.

HENLEY
Management College

Tel: +44 (0) 1491 418803
Email: mba@henleymc.ac.uk
Internet: www.henleymc.ac.uk

the course consists of an elective subject and dissertation. The choice of electives varies from year to year and depends on the study route chosen.

On attendance-based programmes, interactive assessment techniques such as group presentations are often used in addition to formal written papers.

Henley has a Fitness Centre with sauna and steam room. There are also badminton courts, tennis, a golf practice bay, putting, boating, croquet, snooker, boules and a heated open air swimming pool. Full-time MBA students may use the sports facilities (which include tennis, basketball, a weight training room and a multi-gym) and join in social activities on the Regents College campus.

A career development programme is available to all Full-Time MBA candidates offering workshops on interview techniques, self-marketing and career evaluation. Henley has a Career Development Office at Regents College for placement and visits from recruiting companies.

Many students have company sponsorship. UK-based students are eligible for the Association of MBAs loan scheme or may obtain loans directly from banks.

University of Hertfordshire Business School

Address: Mangrove Road, Hertford SG13 8QF
Tel: 01707 285400   Fax: 01707 285410
EMail: mba@herts.ac.uk
Internet: www.herts.ac.uk/EXTREL

Dean: Professor Ben Fletcher

MBA Admissions Officer: Jeannette Toy

MBA Programmes
Full-time Executive MBA: Part-time Executive MBA; Full-time MBA

Programme Details	Full-time Executive	Part-time Executives	Full-time
Duration	1 year	2 or 3 years	1 year
Class Contact	21 hours per week	2 yr: 9 hours per week; 3 yr: 6 hours	18 hours per week
Commencement	October	October/February	October
Which evening/day		Tues eve/Thurs eve/Sat morn	
Application deadline	September 1	September 1	September 1
GMAT Yes/No	Preferable	No	Preferable
Fees EC/Overseas	£6,200/£6,700	2 yr: £7,060 3yr: £7,335	£6,200/£6,700
Annual student intake	20	30	20
Average student age	28	28	22
Min. required experience	3 years	3 years	None
%EC/Overseas	10/90	100/0	30/70
%Men/Women	50/50	70/30	60/40
Number of Professors	2	2	1
Number of Academic Staff	16	16	13

Number of elective courses	2 from 7	2 from 7	2 from 7
Assessment: Exams/Assignments	Both	Both	A
Dissertation/Project	P	P	P

Additional Information
International Links: Arnhem/Zwölle (The Netherlands)

IT facilities: 80 PCs networked; 24 Macs; network access to Digital mainframe; email and Internet access; multimedia facilities, Computer Centre and Library have been integrated to form an Information Resource Centre (with extended access during evenings and weekends)

School Description
The School has an international reputation in the study of Complexity in Management, with an active postgraduate research programme. The School's reputation in research is growing, and is reflected in its rating in the recent HCFCE Research Assessment Exercise.

MBA students are expected to study the full range of functional disciplines to support executive decision-making and to extend their experience of strategic management thinking into areas where the ability to handle complexity in decision-making is at a premium. Students can choose from a range of seven option topics based around Managing Change, Management Development and a range of international options covering the areas of Marketing, Finance and Japanese Management.

Huddersfield University Business School

Address: University of Huddersfield, Queensgate, Huddersfield, West Yorkshire HD1 3DH
Tel: 01484 422288   Fax: 01484 473174
EMail: jacook@hudds.ac.uk/l.m.stansfield@hud.ac.uk
Dean: Mr David Smith
MBA Admissions Officer: John Cook (Full-time)
MBA Admissions Officer: Lyn Stansfield (Part-time)

MBA Programmes
Full-time MBA; Part-time MBA (evenings)

Programme Details	Full-time	Part-time	Top-up from DMS
Duration	15 months	27 months	15 months
Class Contact	15	6 hours per week	6 hours per week
Commencement	September/ January	September	September
Which evening/day		Mon/Wed	Mon/Wed
Application deadline	31 July	1 September	1 September
GMAT Yes/No	No	No	No
Fees EC/Overseas	£4,500/£6,500	£3,850	£1,750
Annual student intake	10	24/30	
Average student age	26	32	
Min. required experience	2 Years	3 years	3 years
%EC/Overseas:		small	small
%Men/Women	60/40	55/45	55/45

Number of Professors	8	8	8
Number of Academic Staff	92	92	92
Number of elective courses	5	4	4
Assessment: Exams/Assignments	Both	Both	Both
Dissertation/Project	D	D	D

Additional Information

Electives not readily available elsewhere: Programme includes systems thinking and crisis management issues. Philosophy of the course focuses on personal development and growth as distinct from strict analytical skills

Other information: Part-time programme includes innovative residential weeks in each year

School Description

A small but active MBA Programme for full-time students from a wide range of backgrounds. Specialisms in strategy available with ample opportunities for research for dissertations.

Part-time programme: Attracts students from a wide range of vocational backgrounds and industrial sectors and sizes. It has a strong philosophy of team and individual development. There is also the flexibility to extend the programme to 39 months for those students with heavy workloads or other pressures.

University of Hull Graduate Management Centre

Address: Graduate Management Centre, University of Hull, 65 Salmon Grove, Hull HU6 7S2
Tel: 01482 466650   Fax: 01482 466652
EMail: l.Fong@mgt.hull.ac.uk
Dean: Professor Richard Briston
MBA Admissions Officer: Mr Louis Fong

MBA Programmes

General MBA (Full-time); Financial Management (Full-time) MBA; Information Management (Full-time) MBA; Executive (Part-time) MBA

Programme Details	Full-time	Part-time
Duration	1 year	2 years
Class Contact	420 hours	360 hours
Commencement	September	variable
Which evening/day		Friday, Saturday and Sunday
Application deadline	1 August	None
GMAT Yes/No	No	No
Fees EC/Overseas	£7,250*	£7,200*
Annual student intake	80	50
Average student age	27	38
Min. required experience	2 years	8 years
%EC/Overseas	44/56	97/3
%Men/Women	55/45	68/32

Number of Professors	2	2
Number of Academic Staff	39	39
Number of elective courses	None	None
Exams/Assignments	Both	A
Dissertation/Project	Both	Both

*subject to confirmation by Senate

School Description

Established in 1927, the University of Hull offers a wide range of academic and social facilities on a spacious, tree-lined campus, together with old and new architecture, making for a pleasant and friendly atmosphere ideal for academic study. The Graduate Management Centre, located in the Faculty of Social Sciences, administers the postgraduate programmes in conjunction with the School of Accounting, Business and Finance and the School of Management. The programmes are designed to serve the needs of professional people accommodating the changes in academic environments and in industry. The staff in both Schools possess high academic credentials and diverse international management consulting experience.

All MBA programmes take one year commencing in September, unless part-time; this usually takes two years. The MBA courses consists of 12 months, taught in an innovative way, with each module consisting of a week of contact with the lecturer, followed by a week of private study by the student. The week of contact consists of lectures, group work, case studies and discussion. All programmes offer traditional material, for example, Human Resource Management and Accounting and Finance and then specialise in an aspect of business. All modules are examined by assignments and written examinations throughout the year. In addition a project or dissertation must be completed.

THE UNIVERSITY OF HULL
THE FACULTY OF SOCIAL SCIENCES
GRADUATE MANAGEMENT CENTRE

STAFF HOUSE • HULL HU6 7RX • UNITED KINGDOM
MASTERS PROGRAMMES • FULL/PART TIME • 01482 466642 • FACSIMILE 01482 466652

The University of Hull offers postgraduate courses based upon the most up-to-date management learning techniques with first-rate facilities, designed to serve the needs of professional people. The University is constantly developing programmes to accommodate changes both in academic environments and in industry.

General MBA

This course offers an education in the most important aspects of modern-day business administration, producing well-informed business people with their own practical training. It focuses on the importance of management, problem-solving and communication skills. Enabling students to gain critical analytical abilities to deal with complex business issues. Offering traditional material, for example, Human Resource Management and Accounting/Finance combined with unique modules such as Creative Problem Solving and Total Quality Management.

MBA Financial Management

Aimed at specialists in accounting or finance, it offers an insight into the important aspects of modern day financial management. Integrating other areas of management such as Organisational Analysis and Human Resource Management to provide specialists in the fields of accounting and finance with an understanding of the relevant aspects of general management

MBA Information Management

The primary objective of the course is to promote the development of hybrid managers of the future. The course allows students to specialise in chosen aspects of information and decision support technologies. Developing people with strong technical and business knowledge.

THE QUEEN'S
ANNIVERSARY PRIZES
FOR HIGHER AND FURTHER EDUCATION
1996

Schools offering an Association of MBAs-accredited programme are indicated by a roundel

The programmes give students an education in the most important aspects of modern-day business, producing well-informed business people with their own practical training as well as enhanced problem solving and communication skills. During the 12 months, students may have the opportunity to be involved with either locally-sited companies or companies which they are already associated with. The programmes are designed to develop middle and senior managers, enhancing their attractiveness and potential employers by introducing them to the most contemporary developments in the area of management. Our students enter a wide variety of careers, some continue with their research studies. Many of our overseas students take up employment in their own countries.

Imperial College Management School

Address: 53 Prince's Gate, Exhibition Road, London SW7 2PG
Tel: 0171 594 9205/9206   Fax: 0171 823 7685
EMail: m.schooleic.ac.uk
Internet: www.ic.ac.uk
Dean: Professor David Norburn
MBA Admissions Officer: Paul Granger (FT MBA)
MBA Admissions Officer: Debbie Johnson (PT MBA)

MBA Programmes
Full-time MBA; Part-time MBA; Public Sector MBA

Programme Details	Full-time ✔	Part-time ✔
Duration	1 year	27 months
Class Contact	500	500
Commencement	October	January
Which evening/day		Friday (day)
Application deadline	July	December
GMAT Yes/No	Yes	No
Fees EC/Overseas	£13,500	£18,800
Annual student intake	150	50
Average student age	29	34
Min. required experience	3	3
%EC/Overseas	57/43	100/0
%Men/Women	108/48	33/15
Number of Professors	11	11
Number of Academic Staff	40	40
Number of elective courses	12	4
Assessment: Exams/Assignments	Both	Both
Dissertation/Project	P	P

Additional Information
IT facilities: Two fully-equipped PC labs with Internet access
Electives not readily available elsewhere: Health Sector Management; Public Sector Management

THE IMPERIAL MBA — VALID FOR A LIFETIME

The Imperial passport will take you to the top! Imperial College enjoys a worldwide reputation for excellence. It is ranked in the top tier by international companies who recruit MBA graduates. Our specialisations are at the cutting edge of business. And we enjoy an ideal location in central London.

Interested? Contact Paul Granger, Admissions Administrator.

Imperial College
MANAGEMENT SCHOOL

53 Prince's Gate, Exhibition Road, London SW7 2PG.
Telephone +44(0)171 594 9205   Fax +44(0)171 823 7685   e-mail m.school@ic.ac.uk

School Description

Located in South Kensington, London, Imperial College Management School sits on the campus of one of the world's most famous academic institutions, allowing students to take advantage of the resources of this well-equipped organisation. These include a recently refurbished sports and leisure complex (which includes an indoor swimming pool and fully equipped gymnasium), language laboratories, and a full student social programme. The Management School's central location means that all the facilities and attractions of London are within easy reach.

The Management School itself has extensive student resources, including excellent library facilities and access to other specialised libraries throughout London. It also has a dedicated computer suite, including four Silicon Graphics Indigo workstations, electronic mail and worldwide Internet access.

The School offers innovative MBA programmes developed through extensive consultation with international employers. In response to increasing change and uncertainty in business, the MBA programmes focus on improving managers' ability to handle economic discontinuity, specifically the management of innovation, technological transfer, and entrepreneurial activity. Students receive a fundamental grounding, not only in functional disciplines such as Marketing and Finance, but also in core processes such as Innovation Management which are of growing importance. This orientation sets the programme apart from traditional MBA programmes which tend to deal with problems of large company administration.

Keele University School of Management

Address: Keele University, Keele, Staffordshire ST5 5BG
Tel: 01782 583425   Fax: 01782 584272
EMail: mna01@keele.ac.uk
Internet: www.keele.ac.uk
Dean: Dr P L Forrester
MBA Admissions Officer: Dr P L Forrester
MBA Admissions Officer: Ms T Burrows

MBA Programmes

Full-time MBA; Part-time MBA (via residentials); Malaysian MBA (in Kuala Lumpur, via residentials)

Programme Details	Full-time	Part-time	Malaysian
Duration	1 year	2 years	2 years
Class Contact	480 hours	220 hours	220 hours
Commencement	September	January	January/July
Application deadline	June	November	November/May
GMAT Yes/No	No	No	No
Fees EC/Overseas	£6,000/£8,500	£5,600	RM28,000
Annual student intake	40	20	25
Average student age	28	38	34
Min. required experience	2 years	2 years	2 years
%EC/Overseas	30/70	95/5	0/100
%Men/Women	50/50	50/50	70/30
Number of Professors	5	5	5
Number of Academic Staff	40	40	40
Number of elective courses	10-12	4	0
Assessment: Exams/Assignments	Both	A	Both
Dissertation/Project	Both	Both	Both

Additional Information

International Links: The Department of Management runs a part-time MBA programme in Malaysia, a part-time distance learning programme in the Netherlands, has major research links with Pacific Asia, Republic of China, India, Eastern Europe, North America, and the EC

Library hours: 0900-2200 every day

IT facilities: Full IT access including internet and email

Electives not readily available elsewhere: Creativity in Business; Individual Development in Organizations; Organizational Psychology

School Description

Keele is one of the UK's leading campus Universities. It was founded in 1949 as a University college and was granted full University status by Royal Charter in 1962. It is located within 617 acres of beautiful Staffordshire parklands and at the centre of the campus is a stately home, Keele Hall (the ancestral home of the Sneyd family). Outside this central area is a variety of accommodation for staff and students ringed by a large area of landscaped lakes and woodlands. Keele has a major commitment to innovation and excellence in graduate education and is at the forefront of interdisciplinary research and learning.

The Keele MBA provides an intensive and intellectually challenging advance study of management combining practical and theoretical elements. Course modules are taught within a strategic and international framework and the course is underpinned by the teaching staff's strong research orientation. In the last UK Research Assessment Exercise the Management School at Keele received a 4A rating justifiably placing the Department within the premier group of Business Schools in the UK. The research focuses on two main areas: empirical and pragmatic studies of strategy, operations, marketing and finance, complemented by a worldwide reputation for organisation theory and the study of human and social issues in management. The Keele MBA reflects these orientations.

The Keele MBA has attracted students from over thirty different countries; interaction with people from different cultures, religions, political systems and business environments is considered an important part of the MBA learning experience. There is also a higher proportion of female students on the Keele MBA than is usual.

There are three main elements to the MBA: core modules; elective modules; and the research dissertation. The core modules provide a comprehensive foundation in management principles and give an insight into the theory, practice and techniques in the main management disciplines. In addition there is a research methods module which assists in the preparation for research and the written dissertation.

KEELE
UNIVERSITY

MASTER OF BUSINESS ADMINISTRATION (MBA)

12 MONTHS FULL TIME
24 MONTHS PART TIME

Keele's Full-time MBA provides a programmed and integrated approach to management development. The Part-time course is taught using a unique combination of weekend residentials and distance learning, making it ideal for the busy practising manager. Both courses are underpinned by the teaching staff's excellent research record – Keele obtained a 4A rating in the recent UK RAE research review placing it amongst the premier research institutions in the country.

Thinking of an MBA .... then think KEELE

For further information and application forms contact:
Linda Scott, Department of Management,
Keele University, Staffordshire ST5 5BG, UK.
Tel: (01782) 583425 Fax: (01782) 584272
EMail: mna09@keele.ac.uk
Internet: http/www.keele.ac.uk/depts/mn/manhome.htm

INSTITUTE OF DIRECTORS

Tailor-made for company directors

Realise your full potential...

In today's highly competitive world, directors need to be able to understand and evaluate key business issues and trends. That is why more and more directors are taking the Institute of Directors' *Diploma in Company Direction,* the only development programme of its kind available through distance learning.

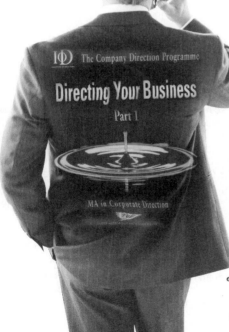

Superb value – The Diploma programme provides material for a full year's study yet costs no more than a typical short course lasting three or four days.

Study when you wish, where you wish and at your own pace.

A lasting resource – The modules for the programme remain a valuable resource of reference for your company in the years ahead.

Take your studies further – once you have completed the Diploma you can continue studying for a *Masters in Corporate Direction* awarded by Leeds Metropolitan University.

Send for your free prospectus
Fax: 0171 240 8018
e-mail: ioddip@ftmanagement.com
Tel: 0171 447 2021
Financial Times Management
128 Long Acre, London WC2E 9AN
Please quote reference no. 101

in association with
**FINANCIAL TIMES
MANAGEMENT**

Kingston Business School

Address: Kingston Hill, Kingston, Surrey KT2 7LB
Tel: 0181 547 7120   Fax: 0181 547 7452
EMail: mba@kingston.ac.uk
Internet: www.kingston.ac.uk/mba

Dean: Professor David Miles

Course Director: Ann Rinsler

MBA Admissions Officer: Karen Hodge

MBA Programmes
Open Learning MBA; Evening MBA

Programme Details	Evening Part-time ✔	Open Learning ✔
Duration	2 years	2 years
Class Contact	350	350
Commencement	September/February	September/February
Which evening/day	Tuesday/Thursday	Friday eve and Saturday
Application deadline	4 weeks before start	4 weeks before start
GMAT Yes/No	Yes or internal tests	Yes or internal tests
Fees EC/Overseas	£9,000	£9,000
Annual student intake	30	100
Average student age	34	34
%EC/Overseas	n/a	n/a
%Men/Women	70/30	70/30
Number of Professors	8	8
Number of Academic Staff	90	90
Number of elective courses	3/14	3/14
Assessment: Exams/Assignments	Both	Both
Dissertation/Project	D	D

Additional Information
International Links: Haarlem Business School (The Netherlands); Napier Business School; Edinburgh; ICBS, Thessaloniki (Greece), Athens, Greece, Natural Academy of Economy, Moscow (Russia)

School Description
Kingston Business School is one of the leading UK and European centres for Business and Management Education, research and consultancy. Over 2000 students are enrolled on Postgraduate Masters and Diploma Courses. The Business School has provided business education for over 25 years. The school is an Institute of Personnel Development Centre of Excellence an ESRC, Centre of Excellence in Small Business Research and has been awarded the accolade 'Excellent' for its teaching by the Government's assessment body, the HEFCE.

The School's educational philosophy is to develop a foundation of sound analytical and critical approaches to problem solving and to equip students with professional competencies immediately applicable to their employment.

Kingston Business School comprises 90 academic staff, 15 visiting Professors and 37 Industrial Fellows, organised into departments which focus on the principal business functions, each with robust subject authority founded upon strong research and practitioner experience.

The MBA was established in 1984. The programme is offered in the innovative Open Learning Mode as well as Part-time Mode over two years. The course constantly evolves to meet the changing challenges and opportunities generated by the dynamic domestic and international business environment.

MBA

at Kingston Business School

Good Managers Invest in People.
The Best Managers Invest in Themselves.

Develop yourself through Kingston's well established, Association of MBAs-accredited programme, rated "Excellent" for teaching.

A flexible programme over 2 years, for professional managers who want to combine study with their busy work schedules.

- OPEN LEARNING - intensive tuition one weekend per month, commences February and September.
- EVENING - weekly attendance, commences September.

You are welcome to attend one of our

Open Evenings

Contact us to find out more

Please telephone the MBA office on 0181 547 7120 fax 0181 547 7452 e-mail mba@kingston.ac.uk web http://www.kingston.ac.uk/mba/

KINGSTON
UNIVERSITY

It is structured to accommodate the needs of business managers enabling them to combine academic study with on-going work. Two modes of attendance are available. The Open Learning Mode provides contact sessions one weekend per month; this has proved advantageous to participants and employers. Alternatively, the Evening Mode takes place on two weekday evenings.

Stage 1 of the MBA consists of eight core modules, starting with technical approaches to identifying and resolving business problems, and moving through the functional approaches to Corporate Strategy. This stage offers a solid base in management theory and practice.

Stage 2 creates opportunities for individuals to develop their specialist interests through three electives and a major business project. Electives vary from year to year, but a typical group would include: Management of Change, International Business, International Marketing, Advance Finance, Information Systems, Small Business Management. The Business Project during Stage 2 of the programme is a substantial piece of consulting work, usually done for a sponsoring firm.

Both Stages are supported by extensive Open Learning material developed by the Business School. The course attracts candidates with a wide range of backgrounds in general, and from middle to senior management positions. Over 200 companies from both the private and public sectors have sponsored students through the programme. The Kingston MBA programme is delivered in the UK, Holland, Greece and Russia.

The Business School is located at the University's Kingston Hill campus, a pleasant wooded site within one hour's travel from Central London, adjacent to Richmond Park and the amenities of rural Surrey. The School has convenient access to the motorway network and to Heathrow and Gatwick airports.

Over £12 million investment in the campus resulted in improved IT, library, teaching and recreational facilities to match the requirements of the programme and the expectations of participants.

Lancashire Business School

Address: University of Central Lancashire, Preston PR1 2HE
Tel: 01772 893712   Fax: 01772 892912
EMail: mandev@uclan.ac.uk
Internet: www.uclan.ac.uk
Dean: Alan France

MBA Admissions Officer: Roger Armstrong (Full-time)

MBA Admissions Officer: Roger Kendle (Part-time)

MBA Programmes
Full-time MBA; Part-time MBA

Programme Details	Full-time	Part-time
Duration	1 year	2½-3 years
Class Contact	12 hrs/wk Semesters 1&2; Semester 3 supervisory meetings	Yr 1 6 hrs/wk; Yr 2 3 hrs/wk; Yr3 supervisory meetings
Commencement	September	September
Which evening/day		Wednesday/ Thursday
Application deadline	September	September
GMAT Yes/No	No	No
Fees EC/Overseas	£6,500 (incl 2 residentials)	£2,900 (incl 2 residentials)
Annual student intake	30	25 plus further 30 in Semester
Average student age	27	35

Min. required experience	n/a	n/a
%EC/Overseas	50/50	100/0
%Men/Women	70/30	50/50
Number of Professors	5	5
Number of Academic Staff	155	155
Number of elective courses	10	0
Assessment: Exams/Assignments	A	A
Dissertation/Project	D	D

School Description

The full-time and part-time MBAs offer students the opportunity to pursue three major themes of Management Theory, Business Performance and Personal Development. The programmes include two residential settings off-campus; the part-time programme embraces a 'live' change management project within an organisation. Stage 2 of the MBA involves the study of Strategic Management, a programme of Research Methodology sessions, and the completion of a major dissertation in the business/management field.

The programmes draw upon the expertise of the 160 academic staff of the Lancashire Business School. Holders of the DMS or equivalent postgraduate general management diploma may seek entry to the MBA at the mid-point in the taught programme.

Lancaster University Management School

Address: Lancaster LA1 4YX
Tel: 01524 594068   Fax: 01524 592417
EMail: mba@lancaster.ac.uk
Internet: www.lancs.ac.uk
Head: Professor Stephen Watson
MBA Admissions Officer: Sarah Gregory (FT)
MBA Admissions Officer: Val Goulding (PT)

MBA Programmes

Full-time MBA; Part-time Consortial MBA; Single Company (British Airways, Bass)

Programme Details	Full-time ✔	Part-time ✔
Duration	12 months	26 months
Commencement	September	September
Which evening/day		Modular (5 days each)
Application deadline	end June	n/a
GMAT Yes/No	Yes	No
Fees EC/Overseas	£10,500	£11,200
Annual student intake	70	30
Average student age	31	35
Min. required experience	3 years	5 years
%EC/Overseas	40/60	100/0
%Men/Women	52/48	60/40
Number of Professors	80	
Number of Academic Staff	80	
Assessment: Exams/Assignments	Both	Both
Dissertation/Project	Both	Both

Additional Information

International Links: Incl Wirtschaftsuniversität, Wien; WHU, Koblenz; Econle Supérieure de Commerce de Lyon; Università Commerciale Lugi Bocconi, Milan; Hochschule, St Gallen; Universidad Comercial de Dusto, Bilbao; Copenhagen Business School, Denmark, HEC, Montreal, Canada.

Library hours: 73 hours per week

IT facilities: Open access and bookable PC and Mac rooms, all connected to the University network; laser printers; technical support; currently 70+ terminals in the School, many more elsewhere on campus

Other information: Special language provision for MBA students; study skills support. Careers Adviser for MBA students located in the Management School

School Description

The Management School has a first class rating in business and management, having been placed in the top 3 business schools by the Higher Education Funding Council for the quality of its research (5 star, meaning 'international excellence') and its teaching (rated 'excellent'). It offers a wide portfolio of specialist masters programmes, a doctoial programme, and many customised in-company courses.

The Lancaster MBA programmes are practice driven but theory led, meaning that there is a special emphasis on applying theory in practice. The full-time MBA provides a major career development opportunity through the organisation based project which each student carries out for the final 3 months of the programme. Small consultancy teams of MBA students, each with an academic supervisor, apply their new knowledge and skills to a current problem or need of one of Lancaster's corporate clients, which range from multinational companies through small enterprises to not-for-profit organisations.

The part-time MBA requires students to apply their skills and knowledge after each 5-day module to a current problem within their employing organisation, offering significant benefits to both the individual student and their employer.

As one of Britain's largest business schools, Lancaster is able to offer breadth and depth, but has a particularly strong reputation in Accounting and Finance, Organisational Behaviour and HRM, Industrial Marketing and International Business.

Both MBA programmes offer a distinctively international development opportunity, taking advantage of the business school's many international alliances with top business schools. Scholarships and bursaries are available for the full-time MBA on application. The campus environment facilitates intensive study but also enjoyable socialising and leisure pursuits through the university's excellent sports facilities and access to two of Britain's most beautiful national parks, The Lake District and The Yorkshire Dales.

The programmes are taught in high quality, purpose-built accommodation on campus.

Leeds University Business School

Address: 11-15 Blenheim Terrace, Leeds LS2 9JT
Tel: 0113 233 2610   Fax: 0113 233 4355
EMail: mbaeng@lubs.leeds.ac.uk
Internet: www.lubs.leeds.ac.uk

Dean: John Hillard (FT)

Melanie Powell (PT)

MBA Admissions Officer: Sarah Heaton

MBA Programmes

(FT) Generic MBA; (PT) Executive MBA; (PT) Evening MBA; (PT) Executive MBA Health and Social Services; (PT) Executive MBA Transport Management; (FT) MBA Marketing

Programme Details

Programme Details	Full-time ✔	Executive ✔	Evening ✔	Singapore
Duration	1 year	2 years	2 years	2 years
Class Contact	400	380-400	380-400	380-400
Commencement	Sept	April/ October	October/ January/ Sept	Jan/ March/ July/Sept
Which evening/day		3 day work-shops	Yr 1: Wed; Yr 2: Tues	weekends and Mon or Tues
Application deadline	August			
GMAT Yes/No	Yes	No	No	No
Fees EC/Overseas	£7–8,000	£7,500	£6,000	S$25,000
Annual student intake	110/130	45/60	25/30	60
Average student age	30	35	33	33
Min. required experience	2 years	5 years	5 years	2 years
%EC/Overseas	25/75	100/0	100/0	0/100
%Men/Women	60/40	50/50	50/50	80/20
Number of Professors	18	18	18	
Number of Academic Staff	80	80	80	
Number of elective courses	28	14	10	5
Assessment: Exams/Assignments	Both	Both	Both	Both
Dissertation/Project	P	P	P	D

Additional Information

International Links: Students on MBA and Masters degree programmes come from more than 30 different countries. Part-time MBA and MBA Finance is delivered in Singapore. There's an Executive MBA for Slovakian health service professionals and a prestigious programme for Indian Managers at Leeds on behalf of the British Council. Staff have also advised on setting up business schools in Hungary, Poland and Romania. Class links with universities around the world including USA, China, Japan, France and Italy.

IT facilities: Comprehensive university-wide computing service has hundreds of computer terminals; two clusters of PCs and a wide range of up-to-date software are available for use by MBA students in the Business School; online business and financial data services

Electives not readily available elsewhere: Foreign languages including: French; German; Japanese

School Description

Leeds University (which received its Royal Charter in 1904) is one of the largest of the long-established universities in the UK with some 22,000 students (including 2,000 international students). Situated on an attractive compact campus location near the centre of a thriving commercial city with excellent shopping and leisure facilities, the University is a leading international centre for research and teaching. The library, which contains over 2.5 million items, is one of the largest academic libraries in the country. The social, cultural and sporting facilities for students are excellent.

Leeds University Business School has five divisions: Management; Accounting and Finance; Industrial and Labour Studies; Economics; Business History. There are over 80 full-time academic staff in the School, including 18 professors. Research centres of excellence include: Centre for Financial Services; Centre for International Business; Centre for Decision Research; Centre for Business History; Centre for Industrial Policy and Performance; Centre for Organisational Behaviour Research and Analysis.

The Full-time MBAs offer generic strength with the opportunity to major in Finance, Marketing or International Business if desired. A wide range of modules are available as options. French, German or Japanese can be studied as a business language option.

Leeds University Business School

Leeds University Business School is one of the leading Business Schools in one of the top UK universities. LUBS derives great internal strengths from the entire University of Leeds with its breadth and depth of departments such as Engineering, Computing, East Asian Studies, Law, and Health Management. These strong links support LUBS extensive teaching, research and consulting activities and the wide range of business relevant degree programmes and short courses.

Among the centres of research excellence are: The International Institute of Banking and Financial Services headed by Professor Kevin Keasey; Centre for International Business headed by Professor Peter Buckley; Centre for Organisational Behaviour Research and Analysis headed by Professor John Hayes; Centre for International Policy and Performance headed by Professor Peter Nolan, and Relationship Marketing and Media Research Centre headed by Professor Paul Michell.

LUBS offers the following MBA programmes accredited by the Association of MBAs:

Full-time MBA (Generic), MBA (International Business), MBA (Marketing), MBA (Finance)

Part-time Evening MBA, Executive MBA, Executive MBA (Health and Social Services), Executive MBA (Transport Management)

The entry requirements for the MBA programmes are typically a good quality first degree and two years work experience for the full-time MBA and five years experience for the part-time MBAs.

In addition to the MBAs we offer the following one year taught Masters programmes:

MA Human Resource Management (IPD accredited)
MA Advertising and Marketing
MSc International Marketing Management
MA Accounting and Finance
MA Economics and Finance
MA Economics

And the following part-time:

MA Credit Management for working professionals.

For further information please contact:

The MBA Office or The Taught Postgraduate Office, Leeds University Business School, 11 Blenheim Terrace, Leeds LS2 9JT, England.

The MBA Office:

Tel: +44 (0) 113 233 2010; Fax: +44 (0) 113 233 4355; Email: MBAenq@lubs.leeds.ac.uk

The Taught Postgraduate Office:

Tel: +44 (0) 113 233 2613; Fax: +44 (0) 113 233 2640; Email: fee@lubs.leeds.ac.uk

LEEDS UNIVERSITY BUSINESS SCHOOL

The Executive MBAs offer special options in Health and Social Services, Transport Management. The School has a strong international focus; it delivers executive programmes for managers from the former Soviet Union countries and from India, and delivers an MBA programme in Singapore.

University of Leicester Educational Management Development Unit

Address: University Centre, Barrack Road, Northampton NN2 6AF
Tel: 01604 30180   Fax: 01604 231136
EMail: emdu@le.ac.uk
Internet: www.le.ac.uk/emdu/index.html
Director: Professor Tony Bush
MBA Admissions Officer: Paul Ryan
MBA Admissions Officer: Marianne Coleman

MBA Programmes
Part-time Educational Management MBA; Educational Management by Distance Learning MBA

Programme Details	Part-time	Distance Learning
Duration	2-5 years	2-5 years
Class Contact	150 hours	n/a
Commencement	Oct/Jan/April	anytime
Which evening/day	Varies	
Application deadline	Varies	None
Fees EC/Overseas	on application	on application
Annual student intake		200
Min. required	3 years	3 years
%EC/Overseas:	95/5	60/40
%Men/Women	30/70	60/40
Number of Professors	1	1
Number of Academic Staff	8	8
Number of elective	n/a	4
Assessment: Exams/Assignments	A	A
Dissertation/Project	D	D

School Description
The Educational Management Development Unit (EMDU) was established in 1992 to provide specialist courses in educational management within the School of Education of the University of Leicester. The MBA in Educational Management is taught in part-time groups in Leicester and Northampton. In addition, students are taught on site within their own schools and colleges, where they may be enrolled for one or more modules of the MBA. The satisfactory completion of one module may entitle a student to the award of Advanced Certificate in Educational Management. Over 600 distance leaning students are now enrolled on the distance learning MBA course. The MBA in Educational Management is open to professionals in education who have a degree, or the equivalent, and who have at least three years teaching experience.

The School of Education at Leicester has a strong research and publications record. The director of the EMDU, Professor Tony Bush, is well-known for his work on theories of educational management. Members of the EMDU have active research interests in many areas including the management of autonomous schools, mentoring and professional development, the management of appraisal, managers in further education, the management of primary education, and women in educational management.

The core text books for the MBA in Educational Management by distance learning are published by Pitman, and the course includes an elective element for four of the five modules. Students are expected to complete five assignments, each of 5,000 words, and a dissertation of 20,000 words.

Students may enrol at any time for the distance learning course, and may negotiate their own study timetable, although it is expected that each assignment will be completed in a maximum of six months. Students are assigned to a tutor who normally provides support through telephone, letter, fax or Email. The course is truly distance learning, with no compulsory attendance or face-to-face tutorials.

Leicester University Management Centre

Address: University of Leicester, The New Building, University Road, Leicester LE1 7RH
Tel: 0116 252 5520   Fax: 0116 252 3949
EMail: lumc@le.ac.uk
Internet: www.le.ac.uk.lumc

Dean: Professor Peter M Jackson

MBA Admissions Officer: Patricia A Greatorex

MBA Programmes
MBA; Finance MBA; Marketing MBA; Total Quality Management MBA

Programme Details	Full-time	Flexible Learning
Duration	1 year	2 years
Class Contact	15 hours	approx 50 hours
Commencement	September	Oct, Jan, April, July
Application deadline	July	4 weeks prior to course start
GMAT Yes/No	Possible	Possible
Fees EC/Overseas	£4,200/£7,350	£5,600/£6,000
Annual student intake	70	708
Average student age	28	28
Min. required experience	2 years	2 years
%EC/Overseas	48/52	30/70
%Men/Women	60/40	70/30
Number of Professors	4	4
Number of Academic Staff	20	20
Number of elective courses	2 or 3	2 or 3
Assessment: Exams/Assignments	Both	Both
Dissertation/Project	P	P

Additional Information

International Links: Yes

IT facilities: Full computer facilities for full-time students. Email for flexible learners

Electives not readily available elsewhere: Public Sector Management, Strategic Management of Technology, Business Process Re-Engineering and IT Marketing, Retailing

School Description

Founded in 1988, the Management Centre is located on-campus in the purpose built New Building (opened in 1995), within easy reach of all University facilities. The Centre offers a range of courses in management studies which combine the highest academic standards with a knowledge of the demands of organisations.

The Leicester MBA is broad-based. Methods and Techniques of Strategy is followed by Methods and Techniques of Analysis (comprising Managerial Economics, Decision and Information Sciences, Marketing, Accounting for Managers, Human Resource Management) and Methods and Techniques of Management (comprising Organisation Analysis and Control, Quality and Operations Management, Strategic Financial Management and Business Policy).

Leicester's strategy for teaching excellence and the development of management skills is through an industry-led approach, which enables particular emphasis to be placed on the use of case-studies and individual and group presentations in enhancing business development, and enables students to adopt a computer-integrated approach to problem solving.

Many students are in employment and return to their employers on completion of the course. Over 100 companies deal directly with the active careers and employment service, which seeks to place MBA students. Located less than 2 miles from the city centre the University offers a well-stocked library, a purpose built computer centre and excellent sports and social facilities including two sports halls, two gyms and several bars and cafes. There are a multitude of cultural clubs, societies and entertainments to accommodate virtually every taste. No financial assistance is available.

Individual programmes accredited by the Association of MBAs are indicated by a tick

Hull Business School
University of Lincolnshire and Humberside

Address: Cottingham Road, Hull HU6 7RT
Tel: 01482 440550   Fax: 01482 473626
MBA Admissions Officers: Jean Kellie; Tim Thompson; Val Skerrow

MBA Programmes
Full-time MBA; Part-time MBA

Programme Details	Part-time
Duration	3 years
Class Contact	7½
Commencement	September
Which evening/day	Monday/Tuesday
Application deadline	August
GMAT Yes/No	No
Fees EC/Overseas	
Annual student intake	45/60
Average student age	33
Min. required	2 years
%EC/Overseas:	1/99
%Men/Women	67/33
Number of Professors	1
Number of Academic Staff	67
Number of elective	5
Assessment: Exams/Assignments	A
Dissertation/Project	D

Additional Information
International Links: Hull Business Schol has strong International links with the Pacific Rim especially Malaysia, Hong Kong; also European initiatives with Spain and eastern European countries such as Hungary and the Ukraine.

Electives not readily available elsewhere: Management and Self Development

Liverpool Business School

Address: Liverpool John Moores University, 98 Mount Pleasant, Liverpool L3 5UZ
Tel: 0151 231 3451   Fax: 0151 707 0423
EMail: j.w.vaughan@livjm.ac.uk
Internet: livjm.ac.uk
Dean: Professor Frank Sanderson
MBA Admissions Officer: John Vaughan

MBA Programmes
Full-time MBA; Part-time MBA (afternoon/evening); Part-time MBA (evening only)

Programme Details

	Full-time	Part-time
Duration	12 months	3 years
Class Contact	15	4-6
Commencement	September/January	September/January/April
Which evening/day		Tues/Weds
Application deadline	August/ December	Applications accepted prior to commencement
GMAT Yes/No	No	No
Fees EC/Overseas	£6,900	£5,400 approx
Annual student intake	30	50
Average student age		35
Min. required experience	3	3
%EC/Overseas:		n/a
%Men/Women		60/40
Number of Professors	4	
Number of Academic Staff	120	
Number of elective courses	8	8
Assessment: Exams/Assignments	Both	Both
Dissertation/Project	D	P

Additional Information

IT facilities: Extensive IT facilities with good availability. Recently opened Learning Resource Centre on site

School Description

Liverpool is an exciting city for students and provides good value as a place to study with accommodation costs below UK average levels. The Business School is located in the heart of Liverpool and provides opportunities for both home based and international students to reach their full potential while enjoying the varied social life offered by the city.

The School has recently re-validated its MBA programme and taken the opportunity to introduce a full-time route. A major strength of the School is its positive commitment to the needs of working managers. This is reflected in the revised programme with an emphasis on the development of management skills to complement knowledge development. Part-time students are assessed largely by work based projects which require them to relate their learning to practical problems within their organisations. Full-time students will be provided with opportunities to study real-life business problems and to apply their learning to practical situations. One important element of the course is that they will be required to undertake a consultancy project for a local organisation as an integral part of their course, this work forming the basis of the final dissertation.

It is intended that routes through the MBA will be offered within the next year. These will build upon the strengths of the University and are likely to include Health Management and Maritime Operations.

Liverpool Institute of Public Administration and Management (LIPAM)

Address: 2 Abercromby Square, University of Liverpool, Liverpool L69 3BX
Tel: 0151 794 2911   Fax: 0151 794 2909
EMail: m.r.davies@liverpool.ac.uk
Dean: Professor Martin R Davies
MBA Admissions Officer: Professor Martin R Davies

MBA Programmes
Full-time Industrialisation and Development MBA; Full-time Environmental Management MBA; Full-time Football Industries MBA

Programme Details	Full-time
Duration	12 months
Class Contact	approx 12
Commencement	September
Application deadline	August 31
GMAT Yes/No	No
Fees EC/Overseas	£3,040/£6,606
Annual student intake	150
Average student age	27
Min. required experience	2-5 years
%EC/Overseas	50/50
%Men/Women	66/33
Number of Professors	2
Number of Academic Staff	17
Number of elective courses	10
Assessment: Exams/Assignments	Both
Dissertation/Project	D or P

Additional Information
International Links: Programmes arranged for UNDP, University of Ljubljana (Slovenia), ILO, local government, newly privatised service industries, Government of South Africa

Library hours: 0900-2100 6 days per week

IT facilities: Yes – both in LIPAM and more generally in the University

Other information: Particular strengths in IT, HRM and Project Management

School Description
Courses: The Institute of Public Administration and Management runs a number of postgraduate and diploma programmes of training both for home and overseas students. They include both an MBA and a Master of Public Administration (MPA). The MBA programme consists of eight course units, of which four are taken concurrently in each of two semesters. Four of the eight units are compulsory; the remaining four are chosen from a list of options. In addition, students undertake a business project as part of their training programme. The compulsory courses are: Industrialisation and Development, Government Business Relations, Business Policy and Organisational Behaviour. MBA course units are partly assessed on a continuous basis. The exam normally represents 50 per cent of the final mark. Course teachers inform students of the specific procedures for continuous assessment by the end of the second week of the course.

Some courses are offered to both MPA and MBA students and involve case studies and simulation exercises in which the interface between the public and private sectors is explored.

The Faculty: LIPAM is a part of the Faculty of Social and Environmental Studies, in which there are approximately 120 full-time staff. In LIPAM, there are 7 full-time and 10 part-time academic staff. Specialist courses are also provided by staff elsewhere in the Faculty.

Accommodation: The University has a number of halls of residence for postgraduate students and their families. University accommodation is guaranteed for students who apply to the student Welfare and Accommodation Officer before 1 June. Assistance is also provided to students to secure appropriate accommodation in the private sector.

Careers Organisation: Many of the Institute's students are seconded from public organisations in various countries of the world. The remainder seek employment through the University's careers service, which organises a continuous programme of recruitment visits by companies and organisations throughout the public and private sectors. In recent years approximately 50 per cent of graduates have returned to their original employment, 45 per cent have found employment via the careers service, and five per cent have proceeded to more advanced studies.

London Business School

Address: Sussex Place, Outer Circle, Regents Park, London NW1 4SA
Tel: 0171 262 5050   Fax: 0171 724 7875
EMail: mba-info@lbs.ac.uk/Charniman@lbs.ac.uk
Internet: www.lbs.ac.uk

Dean: Paul Geroski

Director: Julia Tyler

MBA Admissions Officers: Claire Harniman; Gareth Osborne

MBA Programmes
Full-time MBA; Executive MBA

Programme Details	Full-time ✔	Executive ✔
Duration	21 months	2 years
Class Contact	745 hours	730 hours
Commencement	October	September/ January
Which evening/day		Friday/Saturday + block weeks
Application deadline	June 1 (March 1 for scholarship consideration)	May 31/ September 30
GMAT Yes/No	Yes	Yes
Fees EC/Overseas	£26,000/ £25,000	£26,000/£25,000
Annual student intake	240	120
Average student age	28	32
Min. required experience	3 years	4 years
%EC/Overseas	69/31	88/12
%Men/Women	78/22	74/26
Number of Professors	72	7
Number of Academic Staff	103	103
Number of elective courses	11 from 75	6 from 75
Assessment: Exams/Assignments	Both	Both
Dissertation/Project	P	P

Individual programmes accredited by the Association of MBAs are indicated by a tick

Additional Information

International Links: International exchange programme with 29 top business schools worldwide (open to Full-time and Executive MBA students); regular programme of international exchanges

Library hours: Term-time: 0900-2300 (Mon-Fri); 0900-1700 (Sat); 1300-2100 (Sun)

IT facilities: An extensive intranet is under development, delivering both administrative and academic information

Electives not readily available elsewhere: Strategic Leadership and Corporate Transformation; Languages; Practice for the Design Minded Manager; Information Businesses; Managing East European Operations

School Description

Established in 1965, the London Business School is a graduate school of University of London. Practical and applied teaching and leading-edge research are both fundamental to the School. To support its innovative approach and worldwide reputation, the School has 110 internationally recognised faculty, 45 per cent of whom come from outside the UK.

Both the Executive and Full-time MBA programmes have a strong international focus, with only 20 per cent of the new full-time class come from the UK and the average UK salary of the 1997 graduating class was £48,000 with sign on bonus and benefits on top. An international exchange programme with 29 other top business schools and the international mix of the faculty body adds to this focus.

Core courses for full-time students are taught during the first year; those for the Executive course students are taught on alternate Fridays and Saturdays during the first year, and during block weeks spread throughout the two years. In the second year (last 12 months) students select from an elective portfolio of approximately 75 options, thus tailoring their learning to their specific interests. Full-time students are also expected to graduate with knowledge of a language other than English; language tuition is available throughout the programme. Both programmes have a strong practical element and involve project and group-assessed work.

Most full-time students undertake a summer assignment between the first and second years; over 50 per cent of these typically turn into permanent job offers. This is particularly beneficial for students wishing to change their employment sector in graduation. The average UK salary of the 1996 graduating class was £47,000 (with sign-on bonus and benefits on top); over 58 per cent of the class received two to three job offers (six to seven in some cases) before graduation.

The London Business School Students Association organises many extracurricular activities, ranging from visiting speakers at the business clubs and company-sponsored events, to sports tournaments with other business schools.

Partners of LBS students also run a very active 'Partners Club', which meets regularly.

Information on LBS scholarships is given in the printed materials on the MBA programmes.

London Guildhall University Business School, Department of Management and Professional Development

Address: 84 Moorgate, London EC2M 6SQ
Tel: 0171 320 1528/1570   Fax: 0171 320 1585
EMail: griseri@lgu.ac.uk
Internet: www.lgu.ac.uk
Head: Susan Proudfoot

MBA Admissions Officers: Dr Paul Griseri; Gisèle Guarisco

MBA Programmes
Part-time Evening MBA; Part-time Executive Short Block MBA (new from 1998)

Programme Details	Part-time short block	Part-time evening
Duration	2 years	2 years 3 months
Class Contact	3-day blocks every 5 weeks	6 hours per week
Commencement	late February	End September
Which evening/day	n/a	Mon/Weds
Application deadline	end January	end August
GMAT Yes/No	not normally	not normally
Fees EC/Overseas	£7,000	£7,750
Annual student intake	20	25
Average student age	32	32
Min. required	3 years	3 years
%EC/Overseas:	n/a	n/a
%Men/Women	55/45	55/45
Number of Professors	6	6
Number of Academic Staff	170	170
Number of elective	2	2
Assessment: Exams/Assignments	Both	Both
Dissertation/Project	P	P

Additional Information
International Links: Additional collaborative programme in Moscow, delivered by Moscow International Higher Business School (MIRBIS). Essential course texts supplied free. International study visit in Stage 2

Electives not readily available elsewhere: Financial Risk Management, Strategic HRM, Business Ethics

School Description
Both the evening and executive block programmes are focussed on professional development in service organisations. Participants come from all sectors of the economy. Teaching is highly interactive and aims to help participants make effective practical use of theories and concepts. The programme has a strong international focus, drawing upon links with Business Schools in other countries. There is an emphasis on personal development as the essential tool for putting high level analysis into practice. Direct entry to Stage 2 is possible for candidates with a good DMS or equivalent.

Loughborough University Business School

Address: Ashby Road, Loughborough, Leicestershire LE11 3TU
Tel: 01509 223140   Fax: 01509 233313
EMail: s.e.hollick@lboro.ac.uk
Internet: info.lut.ac.uk/departments/bs/
Dean: Professor Sue Cox
MBA Admissions Officer: Mrs Sue Hollick

MBA Programmes
Executive MBA (evenings) – Loughborough; Executive MBA (evenings) – Peterborough; Corporate MBA; Information and Library Management MBA; Sports and Leisure Management MBA

Programme Details

Programme Details	Part-time	Corporate	Badged
Duration	3 years	3 years	3 years
Class Contact	4 hours		
Commencement	October	October	October
Which evening/day	Wednesday (Thurs at Peterborough)		
Application deadline	August	August	August
GMAT Yes/No	No	No	No
Fees EC/Overseas	£6,000 (£6,500 at Peterborough)		
Annual student intake	60	20	20
Average student age	34		
Min. required	3 years	3 years	3 years
%Men/Women	2/1		
Number of Professors	9	9	9
Number of Academic Staff	44	44	44
Number of elective	6	6	6
Assessment: Exams/Assignments	Both	Both	Both
Dissertation/Project	P	P	P

Additional Information
International Links: Member of a consortium of European business schools which jointly provide an annual international strategic management programme for the benefit of their MBA students. This programme, which is optional, exposes students to international issues more sharply through the collaboration with students and teachers from a wide range of countries.

Library hours: 0900-2200 (Mon-Fri): 0900-1730 (Sat); 1000-2100 (Sun)

IT facilities: Business School computer laboratory containing a network of 25 PCs which is connected to the University's main network

School Description
The rapidly expanding Loughborough University Business School (LUBS) has a reputation for delivering high quality postgraduate and professional management education. The School's teaching has been rated as excellent, and the teaching staff on the MBA programmes are active researchers who remain close to their subjects through links with industry. The MBA programmes are practical, relevant and participative, with an emphasis on professional and personal development. The popular Executive MBA programmes running in identical form at

Loughborough and Peterborough, are complemented by the new Corporate MBA, Information and Library Management MBA and Sports and Leisure Management MBA.

The Executive MBA programmes are studied over three years by attendance at the local centre one evening per week, supplemented by a few full day sessions in Loughborough on Fridays and Saturdays. The core subjects covering the major management functions are complemented by electives and by a personal effectiveness programme. Emphasis is placed on the transfer of skills and knowledge from the classroom to the workplace. The final component of the programme is a substantial project on a topic of the student's choice.

The new Corporate MBA programme covers the same ground as the Executive MBA. However, the students are drawn from a group of sponsoring organisations, each of which nominates a number of participants each year. Attendance at the programme occurs generally in blocks of three days duration.

The Information Management and Leisure MBA programmes are planned to commence in 1998 through joint initiatives between LUBS and other departments at Loughborough University. They are designed in conjunction with senior managers from within the two sectors, thus ensuring that they are practical, contemporary, and relevant to future needs. Attendance is via blocks of study, each of a few days duration.

Luton Business School, University of Luton

Address: Putteridge Bury, Hitchin Road, Luton, Bedfordshire LU2 8LE
Tel: 01582 743945   Fax: 01582 482689
EMail: lbspgrad@luton.ac.uk
Internet: www.luton.ac.uk
Dean: Dr Stephen Pettitt
MBA Admissions Officer: Gillian Butt

MBA Programmes
Full-time, Weekend, Part-time Executive MBA; Specialist MBAs: Financial Management MBA, International Business MBA, Marketing MBA, Technology MBA, Tourism Management MBA

Programme Details	Full-time	After/eve	Weekend	In-company
Duration	1 year	2 years	2 years	2 years
Class Contact	20 hrs (av)	6 hrs	12 hrs per w/e	16 hrs per block
Commencement	October	October	April	November
Which evening/day		Weds	Friday/Saturday	variable
Application deadline	Sept	September	March	
GMAT Yes/No	No	No	No	No
Fees EC/Overseas	£8,000/£6,200	£2,525	£2,675	confidential
Annual student intake	15-20	30	30	15
Average student age	25	35		35
Min. required experience	2-4 years	4 years	4 years	4 years
%EC/Overseas	25/75	100/0	100/0	100/0
%Men/Women	65/35	65/35	65/35	
Number of Professors	4			
Number of Academic Staff	90			

Individual programmes accredited by the Association of MBAs are indicated by a tick

Number of elective courses	4	4	4	4
Assessment: Exams/Assignments	Both	Both	Both	Both
Dissertation/Project	D	D	D	D

Additional Information

International Links: ESC Lyons, EADA Barcelona, University of Utrecht (The Netherlands)

Library hours: 0900-2100 (Mon-Fri) and some weekends

IT facilities: 4 main PC labs (60 PCs)

Electives not readily available elsewhere: MBA Specialist programme: Financial Management, International Business, Marketing, Tourism Management, Technology

Other information: Putteridge Bury is an Edwardian mansion styled on Chequers, set in its own quiet parkland

School Description

Weekend MBA is 4pm to 9.30pm Fridays and 9am to 6pm Saturdays. The course participants meet every 4th weekend and one full week in December. Weekday MBA is 2pm to 9pm on Wednesdays or Thursdays.

New suite of specialist MBAs was launched October 1997 – MBA Financial Management, MBA International Business, MBA Marketing. MBA Tourism Management. MBA Technology.

A new library extension has been recently completed. There is a dedicated postgraduate hall of residence. The university has a wide range of sports facilities.

Manchester Business School

Address: Booth Street West, Manchester M15 6PB
Tel: 0161 275 6311   Fax: 0161 275 6489
EMail: h.dowd@fs2.mbs.ac.uk
Internet: www.mbs.ac.uk

Director: Professor John Arnold

MBA Admissions Officer: Ms Helen Dowd

MBA Programmes

Full-time MBA; Part-time MBA (Day and evening); (REMBA) Residential Executive MBA (weekend study); Public sector MBA; MBA for Lawyers (Day and evenings); Modular MBA for IBM Managers; Distance Learning MBA for Financial Specialists

Programme Details	Full-time ✔	Part-time ✔	REMBA
Duration	18 months	30-60 months	24-36 months
Class Contact	24 per week	3-6 per week	500 hours
Commencement	September	Sept/Jan/April	January
Which evening/day	n/a	Tue (eve) Thurs (eve)	Sat-Tue
Application deadline	30 June	1 month before prog starts	1 month before prog starts
GMAT Yes/No	Yes	Yes	Yes
Fees EC/Overseas	£16,000/£19,000	£14,940 (£830 module)	£19,000
Annual student intake	120	70	10/20
Average student age	28	33	34
Min. required experience	3 years	3 years	4 years

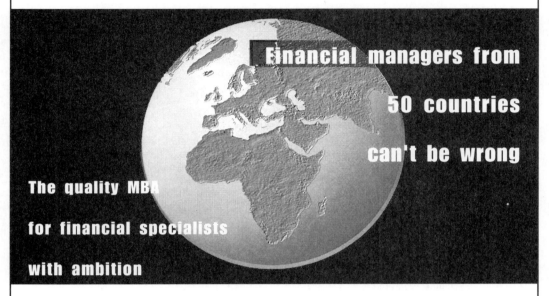

%EC/Overseas	40/60	100/0	100/0
%Men/Women	75/25	50/50	75/25
Number of Professors	15	15	15
Number of Academic Staff	55	55	55
Number of elective courses	40	40	n/a
Assessment: Exams/Assignments	Both	Both	Both
Dissertation/Project	P (D is optional)	P (D is optional)	P (D is optional)

Additional Information

International Links: Large international exchange programme: 50 full-time students go on exchange to over 40 schools in North and Central America, Europe or Pacific Rim

IT facilities: One PC per 5 students; open 24 hours per day

Other information: Career management and Alumni Centre. Students have access to all the facilities of the University of Manchester. All school facilities are contained in one building

School Description

The School was founded in 1965 as one of the two original graduate management schools in the UK. It soon developed its own distinct philosophy: that management education should not be confined to the classroom, but should develop managers who can actually get things done. This has resulted in programmes which stress an action-learning, project-based approach (known as the Manchester Method) with students working together in groups on real-world business problems and opportunities. The School is consistently rated one of the best in Europe. Its teaching and learning were recently rated as 'excellent' by the Higher Education Funding Council for England (HEFCE).

Once on the programme, students are given the flexibility to tailor the content and pace of the programme to suit their individual needs. There is an emphasis on international business, with around 70 per cent of students from overseas, and most students take advantage of the School's extensive international links to spend three to four months on the International Exchange Programme.

The programme is also offered on a part-time modular basis, in partnership with the Manchester School of Management at UMIST. Also available is the Residential Executive MBA, which shapes a programme of management development around the working roles of practising managers. This programme involves block-release attendance for a total of 52 days, only 28 of which are in mid-week. It is offered jointly by MBS. Specialisms at the school include: Innovation, Entrepreneurship, International Business and Strategy.

The Manchester Metropolitan University

Address: Faculty of Management and Business, Aytoun Building, Aytoun Street, Manchester M1 3GH
Tel: 0161 247 3973   Fax: 0161 247 6319
EMail: l.orgee@mmu.ac.uk
Internet: www.fmb.mmu.ac.uk

Dean: Professor Andrew Lock

MBA Admissions Officer: Dr Lawrence Orgee

MBA Programmes

Part-time MBA (late day/evening)

Programme Details	Part-time ✔
Duration	2 years 8 months
Class Contact	4½ hours x 30 weeks
Commencement	May
Which evening/day	Tues/Wed (Year 1/Year2)
Application deadline	March
GMAT Yes/No	No
Fees EC/Overseas	£9,000
Annual student intake	40
Average student age	32
Min. required	3 years
%EC/Overseas:	100/0
%Men/Women	67/33
Number of Professors	1
Number of Academic Staff	25
Number of elective	20
Assessment: Exams/Assignments	Both
Dissertation/Project	D

the
MANCHESTER
METROPOLITAN
UNIVERSITY

Part-Time MBA

One of Britain's largest and most experienced providers of management and business education offers the following 2½ year, part-time modular MBA programme. Designed specifically for experienced managers requiring a general management education, the course is officially recognised and accredited by the Association of MBAs.

The programme includes:
- Core modules encompassing all functional areas of management
- Corporate strategy
- Strategic management of change
- Work based projects
- Wide range of electives

We provide:
- City centre location
- Weekly evening attendance
- Visit to a European Business School
- Individual dissertation support
- Texts for the core programme
- Networking opportunities

For further information about the programme please contact:
The MBA Administrator, The Manchester Metropolitan University,
Faculty of Management and Business, Aytoun Street, Manchester M1 3GH.
Telephone: 0161 247 3713/3717. Fax: 0161 247 6319.

Additional Information
International Links: International Elective Year 1: Prague International Business School, Budapest Business School, EADA Barcelona

Library hours: 0900-2100 (Mon-Fri) 1000-1600 (Sat)

IT facilities: 'Drop in' 110 workstation facilities available in library hours. Additional facilities in Computing Services Suite include extensive software range: wordprocessing, spreadsheets, databases, scanning, printing via network links

School Description
The Faculty of Management and Business is one of the largest of its kind in the country and this is reflected in the comprehensive range of programmes offered. The Faculty's long experience in management education has enabled a particular view to emerge about how managers can best be developed. Consequently, the MBA is designed specially for mature managers, employed in all sectors of the economy, who recognise the need to take part in the process of developing strategic competence through a series of major work-related projects.

The programme entails attendance on 30 evenings per year for the first two years. Modules are studied in blocks of 10 weeks, two at a time, on an evening-only basis. There is also a Management Development Programme which consists of a series of workshops which normally run for two days on Friday and Saturday.

There are nine core modules including Management and Organisations, International Business Development, Accounting for Decision Making, Finance and Organisational Analysis, Human Resource Management and Marketing/Operations. In the second year there are three strategic management modules. Over 20 electives are offered in the areas of Accounting/Finance, Marketing, Organisational Behaviour, Operations Management, Public Sector Management and International Management.

Middlesex University Business School

Address: The Burroughs, London NW4 4BT
Tel: 0181 362 5090   Fax: 0181 362 6069
EMail: headmission@mdx.ac.uk
Dean: Professor David A Kirby
MBA Admissions Officer: Paul Merricks

MBA Programmes
Full-time MBA; Evening MBA

Programme Details	Full-time ✔	Part-time ✔
Duration	1 year	2 years 3 months
Class Contact	15 hours per week	6 hours per week
Commencement	September	October
Which evening/day		Tuesday/Thursday
Application deadline	July	
Fees EC/Overseas	£8,000 approx	£4,000 approx
Annual student intake	45	35
Average student age	28	

Success through management education

MIDDLESEX UNIVERSITY BUSINESS SCHOOL

Middlesex University Business School has a range of high quality postgraduate and professional programmes, attracting students from around the world.

Situated in north-west London, close to the financial and political centre of the country, the Business School offers an exceptionally wide range of post-experience programmes for practising managers including:

- **Master of Business Administration**
  One year full-time

- **Executive Master of Business Administration**
  Two years part-time,
  two evenings a week

Find out more at an open evening, the second Wednesday of each month – ring to book a place:

+44 (0)181 362 5090

Middlesex University
Business School,
The Burroughs,
London NW4 4BT

email: s.sharp@mdx.ac.uk

www.mdx.ac.uk

Min. required experience	3 years	3 years
%EC/Overseas	40/60	75/25
%Men/Women	60/40	65/35
Number of Professors	10	10
Number of Academic Staff	134	134
Assessment: Exams/Assignments	Both	Both
Dissertation/Project	D	D

School Description

Middlesex University Business School offers a range of high-quality postgraduate and professional programmes designed to meet the needs of those pursuing or wishing to pursue a career in business or business-related professions in both the public and private sectors. The post-experience programmes for practising managers and professionals are designed to enable them to meet successfully the challenges of the future by enhancing their knowledge, skills, and professional competence.

The School has a large team of academic and support staff; all of the academic staff have relevant business or professional experience and are active in research and consultancy. To ensure that programmes are at the cutting-edge of best practice, external guest lectures provide input from their own work experience. This expertise in the theory and practice of business and the professions underpins a highly career-directed portfolio of programmes.

The Part-time MBA is a broad management programme designed for practising managers; it aims to develop general managers rather than functional specialists. Outcomes of the learning experience are the acquisition and refinement of professional and intellectual skills required for the analysis of complex corporate problems, and an ability to apply imaginative, yet rigorous, judgement to key business decisions.

Napier University Business School

Address: New Craig, Craighouse Campus, Craighouse Road, Edinburgh EH10 5LG
Tel: 0131 455 5016   Fax: 0131 455 5041
EMail: s.ferrier@napier.ac.uk
Dean: John R Thomson
MBA Admissions Officer: Sheila Ferrier

MBA Programmes

Part-time MBA; Open Learning MBA

Programme Details	Part-time	Distance Learning (UK)
Duration	1, 2 or 3 years depending on entry qualifications	2 years
Class Contact	1150 hours	242 hours
Commencement	October	October
Which evening/day	Wed aft/eve Yr 1, Thur aft/eve Yr 2/3	Fri eve Sat Yr 1 Sat/Sun Yr 2
Application deadline	Mid September	Mid September
GMAT Yes/No	own test	own test
Fees EC/Overseas	£5,165	£5,900
Annual student intake	50	30
Average student age	35	34

Schools offering an Association of MBAs-accredited programme are indicated by a roundel

Min. required	3-5 years	5 years
%EC/Overseas:	nil	nil
%Men/Women	60/40	60/40
Number of Academic Staff	140	140
Number of elective courses	9	8
Exams/Assignments	Both	Both
Dissertation/Project	D	D

Additional Information

International Links: Haarlem, The Netherlands

Library hours: Open 7 days

IT facilities: IT lab on site

School Description

The Business School is one of the largest in Scotland, with over 3,300 students and over 140 academic staff. It offers nine undergraduate degree courses, and has been offering management education at a postgraduate level for over 25 years. The School has strong links with professional institutes and offers a range of courses recognised by several professional bodies.

The Open Learning MBA is a two-year programme which requires attendance at the University on a monthly basis at weekends, allowing students to develop their management career without reducing their commitment to their current job. A significant proportion of the course is assessed by work-based assignments, which allow students to apply course concepts to practical management situations. The programme structure is a progression from individual skills through financial management to corporate perspectives.

Napier is linked with Haarlem Business School, and students have the opportunity to attend a study weekend at the European Business School.

The Part-time MBA and Distance Learning (UK) provides an integrated suite of courses designed to match management development needs to career progression. This programme is structured in three stages (CMS, DMS, MBA), and it may be possible to enter at any of these stages depending on experience and qualifications. It is also possible to exit at any stage with a qualification. There are no bursaries. Students paying for themselves can pay in installments; a career development loan scheme is available via selected banks.

Nene College of Higher Education

Address: Faculty of Management and Business, Boughton Green Road, Northampton NN2 7AL
Tel: 01604 735500   Fax: 01604 721214
EMail: david.shuttleworth@nene.ac.uk; maureen.kelly@nene.ac.uk; roger.willetts@nene.ac.uk
Internet: www.nene.ac.uk

Dean: Mrs Diane Hayes

MBA Admissions Officers: David Shuttleworth (MBA International); Maureen Kelly (MBA for Women); Roger Willetts (Part-time programmes)

MBA Programmes

Full-time International MBA; Full-time MBA (Women returners); Part-time MBA; Top-up Scheme for DMS

Individual programmes accredited by the Association of MBAs are indicated by a tick

Programme Details

	Full-time	Part-time	Full-time MBA (women returners)	MBA Top-up Scheme for DMS
Duration	1 year	1 year	1 year	1 year
Class Contact	15 hours	6 hours	12-15 hours	6 hours
Commencement	October	September/ January	October	September
Which evening/day		Mon/Wed		
Application deadline	September	Aug/Dec	September	August
GMAT Yes/No	No	No	No	No
Fees EC/Overseas	£5,550/ £6,750	£4,780	E.S.F. funded	£2,650
Annual student intake	25	25	25	30
Average student age	27	33	38	33
Min. required experience	1 year	3 years	2 years	3 years
%EC/Overseas	80/20		75/25	
%Men/Women	60/40	80/20	0/100	80/20
Number of Professors	6	6	6	6
Number of Academic Staff	120	120	120	120
Number of elective		8	4	
Assessment: Exams/Assignments	Both	Both	Both	Both
Dissertation/Project	Both	D	D	D

Additional Information
International Links: Full-time MBA (International) Stage 1 taught in Groupe ESC (Poitiers, France) or at Hogeschool Drenthe (Emmen, The Netherlands)
Library hours: 0845-2000
IT facilities: 24 hours

School Description
Nene College is located on the attractive Moulton Park Campus, which occupies almost 70 acres on the edge of the town of Northampton, and which has residential halls for 1,400 students (many with en-suite facilities) mostly built during the past five years. Good sports and social provision has been developed along with teaching accommodation and library and Information Technology facilities.

The Faculty of Management and Business has more than 3,000 students on undergraduate, postgraduate and professional courses.

The Faculty of some 120 academic staff encompasses the Schools of Business and Management; Law and Accounting and Information Systems.

The Sunley Management Centre, a purpose-built residential conference centre which provides consultancy and management development to corporate clients across the UK, is within the Faculty of Management and Business. The part-time MBA, along with other part-time post-experience management programmes, is run at the Management Centre. In 1996 a new part-time MBA programme for Women Returners was launched. The MBA (International) course is housed on the same campus in a purpose-built £4m teaching block which opened in September 1992. This development was based upon the co-operation of the Faculty of Management and Business with international partner institutions it has fostered for more than 12 years.

Northampton is located midway between London and Birmingham, close to junctions 15, 15A and 16 of the M1 with easy access from there to the M5, M6 and M25. By rail, it is on the London (Euston) to Glasgow line with an hourly service to London. London, Birmingham and

Luton airports are all within 80 miles of Northampton. The area is surrounded by major tourist venues within reasonable distance, including Warwick Castle, Coventry Cathedral, Stratford-Upon-Avon, Woburn Abbey, and the historic university cities of Cambridge and Oxford.

Newcastle Business School, University of Northumbria

Address: Northumberland Building, Northumberland Road, Newcastle-upon-Tyne NE1 8ST
Tel: 0191 227 3381   Fax: 0191 227 3893
EMail: donna.etherington@unn.ac.uk; nbadmissions@unn.ac.uk
Director (Acting): Elizabeth Gillott
MBA Admissions Officer: Donna Etherington

MBA Programmes
Full-time MBA; Part-time MBA; MA European Business Administration (FT); MBA Flexible

Programme Details	Full-time	Part-time	MAEB	MBA Flexible
Duration	12-18 months	24-36 months	12-18 months	24-36 months
Class Contact	12	6	12	mainly distance
Commencement	Sept	Sept	Sept	Several
Which evening/day		varies		
Application deadline	August	August	August	None
GMAT Yes/No	if possible	No	if possible	No
Fees EC/Overseas	£5,650–£7,200	£5,000–£6,000	£3,800–£6,800	£5,000–£6,000
Annual student intake	15-20	20+	20	20
Average student age	27	33	25	30
Min. required experience	2 years	2 years	nil	2 years
%EC/Overseas	40/60	100/0	100/0	100/0
%Men/Women	60/40	60/40	50/50	60/40
Number of Professors	4	4	4	4
Number of Academic Staff	140	140	140	140
Number of elective courses	2 from 6	2 from 6	2 from 6	
Assessment: Exams/Assignments	Both	A	Both	A
Dissertation/Project	D	D	D	B

Additional Information
International Links: MAEBA linked with Hochschule für Wirtschaft und Politik, Hamburg (Germany)

Library hours: 0900-2100 (Mon-Fri); 0900-1630 (Sat); 1230-1830 (Sun)

IT facilities: 400 networked PCs; Internet Access, Datacomms; GIS DEC-VAX minicomputers

Other information: FT MBA/MAEBA delivered at Longhirst Campus – purpose built new campus 15 miles from Newcastle with 210 study bedrooms

Individual programmes accredited by the Association of MBAs are indicated by a tick

School Description

The Newcastle Business School (which operates from three sites in the North of England) was assessed as 'excellent' by the Higher Education Funding Council for England (HEFCE) in February 1994. The School is the largest in the North of England with approximately 4,500 students and 170 academic staff offering a wide range of educational opportunities from Certificate and Diploma to MA/MSc and MBA level.

The School operates a fully unitised (modular) programme with learning facilitated in relatively small groups.

Newcastle School of Management, University of Newcastle upon Tyne

Address: Armstrong Building, Queen Victoria Road, Newcastle upon Tyne NE1 7RU
Tel: (0)191 222 5353   Fax: (0)191 222 5857
EMail: School.of.management@ncl.ac.uk
Internet: www.ncl.ac.uk
Dean: Dr Roger Vaughan
MBA Admissions Officer: Professor Jane Hogan

MBA Programmes
Full-time Open MBA; Part-time Open MBA; Rolls-Royce Consortium MBA; MBA in Strategic Telecommunications Management

Programme Details	Full-time ✔	Part-time ✔	Rolls-R	Telecomms
Duration	1 year	2½ years	3 years	2½ years
Commencement	Sept/Oct	Sept/Oct	January	
Which evening/day	n/a	Mon and Fri	Wed-Fri	Fri-Sun
Application deadline	August	August	Jan	
GMAT Yes/No	Yes/500+	No	No	No
Fees EC/Overseas	£7,500/ £9,500	£7,500/ £9,500	£10,500	£15,000
Annual student intake	30	30	15-20	20
Average student age	26	36	35	
Min. required experience	3 years	4 years	5 years	
%EC/Overseas	75	100/0	100/0	
%Men/Women	80/20	71/29	90/10	
Number of elective courses	20+	20+	-	3
Exams/Assignments	Both	Both	Both	A
Dissertation/Project	D	D	P	P

School Description

Newcastle School of Management brings together a wide range of academic departments and research centres, whose work contributes to the breadth and relevance of the MBA and other taught programmes.

The School's practical approach to management education is reinforced by access to leading management research in contexts covering both the public and private sectors, and the School is regularly advised by a group of senior managers from leading national and international organisations.

The unique structure of the School ensures that you will benefit from experience drawn from the many strengths of the University. In summary, Newcastle School of Management combines the benefits of the established research-led approach with a new flexibility.

Schools offering an Association of MBAs-accredited programme are indicated by a roundel

The School draws staff from the departments including Management Studies, Economics, Agricultural Economics and Food Marketing and Computing Science, as well as research centres such as the Centre for Urban Regeneration and Development (CURDS), and the Engineering Design Centre.

Newcastle University's School of Management is dedicated to creating effective managers. To meet this aim, we provide a rigorous and comprehensive MBA programme which will enable managers to: acquire a strong grounding in core management disciplines; choose to study specialist areas of interest from a wide range of electives; and learn within a dynamic, applied research environment. They will be able to adopt an approach to management which combines academic and practical knowledge to reach the best solutions for their organisation, take responsibility for their own development, and manage their own MBA – giving them a firm foundation for life-long learning, and appreciate the demands that the external and internal environments place upon individuals and organisations.

The Business School, University of North London

Address: Stapleton House, 227-281 Holloway Road, London N7 8HN
Tel: 0171 7533333   Fax: 0171 7537061
EMail: admission@unl.ac.uk
Internet: www.unl.ac.uk/bu

Head (Management): Mark Bickerton

MBA Admissions Officer: Sarah Cushnahan

MBA Programmes
Full-time MBA; Day MBA; Evening MBA (Executive); Weekend MBA (Executive); Health and Social Care Management MBA; Education Management MBA; Hospitality Management MBA Museums and Heritage MBA

Programme Details

	Full-time	Part-time	Weekend Management School
Duration	1 year	1½/2½ years	
Class Contact	12-15 hours per week	6 hours per week	W/e alt Sats 9-5
Commencement	September	February	
Which evening/day		Monday and Wednesday	
Application deadline	early September/early January	early September/early January	
GMAT Yes/No	No	No	
Fees EC/Overseas	£7,000/£7,500	£7,000/£7,500	
Annual student intake	50	40	20
Average student age	25	30	30
Min. required experience	2 years	3 years	3 years
%EC/Overseas	40/60		
%Men/Women	50/50	50/50	50/50
Number of Professors	7	7	7

Individual programmes accredited by the Association of MBAs are indicated by a tick

Number of Academic Staff	86	86	86
Number of elective courses	8	8	8
Assessment: Exams/Assignments	Both	Both	Both
Dissertation/Project	D	D	D

Additional Information

International Links: International collaboration with universities in USA, EU, Asia Pacific, Caribbean, Ukraine

Library hours: 7 days a week. Library fully computerised with Internet link

Electives not readily available elsewhere: Managing Change and Innovation, Ethical Management, Cross-cultural Management, Treasury and Financial Management, Tourism Marketing

School Description

This is a modern university business school in London, offering research and consultancy in Management, Transport, Tourism and Hospitality Management, Organisational and Employment Diversity, and Public Sector Management to support the MBA, together with a team of experts and industrial advisors.

The Learning Resource Centre contains networked access to up-to-date learning facilities, and the library hosts the European Documentation Centre, the TUC Library, and the Collection of Tourism Concern.

Executive MBA members work in tandem with their employing organisations and through small learning sets of participants. MBA specialist programmes and day programmes have consulting placements with public and commercial employers. An MBA Conference and Workshop programme runs alongside the main course.

The School provides a tailor-made career planning and job search service to MBA participants.

Competitive bursaries are available for international students.

A full range of cultural and sporting activities is offered.

Nottingham Business School, Nottingham Trent University

Address: Burton Street, Nottingham NG1 4BU
Tel: 0115 9486198   Fax: 0115 9486512
EMail: julian.overton@ntu.ac.uk
Internet: www.nbs.ntu.ac.uk
MBA Admissions Officer: Julian Overton

MBA Programmes

Full-time MBA; Part-time MBA; Executive MBA

Programme Details	Full-time	Part-time	Executive
Duration	1 year	3 years	2 years
Class Contact	av. 16 hours a week	6 hours a week	28 hours per module
Commencement	September	September	November
Which evening/day	n/a	afternoon/eve or 2 eves or weekends	10 x 3½ day modules over the 2 years

Application deadline	no deadline but early application advised	no deadline but early application advised	no deadline but early application advised
GMAT Yes/No	Yes	No	No
Fees EC/Overseas	£7,800	£6,495	£8,500
Annual student intake	25	90	20
Average student age		32	38
Min. required experience	3 years	5 years preferred	5 years
%Men/Women		70/30	90/10
Number of Professors	12	12	12
Number of Academic Staff	112	112	112
Number of elective courses	7	7	n/a
Assessment: Exams/Assignments	Both	Both	A
Assignment	Both	Both	Both

School Description

Nottingham Business School has been providing an experienced and integrated approach to postgraduate and professional education for over 20 years.

The School's envied reputation has been developed in the most straightforward way – by being able to offer flexible and professional services which recognise and satisfy the unique needs of individuals and companies alike; services which enhance performance and give value for money. An extensive portfolio of postgraduate, professional and part-time courses is offered, which are of appeal to a broad range of individuals at different stages of their careers, and which can be taken in a variety of modes including weekends, evenings, day release and distance learning. In all, the School offers a service and value to over 4,000 individual and corporate clients at any one time.

School of Management and Finance, University of Nottingham

Address: University Park, Nottingham NG7 2RD
Tel: 0115 551 5500   Fax: 0115 551 5503
EMail: smf.mba@lin1.smf.nottingham.ac.uk
Internet: www.ccc.nottingham.ac.uk/lizsmf/smf.html

Dean: Professor R Berry

Director: Scott Goddard

MBA Admissions Officer: Ron Hodges

MBA Programmes

General MBA (Full-time and Part-time); MBA in Financial Studies (Full-time and Part-time); International MBA (Full- time); Executive MBA (Part-time); Modular MBA (Part-time one-week intensive blocks); MBA (Health Management); MBA (Education); MBA (Criminal Justice; MBA (Local Government); MBA (Voluntary Sector). All full-time and part-time

The UNIVERSITY *of* NOTTINGHAM

The School of Management & Finance at the University of Nottingham is one of the country's leading management schools.

*The **GENERAL MBA** is a comprehensive international management programme.*

***MBA IN FINANCIAL STUDIES** offers a unique management programme stressing financial management skills. Full-time and Part-time.*

For further details please contact: The School of Management & Finance, Portland Building, University of Nottingham, Nottingham NG7 2RD. Telephone: 0115 951 5500 Fax: 0115 951 5503

Email: SMF.MBA@LIN1.SMF.nottingham.ac.uk
WorldwideWeb: http://www.ccc.nottingham.ac.uk/~lizsmf/smf.html

Both programmes include:
• Excellent choice of electives
• Business Language modules
• Management skills programme
• Practical consultancy projects
• Association of MBAs accreditation
• "Excellent" teaching rating

Other programmes include:
• Executive MBA
• Modular MBA
• International MBA
• MBA (Education)
• MBA (Health)
• MBA (Criminal Justice)
• MBA (Voluntary Sector)
• MBA (Local Government)
• DBA

School of MANAGEMENT & FINANCE

Programme Details

Programme Details	Full-time ✔	Part-time ✔
Duration	1 year	2-4 years
Class Contact	18-21 hours per week	Variable
Commencement	Late September	Variable
Which evening/day		All weekdays and evenings
Application deadline	None – early app. advised	None – early app. advised
GMAT Yes/No	Sometimes	Sometimes
Fees EC/Overseas	£7,980/£9,000 (Gen and fin.)	£9000/9960 (Int, modular)
Annual student intake	85	140
Average student age	30	34
Min. required experience	3 years	
%EC/Overseas	45/65	
%Men/Women	70/30	
Number of Professors	10	
Number of Academic Staff	48	
Number of elective courses	30	
Assessment: Exams/Assignments	Both	
Dissertation/Project	Both	

Additional Information

International Links: France; Germany; USA; Canada more under development
Library hours: 0900-2145 (Mon-Fri); 0900-1645 (Sat)

IT facilities: MBA computer suite plus 24 hour access within the University; local area network with extensive software; CD-Rom facilities; access to computerised databases

Electives not readily available elsewhere: Emerging Market Economies; Portfolio Management and Investment Analysis; Organisational Culture; Insurance; Venture Capital; Financial Fraud and Misconduct; Marketing Research; Entrepreneurship; Japanese Language; Japanese Institutions

School Description

The School of Management and Finance is one of the UK's leading management schools. It is located in a beautiful parkland campus two miles from the centre of Nottingham, the commercial and cultural capital of the East Midlands. The School has high-quality purpose-designed facilities, and was rated 'Excellent' in teaching by the HEFCE in 1994.

The main MBAs of the School are Association of MBAs-accredited, and the MBA programmes were particularly praised in the HEFCE visit. Very good links exist with industry and commerce, and academic posts are sponsored by Boots, Midland Bank, and Norwich Union.

The School is one of the largest providers of taught MBAs in the UK and offers varied programmes with flexible attendance patterns and a wide range of elective subjects. Over 30 electives are offered, including popular subjects such as Business Ethics, Entrepreneurship Law, International Business, and Operations Management. Additionally, the School offers many unusual electives including Emerging Market Economies, Venture Capital, Portfolio Management and Investment Analysis, Insurance and Risk Management, Japanese Institutions, Organisational Culture, and Financial Fraud. Business language electives are available in French, German, Spanish and Japanese.

Students of full-time programmes have the opportunity to undertake practical consultancy projects for companies (ranging from small local concerns to well-known multinational companies) and a management skills programme dealing with presentation skills, assertiveness, conflict resolution, interview techniques, and other practical management needs.

Sporting facilities at the University are first-class, with provision for numerous sports, and a new indoor swimming pool. The active MBA Society provides a mix of social, cultural and sporting activities ranging from a social drink to formal balls.

Students at Nottingham have enjoyed a high degree of success in obtaining positions with well-known UK and international companies.

Open University Business School

Address: Walton Hall, Milton Keynes MK7 6AA
Tel: 01908 653231   Fax: 01908 655072
EMail: oubs-enquiries@open.ac.uk
Internet: oubs.open.ac.uk

Dean: David Asch

MBA Programmes
Distance Learning MBA

Programme Details	Distance Learning ✔
Duration	3 years
Class Contact	5-10 hours per week
Commencement	May and November
Which evening/day	Flexible

The Open University

BUSINESS SCHOOL

"Where will I find time for an MBA?"

Now you can take an Association of MBAs approved MBA without taking time off work – with the Open University Business School.

The school's teaching methods draw on the unrivalled expertise of the Open University and are supported by over 750 tutors offering group tuition and one-to-one feedback on work and assignments.

Our high quality texts, videos, audios and computing materials together with tutor support, informal study groups, day schools and residential schools have been given the highest rating of "Excellent" by the Higher Education Funding Council England

To find out why this is the most popular MBA programme in Europe call 01908 653449 (24 hours) to request our MBA prospectus, quoting SP98L.

OUBS Hotline 01908 653449
http://oubs.open.ac.uk

Application deadline	March and September
GMAT Yes/No	No
Fees EC/Overseas	£9,000
Annual student intake	2,000
Average student age	35
Min. required	7 years
%EC/Overseas:	90/10
%Men/Women	70/30
Number of Professors	15
Number of Academic Staff	80
Number of elective	8
Assessment: Exams/Assignments	Both
Dissertation/Project	P (optional)

Additional Information
International Links: Computer conferencing and training, CD-Rom delivery on some courses. Local tutorials with specialist tutors. Alumni Association of 5,500 MBA graduates. Awarded the Queens Award for Export in 1997.

School Description
The Open University is the world leader in distance teaching. The Business School is a faculty of the University and has been offering an MBA since 1988. Over 5,500 students have graduated with an MBA during that time, making the Business School one of the largest in Europe. The strength of the Open University Business School MBA is that it allows managers to remain in employment whilst studying, as managers study in their own time, tutorials are at weekends, and the residential element held in most of the electives is short in duration.

Schools offering an Association of MBAs-accredited programme are indicated by a roundel

There is a high level of support for managers through the network of thirteen regional offices that select, develop, and monitor the 750 part-time tutors, many of whom are OUBS MBA graduates. Students are encouraged to network through the use of a Computer Conferencing facility. The quality of the materials is excellent, and the learning is relevant to the workplace. Managers are encouraged to transfer the course concepts to work within their organisations.

The programme is in two stages. Stage 1 is either via the open access route of Certificate and Diploma in Management, or via the nine-month accelerated route, 'The Foundations of Senior Management', though entry to this requires an honours degree or professional qualification, and there is a minimum age of 27. Stage 2 focuses on strategy, with a compulsory first course and three strategy-linked electives from a choice of eight.

Oxford Brookes University, School of Business

Address: Wheatley Campus, Wheatley, Oxford OX33 1HX
Tel: 01865 485920   Fax: 01865 485830
EMail: mba@brookes.ac.uk/mdp@hcm.brookes.ac.uk
Internet: www.brooks.ac.uk

Dean: Professor Mary Benwell

MBA Admissions Officer: Jackie Carter

MBA Programmes
Full-time MBA; Part-time MBA; Open Learning MBA

Programme Details	Full-time	Part-time	Open Learning
Duration	1 year	2 years	2 years
Class Contact	12-15 hours per week		n/a
Commencement	September	September	September/March
Which evening/day		Wednesday	
Application deadline	August	August	August/February
GMAT Yes/No	May be required	May be required	May be required
Fees EC/Overseas	£7,650	£7,650	£7,650
Annual student intake	60	30	60
Average student age	28	35	30
Min. required experience	2 years	2 years	2 years
%EC/Overseas	30/70	96/4	65/35
%Men/Women	67/33	67/33	70/30
Number of Professors	1	1	1
Number of Academic Staff	95+	95+	95+
Number of elective courses	20	20	20
Assessment: Exams/Assignments	Both	Both	Both
Dissertation/Project	Both	Both	Both

Additional Information
International Links: Links with more than 100 business schools in Europe, USA, Asia, Africa, and Australasia

Library hours: Term-time: 0900-2100 (Mon-Thurs); 0900-1800 (Fri); 1000-1600 (Sat & Sun). Out of term: 0900-1700 (Mon-Thurs)

OXFORD
BROOKES
UNIVERSITY

*Preparing you for the Challenge
of Senior Management*

AN MBA
CONCERNED WITH AN
INCREASING GLOBAL
MARKET PLACE

- Enrol with Britain's No 1 New University*
- 3 Flexible Study Modes: full time (1 year)
  part time (2 years)   open learning (2 years)
- Programme includes:

  Understanding complex operating environments

  Managing and developing organisations and
  resources

  Developing personal and managerial effectiveness

  Advancing managerial specialisms through
  a wide choice of electives
- Entry to those with a degree and/or relevant
  work experience

*The Times Good University Guide 1996, 1997

FOR BROCHURES/FURTHER INFORMATION, PLEASE CONTACT:

Jackie Carter, School of Business, Oxford Brookes University, Wheatley Campus,
Wheatley, Oxon OX33 1HX. Tel: 01865 485920. Fax: 01865 485905. E-mail: mba@brookes.ac.uk

IT facilities: 24 hour access in Wheatley; 700 computer terminals and PCs (all sites)

Other information: The MBA is a flexible course allowing transfer between modes of study

School Description

Oxford Brookes was founded in 1865 and granted University status in 1992. The School of Business provides courses at undergraduate and postgraduate level for over 2,000 students from all over the world.

The quality of teaching constantly produces outstanding results. Members of the faculty from the School of Business and visiting faculty have significant business experience, and many are actively involved in consultancy and research in addition to teaching.

Most students have considerable business experience, and the numbers on courses are kept small. Interactive teaching methods predominate, with an emphasis on workshops, seminars, and presentations.

The Oxford Brookes multi-mode MBA is based at the Wheatley Campus, set in 65 acres of parkland just a few miles from the centre of Oxford and only two miles from Junction 8 of the M40. The Oxford Brookes campuses at Headington, Oxford are also open to MBA students, and are linked to Wheatley by a free bus service. Facilities for sport and leisure are excellent, and a wide range of residential accommodation is available on the campus and nearby.

Oxford is 50 miles to the west of London and can be reached in about one hour by car, bus or train. The historic city provides the perfect setting for a period of intensive study. It is a renowned centre of learning with many unique traditions, beautiful buildings and a wonderful atmosphere. All this serves to provide an ideal environment and focus for the MBA programme.

Oxford University, Said Business School

Address: The Radcliffe Infirmary, Woodstock Road, Oxford OX2 6HE
Tel: 01865 228477   Fax: 10865 228471
EMail: enquiries@sbs.ox.ac.uk
Internet: www.sbs.ox.uk

Professor John Kay

MBA Admissions Officer: Mrs Alison Mills

MBA Programmes
Full-time MBA

Programme Details	Full-time
Duration	1 year
Commencement	October
Application deadline	March 31
GMAT Yes/No	Yes
Fees EC/Overseas	£15,000
Annual student	120
Average student age	20
Min. required expreience	2 years
%EC/Overseas	30/70
%Men/Women	80/20
Number of Professors	14
Number of Academic Staff	28
Number of elective courses	6
Assessment: Exams/Assignments	Both
Dissertation/Project	P

Additional Information
IT facilities: Workstations linked to University data network, providing access to local databases and information systems, and, through the internet, to worldwide electronic resources; access to information databases such as Datastream, Reuters and Mintel; IT Drop-In Centre and Help Desk provides access to full IT facilities and technical support

School Description
The one-year full-time Oxford MBA is an intellectually challenging programme. The course is designed to combine integrated management teaching with courses which open up broader strategic horizons, drawing on a variety of experts from the wider University community. In its teaching, the MBA is characterised by the traditional Oxford tutorial method, with its close attention to the needs of the individual. The degree is grounded on knowledge rather than management jargon. Its structure provides an integrative approach to the study of management. Modern in outlook, the programme does not simply reproduce the conventional functions of management. Rather, it aims to fuse them into a broader strategic view of the company and that environment in which it operates. Throughout the course there is a strong emphasis on career development and on equipping students for lifelong management learning.

In the summer of the MBA course, students spend two months working with a company or organisation on a specific business study project. This gives students the chance to sharpen their research and analytical skills, and to test and apply the lessons and skills that they have already learnt in the MBA.

As well as belonging to the University, MBA students also become members of an individual college. Colleges provide accommodation, meals, sports and social facilities. Most importantly, they bring together academics and students from a wide cross-section of backgrounds to live and work together.

Oxford is the oldest university, in the English-speaking world, and with its 2,000 senior academics and its 100 faculties, departments and specialist institutes, has become a byword for academic achievement. It draws faculty and students from around the globe, and the Oxford MBA programme fully reflects this internationalism.

University of Paisley

Address: Distance Learning MBA, High Street, Paisley PA1 2BE
Tel: 0141 848 3391   Fax: 10141 848 3395
EMail: kraw-em0@paisley.ac.uk
Director: Mr Kirk Ramsey
MBA Admissions Officer: Mr Wojciech Krawczyk

MBA Programmes
Marketing MBA; Real Estate Management MBA; TQM MBA – all by distance learning

Programme Details	Distance Learning
Duration	3 years
Class Contact	n/a
Commencement	Jan/April/July/Oct
GMAT Yes/No	No
Fees EC/Overseas	£7,500
Annual student intake	100
Average student age	30
Min. required	3 years
%EC/Overseas:	0/100
%Men/Women	70/30
Number of Professors	3
Assessment: Exams/Assignments	Both
Dissertation/Project	Both

Additional Information
International Links: Sites in Hong Kong, Bombay, UAE, Singapore, Pakistan

School Description
The University has pioneered new levels of understanding and developed innovative approaches to tackling vital issues in all areas of management and economics. Its links with industry and commerce extend well beyond the local environment to encompass both national and international companies, as well as major agencies such as Scottish Enterprise and the National Health Service. The Distance Learning programmes take advantage of the University's history of top quality education in business and management studies.

The Distance Learning MBA is ideal for the growing number of managers who wish to develop their careers and enjoy all the benefits of a university while still maintaining their working and family life. The programme is designed to ensure the best delivery and support of all its courses, and all courses are fully validated by the University. The Distance Learning programmes are fully supported through an online facility known as 'Cyber Campus'; this provides an excellent communication channel for students, staff, and local tutors, avoiding the sense of isolation experienced by some students on conventional distance learning programmes.

The electronic bulletin board supports Email, teleconferencing, classroom forums, online reference libraries, and Internet access.

The electronic support system has proven very effective, offering participants the opportunity to study for an MBA at literally any location whilst benefiting from the intellectual exchange from regular contact with course tutors, students, and subject experts.

University of Plymouth Business School

Address: Drake Circus, Plymouth PL4 8AA
Tel: 01752 232859   Fax: 01752 232859
EMail: postgrad.@pbs.plym.ac.uk
Dean: Professor Peter Jones
MBA Admissions Officer: Andy Paddon

MBA Programmes
Full-time MBA; Part-time MBA; MBA (Operations Management)

Programme Details	Full-time	Part-time	Part-time Operations Management
Duration	1 year	3 years	3 years
Class Contact	600 hours	600 hours	600 hours
Commencement	September	September	September
Which evening/day		Monday/ Wednesday	On application
Application deadline	July	July	July
GMAT Yes/No	No	No	No
Fees EC/Overseas	Approx £6,000	Approx £6,000	Approx £6,000
Annual student intake	25	15-20	10
Average student age	25	35	35
Min. required		3 years	3 years
%EC/Overseas	20/80	100/0	100/0
%Men/Women	50/50	60/40	90/10
Number of Professors	4	4	4
Number of Academic Staff	84	84	84
Number of elective courses	2	2	2
Assessment: Exams/Assignments	Both	Both	Both
Dissertation/Project	Both	Both	Both

Additional Information
Electives not readily available elsewhere: Strategic Marketing for Non-profit Sectors

School Description
The University of Plymouth Business School is the centre for management education in the South West, and is located in modern buildings in the city centre, close to the historic waterfront of Sutton Harbour. The faculty's main objective is to enhance participants' capabilities in lifelong learning and research, and a competency orientated approach is taken.

All MBA modules are designed to provide participants with the latest knowledge and management theories to enable them to contribute positively and competently in their business environment. The School has particular strengths and expertise in the fields of business management and marketing.

Postgraduate students have a specially dedicated Management Suite including a computer room and lounge. Previous MBA programme participants have been appointed to senior management positions in a whole range of industries in both the public and private sectors.

Plymouth is located in one of the most attractive parts of the UK, set between the sea and Dartmoor National Park. Its unique position means that a wide range of activities is available locally (various watersports, outward bound activities on Dartmoor, dry skiing and iceskating) as well as the normal facilities provided by a modern city.

University of Portsmouth Business School

Address: Univeristy of Portsmouth, Locksway Road, Milton, Southsea, Hampshire PO4 8JF
Tel: 01705 844056   Fax: 01705 844319
EMail: brownj@pbs.port.ac.uk
Director: Michael Townsend
MBA Admissions Officer: Jill Brown

MBA Programmes
Full-time MBA; Part-time MBA; Global MBA (Full-time)

Programme Details	Full-time	Part-time	Global
Duration	1 year	2½ years	2 years
Class Contact			
Commencement	September	Sept and Feb	Sept and Jan
Which evening/day		Stage 1 Mon; Stage 2 Tues/Wed	
Application deadline	14 September 1998	14 Sept 98, 25 Jan 99	August
Fees EC/Overseas	on application	on application	
Annual student intake	30	40	30
Min. required		2 years	
Number of Professors		6	
Number of Academic Staff		23	
Number of elective			
Assessment: Exams/Assignments	Both	Both	Both
Dissertation/project	D	Both	Both

School Description
The Portsmouth MBA can be studied by either part-time or full-time study modes, depending on individual circumstances. The part-time mode requires attendance on one afternoon and evening per week; the full-time mode obviously requires a more intense attendance pattern. Whichever mode is chosen, the course content is the same and reflects the strong blend of academic and work-place application that distinguishes the Portsmouth programme.

Students must complete a number of core and elective subjects, all set at the strategic level and demanding a high level of critical analysis. There is a wide choice of electives enabling students to study subjects which can assist their career development and interests. Assessment is by both assignment (often work-based) and examination, reflecting some of the key values of the programme.

Students may also study for the award through the Global MBA which requires them to study in Portsmouth for the first semester and then one of six universities in the USA with whom the University of Portsmouth has established strong links, for the second semester. On completion of the taught part of the course, after one year, students must join an organisation, anywhere in the world, to complete their project.

The Portsmouth MBA is delivered by highly qualified staff, most of whom have considerable industrial experience. Teaching embraces a range of techniques including lectures, seminars, workshops, residentials, presentations, role plays, videos, case studies, group work and visits to local organisations. Based on the south coast, Portsmouth Business School occupies a self-contained and attractive site. London is just over an hour away by train and Europe is easily reached via the nearby continental ferry port.

THE PORTSMOUTH MBA PROGRAMME

This 2-year programme, designed for those who hold or aspire to senior general management positions, offers you:

- full-time, part-time, fast-track or global route;
- opportunity to study in USA through Global MBA;
- a practical, industry-relevant approach, with an international focus.

For full details please contact:

Carol Shepherd,
MBA Course Secretary,
Portsmouth Business School,
Locksway Road,
Milton, Portsmouth
PO4 8JF

Telephone: (+44) 1705 844039
Facsimile: (+44) 1705 844319
E-mail: shepherdc@pbs.port.ac.uk
URL: http://www.port.ac.uk

A Centre of Excellence for University Teaching and Research

University of Portsmouth

Queen's School of Management

Address: Lanyon Building, Queen's University of Belfast, Belfast BT1 7NN
Tel: 01232 335381   Fax: 01232 248372
EMail: m.peoples@qub.ac.uk
Internet: www.qub.ac.uk/mgt/
Director: Professor Philip Kitchen
MBA Admissions Officer: Stirling Wisener

MBA Programmes
Part-time Executive MBA

Programme Details	Part-time
Duration	2
Class Contact	24
Commencement	September
Which evening/day	Friday
Application deadline	April (Late apps. considered on their merits).
GMAT Yes/No	Yes
Fees EC/Overseas	£7,500
Annual student intake	25

Individual programmes accredited by the Association of MBAs are indicated by a tick

Min. required	3 years
Number of Professors	7
Number of Academic Staff	24
Number of elective courses	8
Assessment: Exams/Assignments	Both
Dissertation/Project	D

Additional Information
International Links: Usual support services

Library hours: Usual support services

IT facilities: Usual support services

School Description
The Queen's University MBA is a part-time day release programme which extends over two years. It is aimed primarily at public and private sector organisations in Northern Ireland and the border counties of the Republic of Ireland. It is targeted at those in middle management who will be tommorow's top executives; it facilitates progression from technical specialism into general management; and is an approach to management education which aims to develop executive potential by giving a broad understanding of business and management. It aims to develop the following core competencies: development of management skills and techniques; self awareness as a manager and leader; increased personal confidence; enhanced promotional opportunities.

The components of the MBA programme are: Year 1: (Semester 1) Principles of Strategy; Management Information Systems; Marketing Management; Financial Statement Literacy

Year 1: (Semester 2) Organisational Behaviour; Information Resource Management; Negotiating; Research Methods

Year 2: (Semester 1) Leadership; Operations Mangement; Corporate Finance; Advanced Information Resource Management

Year 3: (Semester 2) Value Creation by Management. Students can also select three electives from eight offered, which vary from year to year but may include global marketing management and advanced strategic management.

The University of Reading, The Management Unit

Address: Building 22, London Road, Reading RG1 5AQ

Tel: 0118 931 8180   Fax: 0118 931 6539

EMail: mgt.unit@reading.ac.uk

Internet: www.rdg.ac.uk/MGT

Director: Dennis Beard

MBA Programmes
Open Learning MBA

Programme Details	*Opening Learning*
Duration	22 months
Class Contact	Monthly workshop
Commencement	January/March/June/September/October/November
Which evening/day	Varies
Application deadline	Phone for details
GMAT Yes/No	Not usually

Schools offering an Association of MBAs-accredited programme are indicated by a roundel

Fees EC/Overseas	£6,490
Annual student intake	150
Average student age	35
Min. required experience	4 years
%EC/Overseas	90/10
%Men/Women	65/35
Number of Academic Staff	44
Number of elective courses	6
Assessment: Exams/Assignments	Both
Dissertation/Project	D

Additional Information

Library hours: Term time: 0900-2215 (Mon-Thurs); 0900-1900 (Fri); 0900-1230 (Sat); 1400-1800 (Sun)

School Description

The Reading MBA is a stimulating and practical programme that enables and empowers managers to develop their potential as proactive, responsive, and responsible individuals who can engage hearts and minds in the management process. The programme focuses on business mastery in its widest sense, with a commitment to quality and excellence.

The open learning approach is holistic and rooted in the organisation so that work and study are fully integrated. Assignments are tailored by students to reflect individual and organisational experience and needs. Rigorous and challenging academic knowledge underpins the course material, and action learning ensures transfer of knowledge to the workplace.

The Management Unit (founded in 1990) provides a portfolio of Open Learning Modular Management Development Programmes from first line management to senior executive options such as the MBA and the Masters Strategic Option Programme. To date, the Unit has registered students across all its programmes from a wide spectrum of industry, commerce and local government.

A fundamental principle of the programme is that students are able to compare their performance with best practice, through the use of first class learning materials and a process of continuous assessment of work-related assignments, projects, and dissertations. Other facilities which contribute to their overall development include monthly half-day and full-day workshops led by visiting lecturers, professors and consultants, tutorials, residential workshops, and group-led activities.

The main university campus at Whiteknights is large and modern and features a rural history museum, museums of Greek archaeology and zoology, a film theatre, and an active Music Department with sub-departments of Film and Drama. The London Road campus, which houses the Management Unit, dates from 1904; it hosts a diverse range of facilities and activities.

Individual programmes accredited by the Association of MBAs are indicated by a tick

The Robert Gordon University, Aberdeen Business School

Address: Kepplestone Mansion, Viewfield Road, Aberdeen AB15 7AW
Tel: 01224 263112   Fax: 01224 263100
EMail: s.glenn@rgu.ac.uk
Director: Mr Alex Mackay
MBA Admissions Officer: Sharon Glenn

MBA Programmes
International MBA Full-time Modular; Part-time MBA Evenings/Weekends Modular/Distance

Programme Details	Full-time	Part-time
Duration	1 year	2½ years
Class Contact	500 hours	500 hours
Commencement	September 1998	September 1998
Which evening/day		Yr 1 Mon/Weds; Yr 2 Tues/Thurs
Application deadline	August 1998	August 1998
GMAT Yes/No	Yes (non-graduating overseas)	
Fees EC/Overseas	£6,500	£6,500
Annual student intake	30	30
Average student age	33	33
Min. required experience	3 years	3 years
%EC/Overseas	25/75	86/14
%Men/Women	70/30	70/30
Number of Professors	3	
Number of Academic Staff	50	
Number of elective courses	3	
Assessment: Exams/Assignments	Both	Both
Dissertation/Project	P	P

Additional Information
IT facilities: Extensive
Electives not readily available elsewhere: Offshore Management

School Description
The School has 50 academic staff (all with excellent academic qualifications and a wealth of business experience, often at senior management level) and ten support staff, involved in the teaching of some 800 undergraduates and 300 postgraduate students. The School has five academic divisions: Accountancy; Business Policy and Marketing; Economics and Finance; Human Resource Management; Operations, Logistics and Information Management. It enjoys extensive and well-established links with local and international organisations, developed through a range of teaching, undergraduate placements, research and consulting activities. The School has an excellent record of graduates obtaining appropriate employment; students are able to make use of the University's Careers Service and can capitalise on the School's links with industry.

The MBA programme is delivered in English. A wide range of teaching and learning strategies are adopted, with extensive use being made of case studies to ensure a good blend of theory and best practice. The emphasis is on student involvement, and on drawing from the group the benefit of the considerable experience that students bring to the course. Wherever possible, small group work and teaching are employed. Frequent use is made of outside speakers.

All learning is supported by an excellent information technology environment. Because the School is part of a large faculty, appropriate supervisors are available to meet the specific requirements of each student's dissertation.

Rented accommodation is available in Aberdeen for married students wishing to bring their families with them. Aberdeen has an excellent range of schools and health facilities. For 1998/99 session the Business School will move to new purpose built accommodation within the city but enjoying a wooded site adjacent to one of the city's major rivers.

The majority of the students are self-funded or have company sponsorship, but there are a limited number of bursaries on the full-time programme.

Roffey Park Management Institute

Address: Forest Road, Horsham, West Sussex RH12 4TD
Tel: 01293 851644   Fax: 01293 851565
Director: Val Hammond
MBA Admissions Officer: Kenneth Bull

MBA Programmes
Part-time MBA in Applied General Management by Self Managed Learning

Programme Details	Part-time
Duration	2 years
Class Contact	7 x 1-week residentials + 1 day per month set meetings or 11 x weekends + 1 week summer school + set meetings
Commencement	January/May
Which evening/day	N/A
Application deadline	No set deadlines – applications processed as they are received
GMAT Yes/No	No (Watson GLASER used)
Fees EC/Overseas	£15,300
Annual student intake	50
Average student age	36
Min. required experience	5 years
%EC/Overseas	75/25
%Men/Women	60/40
Number of Professors	5
Number of Academic Staff	19
Assessment: Exams/Assignments	A
Dissertation/Project	Both

Additional Information
International Links: University of Jyvaskyla (Finland): ADQ Consultores, Lisbon (Portugal)

Library hours: 9-5pm

IT facilities: 2 PCs

Other information: General Management Development Programmes, MSc and Research. In-company Programmes

---

Individual programmes accredited by the Association of MBAs are indicated by a tick

School Description

Roffey Park Management Institute offers a unique approach to MBA studies by using self-managed learning, a method which enables managers to design a rigorous learning programme that is tailored both to their needs and those of their organisation. Managers work in small groups or Learning Sets to help them learn and to challenge each other's thinking throughout the two-year programme. The self-managed learning approach creates a climate where effective thinking is valued, where assumptions and styles of managing are challenged, and where excellent learning leads to excellence in action.

Roffey Park is particularly strong in the areas of Change Management, Organisation Behaviour, Human Resource Management, Leadership and Teamworking, Cross-cultural Studies, and Personal Development. The MBA will appeal to experienced managers who wish to develop general management skills and knowledge, and also to grow and develop as people.

The Roffey Park MBA is validated by the University of Sussex and is offered in two modes: seven one-week residential blocks, or eleven weekends and a summer school. Managers also meet in Learning Sets once a month throughout the two-year period. Set in the beautiful surroundings of the Sussex countryside, the Institute offers a range of sports facilities (including a swimming pool and a gym).

Royal Agricultural College, School of Business

Address: Cirencester, Gloucester, Gloucestershire GL7 6JS
Tel: 01285 652531   Fax: 01285 641659
EMail: admissions@royagcol.ac.uk
Dean: Dr Jonathan Turner

MBA Programmes
Full-time European MBA in Food and Agribusiness

Programme Details	Full-time
Duration	1 year and dissertation
Commencement	September
Application deadline	June
GMAT Yes/No	No
Fees EC/Overseas	£5,500
Annual student intake	20 max
Average student age	26
Min. required experience	3 years
%EC/Overseas	90/10
%Men/Women	90/10
Number of Professors	2
Number of Academic Staff	10
Assessment: Exams/Assignments	Both
Dissertation/Project	Both

Additional Information
International Links: Fachhochschule Nurtingen (Germany); Universidad Politecnica de Valencia (Spain); Groupe ESA, Angers (France); Larenstein International Agricultural College, Deventer (The Netherlands)

Library hours: 0900-2100

IT facilities: 3 computer labs – networked

Other information: Studies may commence in the Netherlands, or in the UK, then conclude at any of the five participating schools; 20 taught weeks, 5-wek project, plus Dissertation

School Description
The Business School is dedicated to supporting the needs of the agribusiness, agricultural, food and land management sectors. It has links with over 50 industry associates and a 90+ per cent record of students in work by Christmas following graduation. The School runs an undergraduate business programme and four Masters programmes. It uses an extensive associate lecturer and visiting professor network.

The College has approximately 700 students, with a full range of sporting and welfare activities. Bursaries are available, and loans can be arranged at preferential conditions through a leading Dutch bank.

School of Management, Royal Holloway University of London

Address: Egham, Surrey TW20 0EX
Tel: 01784 443783   Fax: 01784 471517
EMail: m.berry-anton@rhbnc.ac.uk
Internet: www.rhbnc.ac.uk

Dean: Dr Mairi Maclean

MBA Admissions Officer: Maggie Berry Anton

MBA Programmes
Full-time International Management MBA

Programme Details	Full-time
Duration	12 months
Class Contact	20 hours
Commencement	September
Application deadline	rolling – preference to those received by 30 June
GMAT Yes/No	Yes
Fees EC/Overseas	£6,550/£7,725 current
Annual student intake	40/60
Average student age	27
Min. required experience	2 years
%EC/Overseas	33/66
%Men/Women	50/50
Number of Professors	3
Number of Academic Staff	28
Number of elective courses	1 with choice of 3 regional areas of study
Assessment: Exams/Assignments	Both
Dissertation/Project	D

Additional Information
IT facilities: 24 hour computing access. Dedicated Resources Room

Electives not readily available elsewhere: Asia Pacific Business; North American Business; European Business

School Description

Royal Holloway's MBA in International Management is one of several MBAs offered by the University of London, but is distinguished from other London MBAs in numerous ways. Major international firms contributed to curriculum design to ensure that the real needs of managers are met. Attention is paid to historical, political, and cultural forces which forcefully impact upon firms and industries, and to economic factors. Enrolment is deliberately limited.

There are five elements to the MBA; four major teaching blocks and the Research Dissertation. International Management explores the role of major functional specialisms from the perspective of the whole firm; International Business Research provides a comprehensive introduction to quantitative and qualitative methods as mutually reinforcing ways to tackle business problems; International and Comparative Business offers a broad treatment of the major elements necessary to gain knowledge of worldwide economic developments; the Area Study option complements ICB by concentrating on a major regional trading block. The Research Dissertation builds upon the theoretical understanding, empirical knowledge, and methodological skills taught during these taught courses. Value-added activities play a crucial role: business seminars (held several evenings each term), when senior members of the business community address particular issues, and include question and answer periods; management skills development sessions offer practical opportunities to hone important skills in a supportive environment.

Royal Holloway occupies a charming 120-acre site close to Windsor Great Park, in a much less densely populated and far more relaxed area than Central London. However, there is easy access to Central London (20 miles away, 32 minutes by train from Waterloo Station) and Heathrow Airport. Internationalism works two ways within the School, approximately 60 per cent of the intake is from outside the EU (with 25 countries represented), and 40 per cent of the teaching staff obtained their first degrees outside the UK. MBA students benefit from a purpose-built lecture theatre, conference hall, seminar rooms, and a dedicated Resource Room with IT facilities, as well as a computer-based training room.

The Management School, University of Salford

Address: Salford, Greater Manchester M5 4WT
Tel: 0161 295 5530   Fax: 0161 295 5022
EMail: d.c.lavender@man-sch.salford.ac.uk
Internet: www.salford.ac.uk/man-sch

Director: Mr David Lavender

MBA Admissions Officer: Mr David Lavender

MBA Programmes
Full-time MBA; Part-time MBA

Programme Details	Full-time	Part-time
Duration	1 year	2½ years
Class Contact	415	420
Commencement	October	October
Which evening/day		Monday/Saturday
Application deadline	None	None
GMAT Yes/No	No	
Fees EC/Overseas	£6,850	£6,300
Annual student intake	40	30

MANAGEMENT
School

MBA Degree

This is a broadly based degree offering those with no previous qualifications in business the opportunity to gain this widely recognised qualification. The course is offered on a part time or full time basis and introduces you by stages, to the foundation subjects of business, a series of core courses in business strategy and offers a range of specialist electives.

MSc Degree

This specialist degree programme offers those who have had some undergraduate experience of business studies, the opportunity to specialise in some depth in an area of their choice. Courses are offered on a part time and full time basis and cover Human Resource Management, Finance, Marketing, Information Technology, Transport, Management Application and Management Development.

For full details write to: Director of Admissions, University of Salford, Salford, M5 4WT. Fax: 0161 295 5022. Tel: 0161 295 5530. Email: D.C.-Lavender@man-sch.salford.ac.uk

Average student age	26	29
Min. required experience	2 years	2 years
%EC/Overseas	30/70	100/0
%Men/Women	60/40	75/25
Number of Professors	5	5
Number of Academic Staff	27	14
Number of elective courses	15	6
Assessment: Exams/Assignments	Both	Both
Dissertation/Project	D	D

Additional Information

Library hours: 0900-2100 daily

IT facilities: University IT facilities fully networked (24 hours); Management School facilities fully networked (24 hours)

School Description

At Salford we are proud of our vibrant postgraduate community of over 2,000 students working within the supportive context provided by the Research and Graduate College within which the Management School is the provider and local point of all management and business related postgraduate teaching, training and education.

The Salford MBA programme was first launched in 1990 and has attracted students from more than 60 countries during that time. The programme has three main components – the MBA, the Advanced Diploma and the Access Diploma Courses. The full-time MBA has been designed for those whose first degree (or equivalent overseas qualification) is outside the area of business. Former students have typically been graduates in Engineering, Science or the Arts. The part-time MBA programme is a practically based course which combines skill and application

Individual programmes accredited by the Association of MBAs are indicated by a tick

with the development of knowledge and theory and is able to give a real return to sponsoring organisations from the very early weeks of the programme.

The University campus is located in a 34 acre park and riverside site in the heart of Manchester which has a population of 2.5 million. There is an international airport servicing the Far East, USA, Europe. Students enjoy access to concert halls, theatres, art galleries and some of the world's most famous sporting locations, for example Manchester United FC, Old Trafford cricket ground.

SEMS University of Surrey

Address: Stag Hill, Guildford, Surrey GU2 5XH
Tel: 01483 259347   Fax: 01483 259511
EMail: sems@surrey.ac.uk
Internet: www.sems.surrey.ac.uk

Director: Professor P R Gamble

MBA Admissions Officer: Mrs S Gemmill

MBA Programmes
Full-time MBA; Part-time MBA (evening); Distance Learning MBA (UK base); Distance Learning MBA (overseas base)

Programme Details	Full-time	Part-time	Distance Learning
Duration	1 year	2 years	2 years
Class Contact	200+	200+	200+
Commencement	September	September	September
Which evening/day		Tues/Thurs	
Application deadline	N/A	N/A	N/A
GMAT Yes/No	No	No	No
Fees EC/Overseas	£8,250	£8,500	£8,500
Annual student intake	25-30	25-30	25-30
Average student age	27	34	38
Min. required experience	3 years	3 years	3 years
%EC/Overseas	50/50	100/0	40/60
%Men/Women	50/50	70/30	80/20
Number of Professors	1	1	1
Number of Academic Staff	20	20	20
Number of elective courses	6	6	4
Assessment: Exams/Assignments	Both	Both	Both
Dissertation/Project	D	D	D

Additional Information
Library hours: 0900-2200 (during semester); 0900-1700 (during vacations)

IT facilities: 6 laboratories (most open 24 hours per day, seven days per week): campus network utilises FDDI and Ethernet, with connections to the national Super JANET network for access to the Internet

Electives not readily available elsewhere: Export strategy; Decision Making in the European Union; Law of the European Union

Other information: Course fees include set textbooks. A proportion of course delivery is supplemented with electronic support packages

School Description

SEMS is located in new, purpose-built premises on the University of Surrey campus. A significant investment has been made to equip the School with an excellent work environment, attractive seminar rooms and a sophisticated computing and electronic communications system.

SEMS is organised on the Handy Shamrock model of a relatively small core of full-time faculty members supported by a large number of well-qualified and experienced associate staff. Students and staff work together in improving the quality of academic life, with student representation on all key committees.

The MBA programme is offered full-time over one year or part-time over two years. A tutor-supported distance learning version is available in the UK and at several centres overseas, offered over two years. Effective communication links between overseas-based students and staff are provided by telephone, email, fax and teleconference facilities.

The MBA consists of eight modular courses, six of which are core and a dissertation. A wide range of electives is available, with new topics being added from time to time as current research identifies their relevance. An extensive range of sporting activity is available, including cricket, rugby, squash, football (both soccer and American), badminton, tennis, martial arts, climbing and gliding. The University also has a well-equipped professional Health and Fitness club, comprising 60 working stations and around 40 classes in aerobics, step, circuit training etc are held weekly.

The University Careers Service, through its highly experienced careers advisors, provides assistance and guidance on career opportunities. In addition, a comprehensive range of brochures and reference directories is available to assist students in researching and locating appropriate employers.

Sheffield Business School, Sheffield Hallam University

Address: Business and Information Technology Centre, Pond Street, Sheffield S1 1WB
Tel: 0114 2252820   Fax: 0114 2255268
Internet: www.shu.ac.uk

MBA Admissions Officer: Ian Boraston
MBA Admissions Officer: Janet Kirkham

MBA Programmes
Full-time MBA; Part-time MBA; Part-time MBA Management for the Professions

Programme Details	Full-time ✔	Part-time ✔	Mgt for the Profs
Duration	1 year	3 years	2 years
Commencement	end Sept	end Sept + aft/eve weekender block mode	January block mode
Application deadline	August	August	December
GMAT Yes/No	Yes	No	No
Fees EC/Overseas	£7,750	£7,350	£7,740
Annual student intake	50	80	20
Average student age	27	30	30
Min. required experience	1st degreee or equiv	1st degree or post-e	1st degree or post-e
%EC/Overseas	25/75	100/0	100/0
%Men/Women	60/40	60/40	60/40

Number of Professors	7	7	7
Number of Academic Staff	80	80	80
Number of elective courses	3		
Assessment: Exams/Assignments	Both	Both	Both
Dissertaion/Project	Both	Both	Both

Additional Information
International Links: USA, Australia, France, Germany, Netherlands, Czech Republic

Library hours: 6 days per week, normally 0900-2100

IT facilities: 0900-2100 (Mon-Fri); 0900-1800 (Sat)

Other information: Recreation. Accommodation. Visiting speaker Programmes. Residentials (including overseas residential for full-time).

School Description
Sheffield Business School has established a national and international reputation for developing the potential of managers to make strategic contributions to their organisations. To meet the need of organisations in the 21st century, we have now brought together all our management education resources into the Sheffield Business School whose mission is to proved accessible, high quality personal and professional development for its individuals and corporate clients. Sheffield Business School has been delivering postgraduate and professional management development Programmes booth in the UK and around the world since the early 1980s. We have experience of providing a first class education to professional in a wide range of countries including Germany, France, Holland, Finland, Luxembourg, Czech Republic, Bulgaria, Poland, Singapore, Hong Kong, Taiwan, India a USA and the Gulf. Our long list of blue chip clients includes IBM, Hong Kong Shanghai Banking Corporation, Burton Group, American Express and many others.

Sheffield University Management School

Address: 9 Mappin Street, Sheffield S1 4DT
Tel: 0114 222 3346   Fax: 0114 2223348
EMail: sums@sheffield.ac.uk
Internet: www.sums.ac.uk

Dean: Mr Bob Morgan

MBA Admissions Officer: Ms Susan Heyes

MBA Programmes
Full-time MBAs in General Management Accounting; Financial Management; Marketing Management; International Business; Part-time Executive MBA

Programme Details	Full-time ✔	Part-time ✔
Duration	1 year	2 years
Class Contact	200 per semester	23 per module
Commencement	September	October
Which evening/day		Sun/Mon/Tues
Application deadline	August	July
GMAT Yes/No	Yes	Not applicable
Fees EC/Overseas	£6,820/£8,080	£11,500
Annual student intake	40-50	24
Average student age	28	36
Min. required experience	2 years	5 years
%EC/Overseas	30/70	90/10
%Men/Women	60/40	70/30
Number of Professors	9	9
Number of Academic Staff	50	
Number of elective courses	8	all modules tailored
Assessment: Exams/Assignments	Both	Both
Dissertation/Project	Both	D

Additional Information
International Links: Exchange MBA full-time with Aalborg, Denmark, EDHEC, Rennes France and Uppsale Sweden

Library hours: 0900-2130 (Mon-Thurs); 1000-1700 (Fri); 0900-1700 (Sat)

IT facilities: 5 labs within the school, exclusive use of own MBA lab plus off-site remote access

Electives not readily available elsewhere: Leisure Management; Fuel efficiency.

Other information: Nurseries/Playschemes for children of students; Careers Advice and CV preparation; Regional office advice on company projects/consultancy; Health and Counselling services; Chaplaincy and on site Management School prayers; Midland Bank bursary for returners to work.

School Description
Sheffield University Management School is one of the earliest UK Schools to offer the MBA and to be accredited by the Association of MBAs, rated 4 in the latest Research Assessment. Our aim continues to be to provide management education for those seeking a rewarding career.

All students enjoy modern facilities in the current purpose- built premises, opened in 1993. MBA students have their own computing laboratory and reading room. The St George's Library is directly opposite. Self-catering and in-hall accommodation can be arranged from £45 per week, some within walking distance, most within 2-3 miles. All appreciate the convenience and economy of short travel times.

The MBA programme aims to provide an international perspective to the principles and practice of management, satisfying the increasingly global customer and consumer needs. Six core modules across the breadth of disciplines in semester 1; in semester 2, some elect to specialise in Finance, International Business or Marketing, others choose wider electives to gain their MBA in General Management. The Dissertation is on a subject of own choice, supervised by the relevant specialist tutor. Each module is a balance of teaching, self-study and casework which is assessed by coursework and examinations. Projects can be on or off-campus.

The Executive MBA programme provides senior management in both public and private sectors with the opportunity to gain their MBA whilst continuing their key in-post roles. Based on modular assignments, every effort is made to ensure casework is focused on their individual company and delegate issues.

Situated within the city centre and close to all the facilities of a 24-hour city. Sports facilities are available on campus and within the city for sports specialists and the spectator.

Further details on courses, entry requirements, loans and bursaries available on request.

Southampton Business School

Address: Southampton Institute, East Park Terrace, Southampton SO14 0YN
Tel: 01703 319869   Fax: 01703 337438
EMail: June.Fletcher@solent.ac.uk
Dean: Dr John Latham
MBA Admissions Officer: June Fletcher

MBA Programmes
Full-time MBA; Part-time MBA (afternoon and evening); Part-time MBA (Marketing); Part-time MBA (Finance); Part-time MBA (Human Resource Management)

Programme Details	Full-time	Part-time
Duration	1yr/12 months	3 years
Class Contact	14 hours pw	7 hours pw
Commencement	September	October
Which evening/day	Wed/Thurs/Tues (according to level)	Wednesday/Thursday/ Tuesday (according to level)
Application deadline	August	September
GMAT Yes/No	No	No
Fees EC/Overseas	4,900/5,200	
Annual student intake	20	40
Average student age	25	30
Min. required experience	2 years	
%EC/Overseas	33/66	95/5
%Men/Women	70/30	70/30
Number of Professors	3	
Number of Academic Staff	75	
Number of elective courses	3	
Assessment: Exams/Assignments	Both	
Dissertation/Project	Both	

School Description

Southampton Business School is on the South Coast, just over an hour from London, by train, and within easy reach of Bournemouth, Portsmouth and Winchester. Its location is attractive to those who want the facilities of a major city, as well as those who prefer the quiet of the countryside.

Course members have access to excellent sports facilities and a high proportion of participants can be accommodated in custom-built halls of residence. IT and library facilities are constantly upgraded and a range of support services are available, from language classes to IT training.

The initial stage of the programme gives a good grounding in the areas thought necessary for all managers, but there is the opportunity to specialise at later stages of the programme.

University of Southampton, School of Management

Address:, Highfield, Southampton SO17 1BJ
Tel: 01703 593076   Fax: 01703 593844
EMail: ji@soton.ac.uk
Internet: www.soton.ac.uk~managment
Director: Dr Charles Wilkinson
MBA Admissions Officer: Mrs J Ingledow

MBA Programmes
Full-time MBA; Full-time Modular MBA; Part-time Modular MBA

Programme Details	Full-time	Part-time Modular	Full-time Modular
Duration	1 year	2-4 years	1 year
Class Contact	16	2-20	16-20
Commencement	September	September /February	September
Which evening/day		Varies (Student's Choice)	
Application deadline	August	August/January	August
GMAT Yes/No	No	No	Sometimes
Fees EC/Overseas	£8,000	£10,250	£10,250
Annual student intake	40	30	30
Average student age	25	32	29
Min. required		3 years	3 years
%EC/Overseas	60/40	100/0	80/20
%Men/Women	50/50	60/40	60/40
Number of Professors	6	6	6
Number of Academic Staff	30	30	30
Number of elective courses	8	10	10
Assessment: Exams/Assignments	Both	Both	Both
Dissertation/Project	D	D	D

Individual programmes accredited by the Association of MBAs are indicated by a tick

School Description

The Modular MBA is a high quality, well-established programme, designed for experienced managers with at least three years of relevant experience who can also satisfy the normal academic requirements for postgraduate study. On this programme, full-time and part-time students are taught together in ways which ensure that all participants can share and learn from the experience of others.

The Full-time MBA (non-modular) is a new programme which has been developed specifically for graduates without previous managerial experience. It is designed to be stimulating, exciting and challenging, providing bright graduates with an understanding of the key issues in modern management thought and practice.

New members of either programme will join an established management school which has particular expertise in the areas of Accounting, Finance, Management Science, Risk Management, and Information Systems. Programme lecturers are drawn principally from the School of Management and from other relevant departments of the University (such as Law and Economics) as well as from the world of consultancy and professional practice.

A limited number of bursaries are available for privately funded UK students. Students are normally required to have a good honours degree, but the School welcomes applicants with equivalent or overseas qualifications.

Southampton has around 30,000 students, and the entertainment opportunities are plentiful. These include an extensive variety of pubs, places to eat, live music for all tastes, and a multiplex cinema. On campus are a theatre, a film theatre, a concert hall, and a gallery for art and photographic exhibitions.

Southampton is on the South Coast with a mild, sunny climate by English standards! The ancient cathedral cities of Salisbury and Winchester, the beaches of Bournemouth, and the picturesque New Forest are all nearby. Southampton is an excellent centre for sailing and watersports, and offers a dri-ski slope as well as the usual sport facilities.

South Bank Business School

Address: 103 Borough Road, London SE1 0AA
Tel: 0171 815 8245   Fax: 0171 815 8280
Dean: Charles Fenech
MBA Admissions Officer: Lin Mansfield

MBA Programmes
Part-time Day and Part-time Evening MBAs; Full-time International Management MBA; European Management MBA

Programme Details	Full-time International Management	Part-time	European Management
Duration	1 year 3 months	2 years 3 months	1 year 3 months
Class Contact	18	6	18
Commencement	September	September	September (European P/T) January (UK South Bank)
Which evening/day		PTD: Wed PTE: Mon and Wed	
Application deadline	None	None	None
GMAT Yes/No	No	No	No

Fees EC/Overseas	£6,250/£7,900	£6,250/na	1st Sem (Europe Partners) variable; 2nd Sem (South Bank): £2,901
Annual student intake	25	50	50
Average student age	30	34	30
Min. required experience	2 years	2 years	2 years
%EC/Overseas	30/70	N/A	80/20
%Men/Women	60/40	65/35	60/40
Number of Professors	3	3	3
Number of Academic Staff	12	12	6
Number of elective courses	8	8	8
Assessment: Exams/Assignments	Both	Both	Both
Dissertation/Project	P	P	P

Additional Information

International Links: European Partners in Berlin (Germany), Mikkeli (Finland), Rennes (France), and Valencia (Spain)

Library hours: 0830-2100 mainly in term time; 1100-1700 (Sunday)

IT facilities: Extensive, available to 2100 (Mon-Fri) and to 1700 (Sat/Sun)

Other information: Wide range of multicultural societies and clubs; sports complex within Business School

School Description

South Bank University is a large, thriving university close to central London, situated only a mile from the Houses of Parliament, the City's financial centre, and the South Banks Arts Complex. There are excellent tube, bus and rail connections.

The Business School is one of the largest in the UK with over 4,000 full-time and part-time students. The academic staff of over 200 (plus visiting professors and research students) has an extensive range of research interests, and those on the MBA team possess considerable business experience across a wide range of sectors, extensive consultancy experience, and expert teaching skills. Strong international links exist with Europe, the Far East, and the Eastern Bloc.

The South Bank MBA (available in full-time, day releases and evening modes) caters for middle to senior managers from a diversity of backgrounds: private, public, and not-for- profit sectors. Designed to build on the skills, experience and ideas of its participants through extensive group work and workshops, the programme's emphasis is the development of practical skills and experience of direct use to the individual in the workplace. The use of staff with a wide range of practical management and consultancy experience reflects this. Residential weekends (often involving alumni from the School) form an integrative and consolidating function. Alumni play an increasingly important role in the School, providing a useful forum for networking and business ideas, and opportunities, industry and business presentations involving alumni are organised for existing course participants.

Small classes ensure each student's participation and more personal contact with teaching staff. Formal lectures present conceptual material, and participative sessions cover analytical components. A wide range of core studies is used, together with workshops, small group work and presentations. Sessions are generally pragmatic, workplace-orientated, and implementation-focused. MBA classes are held in the Abbey Conference Suite.

The Housing Office can help with accommodation in the University Hall, or with finding accommodation of the student's choice. Students have access to the new Perry Library, up-to-date computing facilities, online databases, modern language learning facilities, and a well-stocked Careers Library.

A career development loan scheme is available.

Individual programmes accredited by the Association of MBAs are indicated by a tick

Staffordshire University Business School

Address: Leek Road, Stoke-on-Trent ST4 2DF
Tel: 01782 294049   Fax: 01782 747006
EMail: bsajlw@staffs.ac.uk
Internet: www.staffs.ac.uk

Dean: C J Brownless

MBA Admissions Officer: Fatima Moran (Full-time); Mike Carrick (Part-time)

MBA Programmes
Full-time MBA; Evening MBA

Programme Details

	Full-time	Part-time
Duration	1 year	3 semesters
Class Contact	400 hours	
Commencement	September	September
Application deadline	August	September
GMAT Yes/No	No	No
Fees EC/Overseas	£4,950/£6,300	£3,100
Annual student intake	60	50
Average student age	23	31
Min. required experience	Nil	Nil
%EC/Overseas	10/90	
%Men/Women	60/40	70/30
Number of Professors	1	1
Number of Academic Staff	15	20
Number of elective courses	3	4
Assessment: Exams/Assignments	Both	Both
Dissertation/Project	D	D

Additional Information
Library hours: 0900-2100

IT facilities: Extensive

Other information: Fees include 4-day UK off-campus course + 1 week abroad course (e.g. USA)

School Description
The full-time course is closely integrated with alternative MSc courses in Marketing, European Management, Tourism Marketing, South-East Asian Management, and Finance.

The first term is a joint course with MBA and these other courses, and qualifies for CBA. A definite decision on MBA route is not needed until November. The second term gives an award of DBA, and it is possible to terminate at this stage. The third term is taught, but students must then continue with their dissertation until the end of September. Dissertation study can be based anywhere in the UK or overseas, and no return is normally necessary after July. Two off-campus study periods are included, one overseas.

The main advantages of Staffordshire University are its central UK location, its modest fee and living costs, the high international student element, and its strong reputation in Marketing and Strategic Management. The campus has full social/recreational facilities and is within the city. Bursaries are not available.

Schools offering an Association of MBAs-accredited programme are indicated by a roundel

Faculty of Management, University of Stirling

Address:, Stirling FK9 4LA
Tel: 01786 467415   Fax: 01786 450776
EMail: mba@stir.ac.uk
Internet: www.stir.ac.uk/management/mba
Dean: Professor L Sparks
Director: Dr P Rosa MBA
MBA Admissions Officer: Dr P Rosa

MBA Programmes
Full-time MBA; Retailing and Wholesaling MBA by Distance Learning; Public Service Management MBA Part-time; Health Care Management MBA Part-time

Programme Details	Full-time
Duration	1 year
Class Contact	280-300
Commencement	mid September
Application deadline	none
GMAT Yes/No	no
Fees EC/Overseas	£7,000/£8,600 1997/98 level
Annual student intake	40
Average student age	26
Min. required experience	depends on academic
%EC/Overseas	43/57
%Men/Women	57/43
Number of Professors	19
Number of Academic Staff	120
Number of elective courses	18
Assessment: Exams/Assignments	Both
Dissertation/Project	D

Additional Information
Library hours: Semester (Mon-Fri) 0900-1200; (Saturday) 0900-1600; (Sunday) 1200-2000

IT facilities: There is a state-of-the-art computing network, linking hundreds of microcomputers and UNIX workstations to central Hewlett-Packard facilities providing file storage, computation, printing and database access. JANET (the Joint Academic Network) provides electronic access to other UK universities and throughout the world. The Faculty of Management and the University have extensive networked laboratory provisions for students. On-line information retrieval and work station providing access to CDD-Roms (in library).

School Description
The University of Stirling was founded in 1967 and is noted for its research excellence and its flexible and innovative approach to teaching, which seeks to cut across conventional barriers between disciplines. The campus is situated two miles from the historic town of Stirling and is one of the most beautiful in Britain, with the teaching buildings and residences set in 300 acres of landscaped parkland, which includes a loch and the splendid Airthrey Castle, built in 1791.

The Faculty of Management is one of the largest University centres of management education in the UK, with over 120 academic staff. Through its six constituent departments, it offers a wide range of programmes covering all areas of management, as well as niche specialisms in areas such as Entrepreneurship, Retail Management, Quality Management and Human Resources Management.

The Faculty has a flourishing postgraduate section, with around 500 postgraduate students undertaking either one of the 25 specialist taught programmes or a research based higher degree. Several courses are available on a part-time basis whilst others can be undertaken by distance learning. A number of specialist centres have been established within the departments to provide a focus for research activity and encourage links with industry and outside organisations through consultancy and management development courses.

All departments are actively engaged in research and invite applications from suitably qualified candidates who wish to pursue a Higher degree by research. A full list of staff research interests is available on request.

Results for Departments appraised in recent SHEFC Teaching Assessments have been extremely positive, with 'excellent' and 'highly satisfactory' ratings.

Stirling has taken the lead among British Universities in bringing together media, computing, networking and library facilities into an integrated information service. The Library houses over 450,000 books and 2,500 journals, and has extensive facilities which include individual study carrels and rooms for audio-visual work. The University has impressive sporting facilities.

Strathclyde Graduate Business School

Address: 199 Cathedral Street, Glasgow G4 0QU
Tel: 0800 661966   Fax: 0141 552 8851
EMail: admissions@sgbs.strath.ac.uk
Internet: www.strath.ac.uk/Departments/SGBS
Director: Professor Chris Greensted
MBA Admissions Officer: Meg Lavery

MBA Programmes
Full-time MBA; Part-time MBA; Mixed Mode MBA; Open Learning MBA; International MBA

Programme Details	Full-time ✔	Part-time ✔	Open-Learning ✔	Mixed Mode ✔
Duration	1 year	3 years	2½ years	2½ years
Class Contact	500	500	100 (approx)	
Commencement	October	October	anytime	October/April
Which evening/day		Tues and Thurs eves		
Application deadline	August/September	August/September	no deadline	September/March
GMAT Yes/No	if degree is non-UK	n/a	n/a	n/a
Fees EC/Overseas	£10,750	£8,925	£8,100	£10,600
Annual student intake	90	80	100+	20+
Average student age	31	32	33	31
Min. required experience	3 years	3 years	3 years	3 years
%EC/Overseas	74	4	20	29
%Men/Women	56/44	62/38	73/27	70/30

Number of Professors	49	49	49	49
Number of Academic Staff	220	220	220	220
Number of elective courses	40	40	40	40
Assessment: Exams/Assignments	Both	Both	Both	Both
Dissertation/Project	P	P	P	P

Additional Information

International Links: France; Turkey; Switzerland; Greece; Hong Kong; Malaysia; Singapore; Bahrain; Dubai; India (New Delhi, Mumbai)

Library hours: SGBS facilities: Business Information Service 0900-1900 (Mon-Thurs); 0900-1700 (Fri); 1100-1700 (Sat)

IT facilities: Two computer labs for SGBS only and access to all University facilities

School Description

Strathclyde Graduate Business School (SGBS) is responsible for the delivery of postgraduate and post-experience business education at the University of Strathclyde. It has been running an MBA programme since 1966, but in recent years has reorganised its delivery along flexible, credit- based lines that allow it to interlock most of its programmes with the MBA and to offer a variety of delivery systems that students can switch between if their circumstances change.

Strathclyde has pioneered the flexible, credit-based approach to the MBA degree. The School offers subsidiary, Certificate in Management and Diploma in Business as part of the programme, both of which count towards the MBA.

The MBA can be followed full-time, part-time, mixed mode or via open learning. There is also a joint programme with Groupe ESC Toulouse in France, where the first six months are spent at Strathclyde working in English and the second six months at Toulouse working in French.

All the Strathclyde MBA versions are very similar in structure, whatever the delivery system. Transfer between most systems is possible. The progarmme, divided into four stages progresses from a compulsory grounding in basic business knowledge to specialised or generalist elective courses and then a final project which can taken abroad. The School has particular areas of strength in Strategic Management, Scenario Planning. IT in Strategic Marketing, Decision-making Behaviour, and Human Resource Management.

The purpose-built school building accommodates teaching and administration and has good facilities including two computer laboratories, a Business Information Service and an audio visual centre. Students also have access to the main university library (350,000 volumes and 1,250 seats) and to very good on-campus sports facilities. On-campus accommodation is available.

University of Sunderland Business School

Address: St Peters Campus, St Peters Way, Sunderland SR6 0DD
Tel: 0191 5153127   Fax: 0191 5152308
EMail: mikemcdonnell@sunderland.ac.uk
Internet: www/sunderland.ac.uk

Director: Professor Graham Henderson

MBA Admissions Officer: Mike McDonnell; Ian Paterson

MBA Programmes

Management Development Programme MBA evenings; Full-time: International Marketing MBA; Human Resource Management MBA; Operations Management MBA; Business Economics MBA; Quality Management MBA

Programme Details

Programme Details	Full-time	Part-time
Duration	1 year	2-3 years
Class Contact	9-12 hours	3-6 hours
Commencement	September	January
Which evening/day		choice
Application deadline	July	Nov/Dec
GMAT Yes/No	No	No
Fees EC/Overseas	£2,600/£5,600	£5,700
Annual student intake	130	50
Average student age	26	35
Min. required experience	2 years	2 years
%EC/Overseas	20/80	100/0
%Men/Women	60/40	75/25
Number of Professors	1	1
Number of Academic Staff	65	65
Number of elective courses	6	2
Assessment: Exams/Assignments	A	A
Dissertation/Project	Both	Both

Additional Information
International Links: International Management Development Program Centres with Network Links

Library hours: 83 hours per week library access during term time

Electives not readily available elsewhere: Product Design and Development. Corporate Responsibility

Other information: State of the art campus – purpose-built in last three years

School Description
The School's strengths are: vocational applied projects/dissertations; personal competence/self development; work based assessment/in-company partnerships (part-time); state-of-the-art teaching campus and IT facilities.

University of Teesside, School of Business and Management

Address: Flatts Lane, Normanby, Middlesbrough TS6 0QS
Tel: 01642 342851   Fax: 01642 342925
EMail: j.m.blee@tees.ac.uk
MBA Admissions Officer: J M Blee

MBA Programmes
Part-time MBA (Day release – 1 day/week, 2 evenings/week)

Programme Details	Part-time
Duration	1-3 years depending on qualifications & experience
Class Contact	180 (min)-540 (max)
Commencement	October 1998
Which evening/day	Wednesday

Application deadline	August 31
GMAT Yes/No	No
Fees EC/Overseas	£1,000/£1,800
Annual student intake	40
Average student age	37
Min. required experience	2 yrs mid management
%EC/Overseas	100/0
%Men/Women	60/40
Number of Professors	1
Number of Academic Staff	55
Number of elective courses	12
Assessment: Exams/Assignments	A
Dissertation/Project	Both

Additional Information

International Links: Haagse Hogeschool, The Hague (The Netherlands); Krakow Academy of Economics (Poland). Both universities are licensed to run the University's MBA

Library hours: 0830-2200 (Mon – Thurs) 0830-1700 (Fri); 1100-1700 (Sat); 1100-2200 (Sun)

IT facilities: Extensive PC facilities dedicated to management courses

Electives not readily available

School Description

The University of Teesside is committed to serving the local community through the provision of a range of part-time courses at a variety of levels. Over 2,500 people are currently studying on part-time courses at certificate, diploma, degree, or postgraduate level. Part-time students come from many different backgrounds; some are studying to improve their employment or career prospects, others are learning more about a subject which interests them. Most are over the age of 21 and live or work in the Teesside area. The University welcomes applications from mature students and many courses will admit suitably experienced applicants without conventional entry qualifications. Mature students will also be considered on successful completion of an Access course.

Courses are delivered at the University's main site, which is within walking distance of the centre of Middlesbrough. Facilities on the main site include the main library, a language centre, and the Students' Union with its bars, shops, and dining areas. Career counselling and other advisory services are also available.

Individual programmes accredited by the Association of MBAs are indicated by a tick

Thames Valley University College of Graduate and Professional Studies

Address: Wellington Street, Slough, Berkshire SL1 1YJ
Tel: 01753 697648   Fax: 01753 697581
MBA Admissions Officer: Nicky Greaves

MBA Programmes
Full-time MBA; Part-time MBA; Open Learning MBA; Pre MBA

Programme Details	Full-time	Part-time	Open Learning
Duration	1 year	2 years	2 years
Class Contact	400 hours	400 hours	150 hours
Commencement	February/October	October	Varies
Which evening/day		Varies	Varies
Application deadline	January/September	September	1 month before commencement
GMAT Yes/No	No	No	No
Fees EC/Overseas	£5,500/£6,500	£2,575	£2,575
Annual student intake	40	120	30
Average student age	28	32	32
Min. required			
%EC/Overseas	60/40	90/10	80/20
%Men/Women	60/40	60/40	60/40
Number of Academic Staff	40	40	40
Assessment: Exams/Assignments	Both	Both	Both
Dissertation/Project	Both	Both	Both

Additional Information
International Links: Voluntary visits

Library hours: 0900-2200 (7 days)

IT facilities: Via purpose-designed Learning Resource Centre and purpose-built Learning Resource Centre

School Description
The college has over 30 years' experience in postgraduate, post-experience and professional education. Fields covered include General Management, HRM, Marketing, Purchasing and Supply, Finance, Accounting, Hospitality, Leisure and Tourism Management, Information Systems, Information Management, Law and English Language. There is a high proportion of full-time staff, who have gained considerable professional experience before joining TVU. This is extended by active engagement in research, writing, teaching and consultancy. Specialist associates also make a valued contribution.

The programme has been designed to enable participants to operate at executive level whilst maintaining a capability to remain lifelong learners. The analysis and implementation of strategy is of particular importance. Professionals and managers at every level and from all sectors of the economy currently study at TVU.

Schools offering an Association of MBAs-accredited programme are indicated by a roundel

Ulster Business School

Address: University of Ulster at Jordanstown, Shore Road, Newtownabbey, County Antrim BT37 0QB
Tel: 01232 368882   Fax: 01232 368948
EMail: ca.lavery@ulst.ac.uk
Dean: Professor Stephen Parkinson
MBA Admissions Officer: Ms Conac Lavery

MBA Programmes
Full-time MBA; Part-time MBA; International MBA

Programme Details	Full-time	Part-time
Duration	1 year	3 years
Class Contact	15 hours per week	7 hours per week
Commencement	September	September
Application deadline	April	April
GMAT Yes/No	Yes	No
Fees EC/Overseas	£3,700/£7,000	£3,000
Annual student intake	45	120
Average student age	23	35
Min. required experience	3/4 years	3 years
%EC/Overseas	10/90	100/0
%Men/Women	50/50	70/30
Number of Professors	2	2
Number of Academic Staff	20	20
Number of elective courses	14	14
Assessment: Exams/Assignments	Both	Both
Dissertation/Project	Both	Both

Additional Information
International Links: McLaren Graduate Business School UCSF; many European business schools, Irish Institute for European Affairs, Leuven (Belgium)
Library hours: Extensive hours and facilities
IT facilities: Extensive laboratory hours and facilities

School Description
The highly popular and successful three-year Part-time MBA consists of 22 modules and a management dissertation, taken by attending lectures one afternoon and evening per week, combined with residentials, group work and self-directed learning.

The full-time programmes are taken over three or four semesters (12-18 months) and by a combination of lectures, international residentials and local workshop sessions, group working and self-directed study.

The Ulster Business School, a faculty of the University, has sports, cultural, library and computer facilities available. The School has strong links with the business and academic world, nationally and internationally.

A wide range of electives is offered, allowing participants to choose a generalist or specialist MBA.

Institute for Financial Management (University of Wales, Bangor and Manchester)

Address: University of Wales, Bangor, Gwynedd LL57 2DG
Tel: 01248 371408   Fax: 01248 370769
EMail: R.Henry@bangor.ac.uk
Internet: www.bangor.ac.uk/ab/ifm/home.htm
Director: Robert Henry
MBA Admissions Officer: Dr Alistair Benson

MBA Programmes
Distance Learning MBA

Programme Details	Distance Learning
Duration	Approx 3 years
Class Contact	250 hours
Commencement	January/July
GMAT Yes/No	No
Fees EC/Overseas	£4,750-£7,500 (plus project fee)
Annual student intake	Approx 400
Average student age	34
Min. required	3 years management
%EC/Overseas:	40/60
%Men/Women	70/30
Number of Professors	6
Number of Academic Staff	36
Number of elective	9
Assessment: Exams/Assignments	Both
Dissertation/Project	Both

Additional Information
International Links: Student support centres at a number of overseas locations; overseas residential workshops provided by UK faculty

School Description
The University of Wales, Bangor/Manchester Business School Distance Learning MBA commenced in January 1992. Within two years the number of students enrolled on the programme approached 500 drawn from over 50 countries, an autonomous administration (the Institute for Financial Management) had been established, a network of overseas bases for the operation of the MBA had been brought online, and a number of corporate relationships had been successfully established. The total number of students enrolled to date is over 1,400.

The success of the MBA reflects both the standard and quality of the courses offered and the need for a financial management qualification in the international business community. The Degree has recognised academic strength and integrity; it is delivered in distance learning format, which is the growth area in the MBA arena, and it incorporates a high level of faculty/peer groups contact (essential in any high quality MBA). Its modular structure lends itself easily to the development of links with corporate and professional institute training programmes, and it is international in its approach in an area in which English is the common language.

This is a demanding and rewarding MBA, which carries the names of a world-ranking business school and two of Britain's major traditional universities.

University of Wales College, Newport

Address: Department of Business and Management, Allt Yr Yn Campus, PO Box 180, Newport NP9 5XA
Tel: 01633 432366   Fax: 01633 432307
EMail: uic@newport.ac.uk
Internet: www.newport.ac.uk

Acting Head of Department: Mr T H Williams

MBA Admissions Officer: Neil Wellard and Brent Stephens

MBA Programmes
Full-time MBA; Part-time MBA

Programme Details

Programme Details	Full-time	Part-time
Duration	1 year	3 years
Class Contact	12	6
Commencement	October	October
Which evening/day		various
Application deadline	August	August
GMAT Yes/No	No	No
Fees EC/Overseas	£4,000/6,345	£4,000
Annual student intake	25	90
Average student age	28	30
%EC/Overseas	15%	
%Men/Women	83/17	80/20
Number of Academic Staff	27	27
Number of elective courses	4	8
Assessment: Exams/Assignments	Both	Both
Dissertation/Project	D	D

Additional Information
International Links: The Department has links with the other academic institutions within the university of Wales, and is engaged in collaborative ventures in China, Malaysia, Greece and as a link department with colleges in Spain

School Description
Located on a single campus in a pleasant residential area overlooking Newport, the largest town in South-East Wales, the department caters for the needs of undergraduates, postgraduate and professional students with awards of the University of Wales BTEC and key professional bodies. With near 1,700 students enrolled in 1997/98, 460 full-time and 1,060 part-time, the department ranks as one of the largest providers of part-time higher education in Wales. Yet in business school terms it remains a small department, offering challenging programmes in a supportive environment. It has sound grounds for boasting a particular strength in finance and accounting.

The department offers post-experience and postgraduate management programmes at certificate, diploma and masters levels. The programmes are modular and allow for credit accumulation and transfer, as well as accreditation of prior achievement and entry with advanced standing. Programmes are offered on a full-time and part-time basis, and can also be tailored to the needs of individual organisations.

Individual programmes accredited by the Association of MBAs are indicated by a tick

University of Wales Institute Cardiff Business School

Address: Colchester Avenue, Cardiff CF3 7XR
Tel: 01222 506370   Fax: 01222 506932
EMail: tcockburn@uwic.ac.uk
Director: Thomas Cockburn
MBA Admissions Officer: Trefor Lewis

MBA Programmes
Full-time and Part-time MBA; Hospitality MBA; Food Production Management MBA; Banking and Finance MBA; Human Resource Development MBA

Programme Details	Full-time	Part-time
Duration	1 year	2 years
Class Contact	12	6
Commencement	September/February	September/February
Which evening/day	1 afternoon and 1 evening	
GMAT Yes/No	No	No
Fees EC/Overseas	£3,500/£7,460	£3,100
Annual student intake	100	40
Average student age	28	32
Min. required experience	1 year	1 year
%EC/Overseas	50/50	95/5
%Men/Women	80/20	50/50
Number of elective courses	26	26
Assessment: Exams/Assignments	Both	Both
Dissertation/Project	D	D

Additional Information
Electives not readily available elsewhere: Managing Achievement

School Description
The UWIC MBA consists of 4 core modules, 2 electives and a dissertation of between 18,000 to 20,000 words. There are 26 electives available when demand is sufficient. The programme is based in the UWIC Business School at the Colchester Avenue Campus which has been acclaimed for 3 centres of expertise: the WDA-Accredited, Food Industry Centre; the Centre for the Leisure Industries; the Centre for the Support of Lifelong Learning.

UWIC is a University College of the Federal University of Wales and is one of the UK's leading centres for university sport. Strong links are in place with such institutions as the Wales quality centre and innovation Wales as well as many local organisations and multi-national companies. Part scholarships are available for commonwealth citizens.

Warwick Business School, University of Warwick

Address: Coventry CV4 7AL
Tel: 01203 524306   Fax: 01203 523719
EMail: inquiries@wbs.warwick.ac.uk

Dean: Peter Doyle

MBA Admissions Officer: Pauline O'Sullivan

MBA Programmes
Full-time MBA; Evening MBA; Distance Learning MBA; Modular MBA

Programme Details	Full-time ✔	Evening ✔	Distance Learning ✔	Modular ✔
Duration	1 year	3 years	3-4 years	3 years
Class Contact	18 hours per week	6 hours per week	72 hours	40 hours per module
Commencement	October	April	January or July	November/ December
Which evening/day	Monday, Tuesday, Wednesday, Thursday			13 x 1 week modules and workshops
Application deadline	July	Rolling procedure	31 October/31 May	Rolling procedure
GMAT Yes/No	Yes	may be required	may be required	may be required
Fees EC/Overseas	£14,000	£12,164	£7,210/ £7,840	£13,750 and accommo- dation
Annual student intake	120	60	approx 350	50
Average student age	29	32	32	33
Min. required experience	3 years	4 years	3 years	4 years
%EC/Overseas	55/45	94/6	65/35	93/7
%Men/Women	70/30	76/24	77/23	75/25
Number of Professors	22	22	22	22
Number of Academic Staff	166	166	166	166
Number of elective courses	30	14+ modular and DL	6 DL + optional mods	20
Assessment: Exams/Assignments	Both	Both	Exam	Both
Dissertation/Project	Both	Both	Both	Both

Additional Information
International Links: 49 agreements with high-ranking educational establishments worldwide; MBA modules taught in locations such as Hong Kong, Brussels and Toulouse; DLMBA partners in Singapore, Sweden, Hong Kong, Greece; UK partner in 'UK-Berkeley Business Scholarship Program'

Library hours: 0900-2130 (Mon-Fri); 1200-2000 (Sat); 1300-2100 (Sun)

IT facilities: 23 dedicated MBA terminals plus additional 54 dedicated postgraduate terminals

Electives not readily available elsewhere: EU Regulations (with Solvay Business School,

Brussels), Corporate Environmental Management (with Aarhus School Management, Denmark), European Banking and Finance (with ESC Toulouse, France)

Other information: Purpose-built MBA teaching centre; foreign language laboratory; full sporting and social facilities on campus; major arts centre

School Description

With dual strengths in both research and teaching, Warwick Business School is internationally renowned, with over 230 staff and 17 major programmes of study attracting 3,000 students around the world. This all-round quality has enabled the School to achieve highly-prized rankings for the excellence of both its research and teaching from the Higher Education Funding Council for England. Founded in 1967, the School is an integral part of the University of Warwick.

Research, teaching and practical application are closely interwoven at Warwick Business School, an approach which enriches the learning experience. The Warwick MBA combines academic rigour and practical relevance, and is offered through a flexible range of four programmes to meet the diverse needs of organisations and managers. In addition to the 12-month Full-time MBA, Warwick has developed three MBA study routes for managers studying alongside employment; the Evening MBA; the Distance Learning MBA (which has around 1,500 students world-wide); the Modular MBA. All four study routes are accredited.

All Warwick's MBA programmes comprise core courses, a broad choice of elective courses, and a management project in the latter stages which provides an opportunity to test and apply a whole range of knowledge and techniques learned during the programme. Continual updating keeps the Warwick MBA at the forefront of management thinking, most recently reflected in the Full-time programme for 1996, which now places even greater emphasis on managing internationally, the management of innovation, and the practical issues of implementing strategy.

Four scholarships are available for the Full-time MBA, worth £4,500 each, of which two are for women (one UK, one overseas), one for a North American national, and one for a Public Sector employee.

Warwick MBA graduates have excellent career prospects, and through the varied activities of the School's MBA Alumni Association, they can keep up-to-date. It has a membership of about 3,500 worldwide.

University of Westminster

Address: 35 Marylebone Road, London NW1 5LS
Tel: 0171 911 5000/5020   Fax: 0171 911 5703
EMail: marob@wmin.ac.uk
Internet: www.wmin.ac.uk

Director: John Wooton

MBA Admissions Officer: Ms Ramila Mistry

MBA Programmes

Full-time MBA; Part-time MBA (evenings only); Part-time MBA/afternoon and evening); MBA Design Management by Distance Learning

Programme Details	Full-time	Part-time ✔
Duration	1 year	2 years
Class Contact	15 hours per week	6 hours per week
Commencement	September/February	September/February
Which evening/day	Tues/Thurs	
Application deadline	September/February	September/January
GMAT Yes/No	Not obligatory	Not obligatory
Fees EC/Overseas	£7,750	£5,204
Annual student intake	50	90
Average student age	29	30
Min. required experience	3 years	3 years
%EC/Overseas	45/75	n/a
%Men/Women	60/40	60/40
Number of Professors	2	2
Number of Academic Staff	.103	103
Number of elective courses	2	2
Assessment: Exams/Assignments	Both	Both
Dissertation/Project	P	P

Additional Information

International Links: Visiting faculty from overseas universities

Library hours: Term time: 0915-2100 (Mon-Thurs); 0915-1700 (Fri); 1100-1600 (Sat, Sun); Vacations 0915-1700 Mon-Fri and one eve a week

IT facilities: 19 microlabs (342 workstations – IBM compatible) 4 Microlabs (70 workstations – Macintosh computers)

School Description

The MBA programmes are taught within the Westminster Business School and the Harrow Business School. The part-time modes are Association of MBAs accredited courses. The full-time mode and the MBA Design Management distance learning course have not been offered for a long enough period to qualify yet for Association of MBAs accreditation.

The Schools are prominent in research, in particular in such areas as education, training and the labour market, the future of work and franchising.

The part-time MBA modes have been run for some 15 years and thus the Faculty has considerable experience of these courses. Both the part-time and the full-time courses allow for some elective specialisation with a wide range of choice.

All MBA students complete a project/dissertation. In the case of part-time students these are normally organisation related to benefit employers. For full-time students some project opportunities are related to work commissioned by organisations as a form of consultancy.

DMS graduates with good marks may be eligible for direct entry to Stage 2 of the part-time and full-time MBAs.

Wolverhampton Business School

Address: University of Wolverhampton, Shropshire Campus
Tel: 01902 321789   Fax: 01902 321724
EMail: wbs.marketing@wlv.ac.uk
Internet: www.wlv.ac.uk
Dean: Dr Bryony Conway

MBA Programmes
Full-time MBA; Part-time MBA; MA Public Policy and Resource Management (Part-time); MSc Marketing Management (Full-time)

Programme Details	Full-time	Part-time	In Company
Duration	1 year	3 years	3 years
Commencement	January	October/ February	
Which evening/day		Monday/Thursday (incl)	
Application deadline	November	October/ February	
GMAT Yes/No	Yes	No	N/A
Fees EC/Overseas	£5,700	£5,070	N/A
Annual student intake	50	70	Variable
Average student age	30	35	35
Min. required experience	2 years	5 years	3 years
%EC/Overseas	50/50	100/0	
%Men/Women	70/30	60/40	50/50
Number of Professors			
Number of Academic Staff	95	95	95
Number of elective courses	8	6	14
Assessment: Exams/Assignments	Both	Both	Both
Dissertation/Project	D	D	D

Additional Information
Library hours: Learning Centres open 60 hours per week, including evenings and weekends in term-time.

IT facilities: IBM PC 486, email (internal and external)

School Description
Wolverhampton Business School, one of the first to award an MBA, has substantially expanded its portfolio of postgraduate qualifications in recent years. It offers a relevant and practical programme that reflects the current and future needs of managers and their organisations.

The internationally-recognised Wolverhampton MBA offers a high standard of teaching, scope for significant personal research and practical input, the maximum choice of subjects, and flexibility of study. Full-time, part-time and dedicated in-house programmes are available, and allow for day and/or evening study.

All participants complete a programme of study in a range of Management Development core skills, including marketing, finance, information systems, and human resource management, together with modules designed to develop personal managerial effectiveness.

Participants can choose between the broadly-based general management course leading to a Diploma or the MBA, or elect to follow a more targeted route leading to a specialist Masters degree in the areas of Marketing, Human Resources or Public Policy.

All of the School's taught Masters programmes have a significant research-related component at both Diploma and Masters stages.

Europe

CESMA MBA – E.M. LYON
(formerly Groupe ESC Lyon)

Address: 23 avenue Guy de Collongue, BP 174, 69132 Ecully Cédex, France
Tel: +33 4 78 33 78 65   Fax: +33 4 78 33 78 55
EMail: cesmamba@groupe.esc-lyon.fr
Dean: Bernard Belletante
Programme Director: Judith Ryder
MBA Admissions Officer: Jacqueline Del Bello

MBA Programmes
Full-time MBA; Part-time MBA

Programme Details	Full-time ✔	Part-time
Duration	1 year	2 years
Class Contact	900 hours	900 hours
Commencement	September	September
Which evening/day		Friday/Saturday twice per month
Application deadline	June 15	June 15
GMAT Yes/No	Yes	Yes
Fees EC/Overseas	99,000 FF	120,000 FF
Annual student intake	60	30
Average student age	30	33
Min. required experience	2 years	4 years
%EC/Overseas	78/22	100
%Men/Women	80/20	92/8
Number of Professors	10	10
Number of Academic Staff	85	85
Number of elective courses	38	20
Assessment: Exams/Assignments	Both	Both
Dissertation/Project	P	P

Additional Information
International Links: Cranfield School of Management – double degree (UK); double degree (Argentine); Lancaster University (UK); ESADE
(Spain); HEC Montréal (Canada); Carnegie Mellon University (USA).

Library hours: 0900-1900 (Mon-Fri); 0900-1200 (Sat)

IT facilities: Email; CD-ROM; fully equipped computer labs

Other information: Selection is based on a written publication, a personal interview, and test results (GMAT, TOEFL and French proficiency tests).

School Description
As a French 'Grande Ecole' with an international orientation, E.M. Lyon is one of Europe's leading management education and research centres. Its activities rest upon three pillars; graduate management education (Cesma MBA, ESC Lyon Master's in Management, specialised

Masters programmes. Doctorate in Management), management development and research.

The aim of the Cesma MBA is to train managers who have an integrative vision of the business world and who are immediately operational upon graduation in a multicultural and an international environment. Teaching content is highly practical with an emphasis on developing managers as decision-makers.

The Cesma MBA is a bilingual programme taught in both French and English. Participants can choose to take first term core course in the language of their preference. This is particularly important for those with an intermediate level in French who can perfect their French while studying in English. For the remainder of the programme courses are taught either in French or in English, depending on the faculty member concerned.

Alongside the traditional MBA curriculum (including Finance, Marketing Strategy), cross-functional courses and executive- format seminars are programmed at regular intervals. In addition, each participant pursues a professional project. In term 3, participants choose from 38 electives in order to continue with a generalist approach or to concentrate on a specific area of management. In term 4, participants army choose between going abroad or putting their knowledge into practice by undertaking a field of study, a consulting or a company start-up project.

Counsellors from E.M. Lyon Careers and Orientation Department offer individualised support and advice to participants in planning their career and in their search for employment.

The Part time Cesma MBA lasts over two years and is identical in content to the Full time programme. Participants attend classes on Fridays and Saturdays twice a month, and take part in four one-week seminars each year.

School of Business Studies, University of Dublin, Trinity College, Dublin

Address: University of Dublin, Trinity College, Dublin 2
Tel: +353 1 608 1024   Fax: +353 1 679 9503
EMail: businq@ted.ie
Internet: www.tcd.ie/Business_Studies/MBA/
Chairperson: Professor Paul Coughlan
MBA Admissions Officer: Catherine Williams

MBA Programmes
Full-time MBA

Programme Details	Full-time
Duration	1 year
Class Contact	700 hours
Commencement	October
Which evening/day	n/a
Application deadline	June 30
GMAT Yes/No	Yes
Fees EC/Overseas	IR£9,000
Annual student intake	up to 40
Average student age	29
Min. required experience	3 years
%EC/Overseas	39/61
%Men/Women	70/30
Number of Professors	8

Number of Academic Staff	25
Number of elective courses	None
Assessment: Exams/Assignments	Both
Dissertation/Project	P

Additional Information

Library hours: Copyright Library 0900- 2200 (Mon-Fri); 0930-1300 (Sat)

IT facilities: All MBA syndicate rooms with Internet access

Other information: The School of Business Studies is located on the Trinity College campus – a 400 year old internationally renowned university in the centre of Dublin, a cosmopolitan capital city.

School Description

Trinity College, Dublin, one of Europe's oldest universities, offers a one-year MBA programme which attracts students of diverse backgrounds from all over the world. Trinity College celebrated its 400th anniversary in 1992; it is the oldest university in Ireland. The campus, set in attractive parklands and gardens, occupies an enviable position in the heart of Ireland's capital, and provides immediate access to the business and cultural life of the city.

The Trinity MBA is a general management programme with a broad but integrated core. Running for over 30 years, it is designed for creative, articulate, and strategically-oriented young managers with strong analytical and interpersonal skills who can operate in an international environment. The course is full-time and organised in five modules: Programme Orientation; Analysis for Decision-making; Making Decisions; Managing Strategically; Company Project.

The Company Project is a key element of the programme. Groups of five or six participants work with, and report to, the top management team on major strategic concerns of co-operating companies.

Students are required to commit an average of 70 hours per week to the Programme. Teaching methods combine lectures, seminars, case method, project work, computer simulation, and independent reading seminars. Assessment is by a combination of individual and group project work, class participation, and written examination.

THE TRINITY MBA

A one year, full time, intensive and intimate programme for managers and professionals aiming at General Management and membership of a global network of Trinity Alumni

The next Programme
runs from October each year

School of Business Studies
University of Dublin
Trinity College
Dublin 2
Ireland

To apply contact: Catherine Williams
Administrative Coordinator
Tel: +353-1-6081024
Fax: +353-1-6799503
e-mail: businq@tcd.ie
web: http://www.tcd.ie/Business.Studies/MBA/

Individual programmes accredited by the Association of MBAs are indicated by a tick

Graduates have effected significant career changes on the basis of this Programme. The positions offered to graduates range from senior management to critical middle management functions. In order to facilitate job-searching after the Trinity MBA, the School organises a programme of activities, including career management workshops, in-School recruitment events, and targeted distribution among alumni and potential employers of the Class Directory.

European School of Management (EAP)

Address: 6 avenue de la Porte de Champerret, 75838, Paris cedex 17, France
Tel: +33 1 44 09 33 30/32   Fax: +33 1 44 09 33 35
EMail: mba@eap.net
Internet: www.eap.net

Dean: Farhad Rad-Serecht

MBA Admissions Officer: Christine Hauser

MBA Programmes
Full-time MBA; International Executive MBA; A modular program taking place in 5 countries over a period of 16 months. In addition, tutoring through Internet and an International Consulting Project assigned to each participant.

Programme Details	Full-time ✔	Other
Duration	1 year	16 months
Class Contact	30 hours per week	
Commencement	January 1998	July 1998
Which evening/day		14 weeks residential courses
Application deadline	10 December 1997	end January
GMAT Yes/No	Yes	
Fees EC/Overseas	125,000 FF	80,000 FF
Annual student intake	Maximum 40	30
Average student age	32	
Min. required experience	3 years	4 years
%EC/Overseas	68/32	new programme
%Men/Women	84/16	new programme
Number of Professors	35	35
Number of Academic Staff	30	30
Number of elective courses	6	2
Assessment: Exams/Assignments	Both	Both
Dissertation/Project	P	P

Additional Information
International Links: 4 European schools – Paris, Berlin, Oxford, Madrid

Library hours: 0900-2000 (Mon-Thurs); 0900-1700 (Fri); 1000-1600 (Sat)

IT facilities: CD-ROMs; Kompass France; Ekod; Diane; ABI-Inform: Myriade; Grolier; Internet; email

Other information: Audiovisual equipment; Language Laboratory; Restaurant; Gymnasium and scheduled sports activities available to all participants

School Description
EAP is the European School of Management. With a cross-border presence in four European countries (France, Germany, Spain and the United Kingdom) an an international faculty from 14

countries, EAP is able to expose its exclusively post-experience MBA participants from around the world to the multiple realities of business practice and business culture in Europe. Managing in and from a European base is its strength.

Its goals are to develop the participant's confidence to operate internationally and to empower him/her to apply new skills and attitudes in complex environments. Three blocks of learning deliver the outcome: building confidence with business fundamentals; shaping the international future of the business; confronting challenges in the international business arena.

The MBA programme (12 months in Paris in English) places heavy emphasis on teamwork and project management in an international context. Performance in complex business environments internationally is the leitmotif and bottom line. The last phase of the programme is a real consulting project which provides the opportunity to put into practice the learning gained during the course.

The course covers a wide range of subjects from fundamentals to specialisations. In total there are over 650 hours of teaching made up of 22 modules of between 21 and 30 hours each. Teaching methods include a combination of lectures, case studies, team assignments, and field trips. During each phase there is a field trip to one of EAP's other locations: Berlin; Madrid. The aim is to provide direct contact with live business practices in different European cultures. Of critical importance to EAP is bringing the participants back to business. There is, throughout the programme, strong emphasis on job search and career development (through seminars and workshops).

Financing and sponsoring organisations include the Royal Academy of Engineering, Rotary International and FONGECIF, the French managers professional association.

Ecole Nationale des Ponts et Chaussées – Graduate School of International Business

Address: 28 Rue des Saints-Pères, 75343 Paris Cedex 07, France
Tel: +33 1 44 58 28 52   Fax: +33 1 40 15 93 47
EMail: mib.admit@paris.enpc.fr
Internet: www.enpc.fr/mib/pres.htm
Dean: Professor Celia Russo
MBA Admissions Officer: Mayaléne Crossley

MBA Programmes
Full-time MBA; Executive MBA; specialised MBAs

Programme Details	Full-time ✔
Duration	13-15 months
Class Contact	30-45 hours week
Commencement	October
Which evening/day	1st Monday
Application deadline	August
GMAT Yes/No	Yes
Fees EC/Overseas	110,000FF
Annual student intake	60
Average student age	30
Min. required experience	3 years
%EC/Overseas	25/75
%Men/Women	69/31
Number of Professors	10

Number of Academic Staff	30
Number of elective courses	45
Assessment: Exams/Assignments	Both
Dissertation/Project	Both

Additional Information

International Links: International exchange programs in Argentina, Czech Republic, Hong Kong, Japan, Poland, Slovenia, UK, United States

Library hours: 0930-1745; 0930-1930 (Tues & Thurs)

IT facilities: Centre de documentation Contemporaine et Historique: total holdings of 150,000 volumes, 200 microforms, 700 current periodical subscriptions. CD-ROM player(s) available for graduate student use. Recommended that students should have own computer.

Other information: The school is located in the heart of Paris in the famous district of St Germain-des-Prés, close to other prestigious schools and universities.

School Description

The ENPC, founded in 1747, has run the MBA programme since 1988. The student body and faculty are both highly international. Most faculty are visiting – coming either from business schools in the rest of Europe, Asia and North America, or are practising executives from the international corporate scene in France.

The Graduate School of International Business programme is flexible but intensive and places emphasis on: international finance and marketing; the management of technology; marketing, operations and strategy.

Students can also choose to concentrate on a geographical area: Europe, North America, or Asia. This would involve study at ENPC, study at a university in the area, and undertaking a project in the area. The in-company project lasts 4-6 months, usually takes place outside the student's native country, and is seen as a key element in final job placement.

The programme is taught entirely in English but students are required to achieve a good knowledge of French before graduation.

Esade

Address: Avenida de Pedralbes, 60-62, 08034, Barcelona, Spain
Tel: +34 3 280 29 95   Fax: +34 3 495 20 77
EMail: info@esade.es
Internet: www.esade.es
Director: Lluis M Pugès
MBA Admissions Officer: Catalina Pons

MBA Programmes
Full-time MBA; Part-time MBA

Programme Details	Full-time ✔	Part-time
Duration	21 months	23 months
Class Contact	1500 hours	1300 hours
Commencement	September	September
Application deadline	June 30	June 30
GMAT Yes/No	Yes	Yes
Fees EC/Overseas	4,400,000 pesetas	3,400,000 pesetas
Annual student intake	125	100

Average student age	26	29
Min. required experience	1–2 years recommended	3 years
%EC/Overseas	85/15	100/0
%Men/Women	65/35	77/23
Number of Professors	169	169
Number of Academic Staff	248	248
Number of elective courses	134	100
Assessment: Exams/Assignments	Both	Both
Dissertation/Project	None	None

Additional Information

International Links: The MBA International Exchange Programme: 18 schools in the USA; 3 in Canada; 10 in Europe; 4 in Latin America; 2 in Australia; 10 in Asia

Library hours: 0800-2200 (Mon-Fri); 0930-2000 (Sat)

IT facilities: The Data Processing Centre is a support service for the ESADE Business School's student body, teaching, research, administrative and service staff and is open daily from 0900-0200. There is an advisory service for students and faculty

Other information: The Spanish and International Placement Service is unique in that it arranges students' internships, helps graduating students to find entry-level jobs, and provides counselling and opportunities for alumni seeking a mid-career change for advancement

School Description

ESADE is a private business school founded in 1958 to teach general and applied management skills, encourage a spirit of entrepreneurship, and foster a sense of business ethics. In the course of 38 years, more than 16,000 men and women have passed through ESADE.

ESADE programmes attract students from throughout Spain and abroad. The foreign student population, representing 30 different countries, currently accounts for an increasing percentage of graduate enrolments. There is increasing emphasis on cross-cultural management skills, an internationally oriented curriculum, and co-operation and exchange agreements with leading European organisations and with management schools throughout the world.

The MBA is a two-year full-time graduate programme. It is a generalist programme that provides a global view of business operations and developing management skills which will enable graduates to work well in any type of company and/or executive position. Special attention is paid to developing analytical skills and an ability to make decisions in a changing environment whilst remaining steadfastly committed to ethical behaviour and social responsibility. Once ESADE students have mastered the fundamentals of management, they complete their education by choosing a major in a specific sector of activity and undertaking in-depth studies in their particular field of interest.

The programme's international focus is evident throughout the entire two years; both the faculty and student body come from a variety of cultural backgrounds, all subjects are examined in an international context, and a number of courses deal with specific international issues. In addition, there is a large student exchange programme.

Non-Spanish speakers enrolled in the English-language programme have the opportunity to become fluent in Spanish with courses in the ESADE Language School as part of the MBA curriculum. Students who are fully fluent in English and Spanish at the time of enrolment may opt for French or German classes.

HEC MBA Program

Address: 1, rue de la Libération, 78351 Jouy-en-Josas Cedex, France
Tel: +33 1 39 67 73 79   Fax: +33 1 39 67 74 65
EMail: denoyellep@hec.fr
Internet: www.hec.fr
Professor Jean-Loup Ardoin
MBA Admissions Officer: Pantéa Denoyelle

MBA Programmes
Full-time MBA

Programme Details	Full-time ✔
Duration	16 months
Class Contact	55 hours/week
Commencement	Sept or January
Application deadline	Early June, Early Nov
GMAT Yes/No	Yes
Fees EC/Overseas	125,000 FF for 16 months
Annual student intake	150-200
Average student age	28
Min. required experience	Average 5 years
%EC/Overseas	43/57
%Men/Women	80/20
Number of Professors	106
Number of elective courses	85
Assessment: Exams/Assignments	Both
Dissertation/Project	P

Additional Information
International Links: Students drawn from 30 different nationalities worldwide; bilingual teaching; major international companies on board of founders, such as Crédit Lyonnais, Bouygues, Ernst & Young, Procter & Gamble.

Other information: HEC is located in a 240 acre green setting, where everything has been done to foster relaxation, exchange of information and mutual support. The aim is to encourage a mixture of cultures, a commitment by the school much appreciated by the students.

There are 1400 bedrooms, 50 apartments, (all rooms on campus are cabled enabling access to library databases and internet), a cafeteria, a language centre, a day-care centre, a printing shop, an infirmary and an ecumenical chapel. Sporting facilities include a soccer stadium, a basketball court, a 2000 square-meter gymnasium, a nine-hole golf course, a martial arts center, tennis courts and a climbing wall. Each year, a European inter-MBA tournament takes place on the HEC Campus. This event brings together the best sportsmen and women from Europe's leading business schools for a three-day event.

School Description
The HEC MBA Program (ISA) is offered in September and January and is a 16 month, full-time course. The limited class size allows participants to maximize on both student-faculty as well as cross-student interactions.

The program is articulated around two main elements. The first element is the Core International Management Program (CIP); the second element is the possibility to personalize the curriculum.

ISA emphasizes knowledge of languages as an important part of the learning process. In addition to bilingualism in both French and English, the program offers the opportunity to learn a third or even a fourth language.

The HEC foundation unites over 40 prestigious multinational companies. Each company supports HEC's ambitions, participates in its strategic orientation, and ensures a concrete link between the educational and business worlds. In particular, they promote research programs in management sciences and encourage international projects.

The HEC Alumni Association and the ISA Alumni Association officially merged this year to form the HEC School of Management Alumni Association.

Each year about 130 companies come to recruit directly on campus. In addition to this close contact with the corporate world, the HEC MBA provides students with a range of support services to assist them in their career orientation. These include monthly conferences on employment with the participation of head-hunters, personal assessments, and job search workshops.

Helsinki School of Economics and Business Administration

Address: Leppasuonkatu 9E, 00100, Helsinki, Finland
Tel: +31 358 9 4313 8743   Fax: +31 358 9 4313 8613
EMail: dasilva@hkkk.fi
Internet: www.hkkk.fi./mbafi

Dean: Dr Heikki Topi

MBA Admissions Officer: Christina da Silva

MBA Programmes
Full-time International MBA in International Business Finance, Digital Technology Management; Executive MBA

Programme Details	Full-time ✔	EMBA Other
Duration	min 16 months	18 months
Class Contact	45 per module	20 per module
Commencement	May	March
Application deadline	Sept 15 and May 15	January 15
GMAT Yes/No	Yes	No
Fees EC/Overseas	65,000 FIM/18,500 US$	120,000 FIM + VAT
Annual student intake	60	36
Average student age	31	38
Min. required experience	2 years	5 years
%EC/Overseas	81/19	90/10
%Men/Women	57/43	65/35
Number of Professors	0	
Number of Academic Staff	3	2
Number of elective courses	48	n/a
Assessment: Exams/Assignments	Both	Both
Dissertation/Project	P	P

Additional Information
International Links: Links with numerous schools worldwide in USA, Switzerland, Thailand, India, Japan, Singapore, Korea, Australia

IT facilities: 25 Intel-based PCs with MS Office and Internet tools and an HP laser printer are available for student use in two computer laboratories.

Electives not readily available elsewhere: Management of information technology; Technology Commercialisation; Managing Multimedia Development for internet/intranet; Marketing of High Technology Products; Electronic Commerce; Modern Database Management; Collaborative Computing

Other information: The Library in Helsinki, one of the oldest and finest in Scandanavia, is at the forefront of modern library systems

School Description

The MBA programme at the HSEBA is a truly global experience with an international student body, highly qualified faculty members who come from top business schools around the world, English as the language of instruction and a strong emphasis on international issues in the programme content. Our programme will not only provide you with the knowledge required to operate successfully in international business but also the skills that every modern leader needs and a contact network that will last for the rest of your life.

The extensiveness and intensity of the programme allow us to integrate specialisms with a strong general management orientation. The programme consists of ten required core courses and 13 electives, four of which are normally taken a semester-long period a partner institution abroad.

The core courses provide our students with the broad, integrative overview of business that general managers need. The areas covered include: the external environment of the firm (economics), the internal environment of the firm (organisational behaviour), functional business areas (marketing, accounting, finance, operations), and managerial skills (quantitative methods, managerial communication, personal productivity computing tools).

In Helsinki, the Programme has from the start in 1984 offered concentrations in Finance and in International Business (including International Management and Marketing). In both areas, renowned professors from North America, Europe, and Asia engage the students in an interactive learning experience that provides them with the latest knowledge and skills in these vitally important areas. On our Mikkeli campus, we are very proud to be able to offer a concentration in Digital Technology Management in our state-of-the-art technology environment; this specialisation focuses on the utilization of telecommunications and multimedia technologies.

A high level of personal interaction has always been one of the trademarks of our programme. Class sizes are never too large, and our professors are a carefully selected group who can lead the class meetings so that the contributions of students with a variety of backgrounds become fully utilised. The intensity of the courses, which meet five days per week three hours every day, engages everybody in the educational process and teaches the students essential skills in stress and time management, teamwork, defining priorities, and finding the essential quickly from a large set of materials. Even when instructional technology is heavily utilised, as is increasingly the case especially on our Mikkeli campus, intensive interaction between the professor and the students and amongst the student is an essential part of the Programme.

The MBA Finland is an association of MBA graduates and students in Finland. In addition to its annual meeting, the association conducts a yearly Business Seminar, arranges excursions to different corporations and organisations and organises social gatherings for the alumni, thus providing them with a forum for exchange of experiences and ideas.

The Alumni Relations Office of the HSEBA keeps track of its alumni and publishes *the Graduate*, a newsletter for alumni, four times per year. It also cooperates wth MBA Finland in arranging various activities.

IESE International Graduate Schools of Management

Address: Avenida Pearson, 21, 08034 Barcelona, Spain
Tel: +34 3 253 4229   Fax: +34 3 253 4343
EMail: MBAinfo@iese.es
Internet: www.iese.es
Professor: Professor Eduardo Martinez-Abascal

MBA Admissions Officer: Pablo Aguilar

MBA Programmes
Full-time MBA

Programme Details	Full-time ✔
Duration	1¾ years
Class Contact	27.5 hours
Commencement	September
Which evening/day	N/A
Application deadline	1 May
GMAT Yes/No	Yes
Fees EC/Overseas	4,600,000 pesetas
Annual student intake	210
Average student age	26
Min. required experience	2 years
%EC/Overseas	72/28
%Men/Women	77/23
Number of Professors	114
Number of Academic Staff	114
Number of elective courses	60
Assessment: Exams/Assignments	Both
Dissertation/Project	N/A

Additional Information
International Links: Exchanges with: UC Berkeley; University of Chicago; Columbia; Tuck; Duke; INCAE; IPADE; Keio; Kellog; LBS; MIT; Western Ontario; Wharton; China- Europe International Business School

Library hours: 0800-2100 (Mon-Fri); some Saturdays

IT facilities: 60 Personal Computers, 20 MacIntosh computers, all equipped with CD-Roms; Internet, Intranet, e-mail; laser printers available to students.

Electives not readily available elsewhere: Global Roll-out Workshop (GROW)

School Description
IESE is the International Graduate School of Management of the University of Navarra. In 1964, with the help of an advisory committee of professors from the Harvard Business School which still meets annually, IESE established Europe's first two-year MBA programme. An important step towards internationalisation was taken in 1980, when the MBA course became bilingual (English-Spanish). Thus, students not only complete a rigorous MBA, but emerge from the programme fluent in two of the world's most important languages of commerce.

The two-year, full-time programme is a general management course on which the main teaching tool is the case method, supported by lectures, discussion presentations, computer work and group projects. A variety of cases are utilised from international sources, as well as some of the over 120 cases published annually by the IESE faculty. Work groups, organised to be as diverse as possible in terms of nationality and also educational and professional background, meet everyday to discuss real business situations. The objective of the MBA is to develop not only technical knowledge, but also personal skills and leadership qualities.

The programme structure is such that first-year students are divided into three sections of approximately 70 students each. The English-speaking section includes many students who do not speak Spanish when they begin. An intensive Spanish course prior to the start of the first term and language tuition throughout the first year are provided. The first year consists of a 15-course structured programme, as well as a three-month internship during the summer. In the past, these internships have included opening a new plant abroad, reshaping the definition of job functions, or designing a new marketing plan. Students are paid for this work and it provides them with an opportunity to return to the business world and put into practice the fresh ideas and new skills they have acquired during their first year. In the second year students select 15 elective courses taught in English or Spanish.

IESE offers Global Roll-out Workshop (GROW), an innovative multi-disciplinary approach to simulating a virtual global organisation, which links students on the campuses on IESE, the Darden School, and Manchester Business School through use of the Internet and video-conferencing. Participants form multinational teams and are challenged with developing a global marketing strategy for a real company, with input from the company's management regarding their internal and external environments. It is a three-dimensional process: local market issues; global functional issues; global strategy.

International Institute for Management Development (IMD)

Address: Chemin de Bellerive 23, 1007, Lausanne, Switzerland
Tel: +41 21 618 02 98   Fax: +41 21 618 0615
EMail: mbainfo@imd.ch
Internet: www.imd.ch
Dean: Professor Dominique Turpin
MBA Admissions Officer: Marianne Wheeler

MBA Programmes
Full-time MBA

Programme Details	Full-time ✔
Duration	January-December
Class Contact	900 hours per year
Commencement	January
Which evening/day	Monday-Saturday (Half-day Saturday)
Application deadline	various throughout the year
GMAT Yes/No	Yes
Fees EC/Overseas	SFr 33,000
Annual student intake	83
Average student age	31
Min. required experience	3 years min average
%EC/Overseas	0/100
%Men/Women	78/22
Number of Professors	27
Number of Academic Staff	6

Individual programmes accredited by the Association of MBAs are indicated by a tick

Number of elective courses	10
Assessment: Exams/Assignments	Both
Dissertation/Project	International Consulting Project

Additional Information

Library hours: 0830-2000

IT facilities: Portable PC required for each student; 30 PCs available

Other information: Software – Word, Excel, Powerpoint, Internet access, e-mail access to on-line and CD-rom based databases

School Description

Situated in Lausanne, on Lake Geneva and in the heart of French-speaking Switzerland, IMD is just 45 minutes from Geneva. Both Geneva and Lausanne are prominent university centres and the area offers a rich variety of music, theatre, exhibitions and special events.

IMD offers an intensive 11-month general management MBA aimed at managers with significant career progression, strong intellectual ability, and an international outlook.

Among the school's strengths is its participant to faculty ratio of 3 to 1, an international environment with 35 nationalities represented in the student body and 20 nationalities among the faculty, and a practical, hands-on approach to learning with the International Consulting Projects. International Consulting Project clients include General Motors, PepsiCo, Baxter and Club Med. Another unique feature is the Team Initiated Enterprise (TIE) projects which give participants the opportunity to plan and create an enterprise and see it through until completions. The scope of the projects is diverse and often humanitarian in nature.

Typical electives include: Managing Change; Entrepreneurship; Leadership; Sales Force Management; Financial Instruments; Manufacturing for the Year 2,000; Information Technology; Management in Asia; Business Economics.

IMD graduates are traditionally recruited by leading organisations throughout the world. A profile of the year's class is distributed to over 2 000 organisations throughout the year and a résumé portfolio with detailed descriptions of each student is distributed to over 250 organisations worldwide. Companies are invited to interview candidates on campus during the second half of the year. In 1996, 94% of the class received at least one job offer by graduation, with an average of three offers per participant. The average salary for 1996 was US$106K, and the average increase vs pre-MBA salary was 75%.

IMD graduates have a wide choice of career opportunities, with 60% of the 1996 class entering industry, 24% choosing consulting and 16% choosing finance.

INSEAD (The European Institute of Business Administration)

Address: Boulevard de Constance, 77305 Fountainebleau Cedex, France
Tel: +33 1 60 72 42 73   Fax: +33 1 60 74 55 30
EMail: admissions@insead.fr

MBA Programmes

Full-time MBA

Programme Details	Full-time ✔
Duration	1 year
Class Contact	528+ hours
Commencement	January/September
Application deadline	August/April

GMAT Yes/No	Yes
Fees EC/Overseas	155,000FF
Annual student intake	600
Average student age	28½
Min. required experience	Nil
%EC/Overseas	60/40
%Men/Women	80/20
Number of Professors	101
Number of Academic Staff	101
Number of elective courses	Approx 60
Assessment: Exams/Assignments	Both
Dissertation/Project	P

Additional Information

Library hours: 0800-2300

IT facilities: 150 micros for student use; Internet access; network connections for laptop users; Internet & Intranet access; internal & off-campus access to messaging system; fully networked amphitheatres; access to on-line & CD-ROM based databases; 40 servers using NT

School Description

For over 35 years INSEAD's integrative management approach has prepared executives for managing in an international environment. Close ties with the business community guarantee the relevance of its activities, while significant investments in research nourish up-to-date and innovative teaching.

The 520 MBA participants represent over 50 different nationalities. Not only is the group as a whole international, but each individual has an international outlook, with over two-thirds of INSEAD's MBA participants speaking three or more languages, and over half the class having studied or worked abroad.

Successful applicants demonstrate strong academic capacities, proven professional achievement, language skills, and the ability and willingness to contribute to the programme.

Expert faculty representing more than 20 nationalities ensure that teaching and research remain intimately tied to real business practices and current concerns.

The INSEAD experience broadens both professional and personal horizons, and can be the catalyst for achieving long-term career objectives. Over 100 leading corporations recruit on-campus, and have identified the INSEAD MBA as a rich source of international management talent.

Institut d'Etudes Politiques de Paris – MBA Sciences Po

Address: 174 Boulevard Saint Germain, 75006, Paris, France
Tel: +33 1 45 44 87 43   Fax: +33 1 45 44 88 92
EMail: mba@sciences-po.fr
Internet: www.sciences-po.fr

Dean: Professor Jean-Jacques Rosa

MBA Admissions Officer: Ms Isabelle de Saint Martin

MBA Programmes

Full-time Bilingual (English-French) MBA

Programme Details

	Full-time ✔
Duration	9 months
Class Contact	20 hours per week
Commencement	January
Application deadline	15 November
GMAT Yes/No	Yes
Fees EC/Overseas	£10,000
Annual student intake	40
Average student age	30
Min. required experience	3 years
%EC/Overseas	45/55
%Men/Women	70/30
Number of Professors	50
Number of Academic Staff	60
Number of elective courses	5
Assessment: Exams/Assignments	Both
Dissertation/Project	Both

Additional Information

Library hours: 0800-2000

IT facilities: Computer rooms/Internet

School Description

The Institut d'Etudes Politiques de Paris (Sciences Po), which succeeded the Ecole Libre des Sciences Politiques (founded in 1871), is located in the heart of Paris. More than 4,500 students are enrolled in its undergraduate and graduate programmes, which are served by a 1,200 member faculty – of which 30 per cent are engaged in the business world, and another 30 per cent in top level civil service.

The chief objective of MBA Sciences Po is to provide capable young business people with the concepts and methods necessary to succeed in positions of major responsibility in the international market. The MBA emphasises the study of social and economic sciences in European and International institutions in order to provide a global understanding of the marketplace.

MBA Sciences Po offers students a general overview of business practice and focuses on creating the ability to synthesise information from a managerial perspective. Using a wide variety of disciplines, students are exposed to a thorough examination of the hurdles facing international companies today. Classes are conducted in French (50%) and English (50%) whereas course material is entirely in English. The intensive programme of nine months is divided into four periods: three periods of 10 to 12 weeks, each of which is followed by a week of examinations; and one period of two weeks devoted to career development.

Designed to match students profiles with corporate demands, FORUM MBA, Sciences Po introduces students to their particular areas of interest. A booklet of students' resumés is sent to recruiters in advance, making personal interviews a more efficient process. Recognising the importance of the job search. Sciences Po continually promotes relations with the professional community. Conferences, lectures and informal breakfast meetings – at which students can meet key professionals from a wide variety of fields – are held throughout the programme.

Instituto de Empresa

Address: Marla de Molina 13, 28006, Madrid, Spain
Tel: +34 91 568 9610   Fax: + 34 91 411 5503
EMail: admissions@ie.ucm.es
Internet: www.ie.ucm.es

Director: Diego del Alcazar

MBA Admissions Officer: Margarita Alonso

MBA Programmes
Full-time; Part-time; International MBA; MBA International Trade

Programme Details	Full-time	Part-time	International MBA ✔	MBA Int Trade
Duration	10 month	12 month	15 month	10 month
Class Contact	1000	900	1100	1000
Commencement	Oct/Feb	October	October	October
Which evening/day	Mon-Fri	Thurs and Fri evening, Sat morning	Mon-Fri	Mon-Fri
Application deadline	Rolling	Rolling	Rolling	Rolling
GMAT Yes/No	Yes	Yes	Yes	Yes
Fees EC/Overseas	2,200,000 Ptas	2,200,000 Ptas	2,750,000 Ptas	2,200,000 Ptas
Annual student intake	300	65	56	50
Average student age	25	27	27	25
Min. required experience	2-3 years	3 years	3 years	2-3 years
%EC/Overseas	85/15	85/15	70/30	85/15
%Men/Women	65/35	65/35	65/35	65/35
Number of Professors	210	210	210	210
Number of elective courses	32		32	32
Assessment: Exams/Assignments	Both	Both	Both	Both
Dissertation/Project	Both	Both	Both	Both

Additional Information
International Links: Strong international links with Latin American countries, exchange programmes, intensive Spanish course (September) and classes during International MBA programme

Library hours: 0900-2200 with databank. Lodgement database available

IT facilities: Classes and Team work rooms with individual Internet access, Computer laboratories

School Description
Founded in 1973, and a member of the most prestigious of business school associations, Insitituto de Empresa is renowned for its excellent entrepreneurial education, for its constant support of the creation of new enterprises, and for being one of the most important opinion forums.

The Institute offers an International MBA (a 15-month programme covering the basic MBA core, assessed internship or an exchange visit, an elective period, and a World Reality seminar), Full-time or Part-time MBAs (consisting of the basic MBA core and electives), and an MBA in Foreign Trade (consisting of the basic MBA core and electives focused on international commerce).

Individual programmes accredited by the Association of MBAs are indicated by a tick

INSTITUTO de EMPRESA

1973 - 1998
25 ANIVERSARIO

The success of the Institute lies in three essential aspects; the excellence of the faculty (both full-time and part-time, but all in constant contact with business reality through research, consultancy, and publishing); the constant updating and adaptation of the programmes to meet the requirements of an entrepreneurial market in constant evolution; the alumni, selected after a very demanding process.

The Career Management Centre deals with over 1,200 job offers per year.

The Alumni Association maintains a contact network through the organisation of activities such as conferences, seminars, continuity courses, and social events.

The Institute is placed in the very heart of the business core of Madrid, which offers an excellent framework for the international exchange of cultures, opinions, and talents. Bursaries are available.

Nijenrode University, The Netherlands Business School

Address: Straatweg 25, 3621 BG Breukelen, Netherlands
Tel: +31 346 291 607   Fax: +31 346 250 595
EMail: mba@nijenrode.nl
Internet: www.nijenrode.nl
Assoc Dean: Dr Karel J. Samson
MBA Admissions Officer: Natasha van Dalen

MBA Programmes
Full-time International MBA; Rochester/Nijenrode Executive MBA

Programme Details	Full-time ✔	Executive
Duration	1 year	1½ years
Class Contact	1000 hours	600 hours
Commencement	October	January
Which evening/day	N/A	Friday/Saturday
Application deadline	May 15	November 15
GMAT Yes/No	Yes	No
Fees EC/Overseas	DFL 3,8000	DFL 95,000 (all incl)
Annual student intake	70	40
Average student age	29	36
Min. required experience	2 years	10 years
%EC/Overseas	40/60	85/15
%Men/Women	75/25	85/15
Number of Professors	30	30
Number of Academic Staff	50	50
Number of elective courses	20	0
Assessment: Exams/Assignments	Both	Both
Dissertation/Project	Both	P

Additional Information
International Links: International student body (22 nationalities); International faculty (12 nationalities); International Advisory Board (16 nationalities); very close contacts with the international business community

Library hours: 0830-2400 (Mon-Fri); 1200-2400 (Sat-Sun); 24 hour access to library databases

IT facilities: 90 networked personal computers with 24-hour access to most recent Windows and DOS applications, worldwide databases, Internet, email, etc.

Other information: The Nijenrode campus features student housing (private rooms – the majority of students live on campus) sports facilities, restaurant, bars. Classrooms are equipped with the latest state-of-the-art multimedia and computer facilities

School Description
Nijenrode University is a pioneer among European business schools, both chronologically and in terms of approach. Founded in 1946 by and for business it is one of the leaders in Europe. The emphasis is on developing 'whole' business people. The ability to work and communicate effectively in a multicultural situation is central to the Nijenrode style.

The 12-month Nijenrode International MBA programme, taught in English, includes two terms of course work – core courses, expert modules and electives – and a challenging 3-month company-sponsored project. Participants work intensively in small groups with colleagues from many different backgrounds and cultures. The MBA class is traditionally composed of some 20 nationalities. Participants have an average of five years of full-time work experience.

The Rochester-Nijenrode Executive MBA programme offers an integrated sequence of courses and management workshops aimed at a balanced study of business functions and managerial competencies. The programme takes 18 months to complete; this is made possible by the Universities' comprehensive teaching and learning formula, careful screening of candidates, a faculty dedicated to their students in a way that transcends the usual nine-to-five parameters, extensive reliance on study teams, and an intensive summer programme in the USA at the University of Rochester. After successful completion of the programme, students receive two MBA degrees, one from the Univesity of Rochester and one from Nijenrode University.

NIMBAS Graduate School of Management

Address: PO Box 2040, 3500 GA Utrecht, Netherlands
Tel: +31 30 230 30 50   Fax: +31 30 236 73 20
EMail: nimbas@compuserve.com
Internet: www.nimbas.com
President: Dr Joséphine B P M Borchert-Ansinger
MBA Admissions Officer: Mrs Rosemary Korte-Taylor

MBA Programmes
One-year full-time MBA: Utrecht, The Netherlands and Aachen, Germany; Two-year part-time MBA: Utrecht, The Netherlands, Bonn and Mainz, Germany; Two-year executive MBA: four-country programme; modular format MBA programmes in International General Management

Programme Details	Full-time MBA Utrecht, and Aachen ✔	Part-time MBA Utrecht ✔	Executive MBA ✔	Part-time MBA Bonn & Mainz
Duration	1 year	2 years	2 years	2 years
Commencement	September	September	September	September
Which evening/day		Tuesday evening	Modular	Friday evening and alternate Saturdays (0930-1630)
Application deadline	May 31	May 31	May 31	May 31
GMAT Yes/No	Yes	Yes	Yes	Yes

Schools offering an Association of MBAs-accredited programme are indicated by a roundel

Fees EC/Overseas	DM 34,350/ DFL37,500	DFL 47,500	DFL 6,000	DM 45,500
Annual student intake	50	40	28	35
Average student age	29	34	36	34
Min. required experience	3 years	4 years	5 years	4 years
%EC/Overseas	80/20	15/85	75/25	20/80
%Men/Women	50/50	80/20	80/20	70/30
Number of Professors	17	17	17	17
Number of Academic Staff	50	50	50	50
Number of elective courses	15	15	15	15
Assessment: Exams/Assignments	Both	Both	A	Both
Dissertation/Project	P	P	P	P

Additional Information

International Links: York University Toronto (Canada); Carnegie-Mellon (USA); University of Bradford Management Centre (UK); University College Dublin (Ireland)

School Description

NIMBAS Graduate School of Management is the Associate Institute of the University of Bradford in the UK and is nearing a decade of providing state-of-the-art international management education. In addition to its one-year full-time, two-year part-time and four-country modular Executive MBA programmes offered in the Netherlands, NIMBAS has also become very successful in Germany in the last few years.

The Association of MBAs-accredited NIMBAS-Bradford MBA programmes lead to the worldwide-recognised degree of Master in Business Administration from the University in Bradford in the UK. The Bradford MBA degree is officially recognised in Germany by the Kultusministerkonferenz. There are very few foreign MBA institutes in Germany which have received official recognition.

Individual programmes accredited by the Association of MBAs are indicated by a tick

NIMBAS offers International General Management MBA Programmes with optional specialisations in Environmental Management, International Marketing Management and Financial Management: These are One-year Full-time MBA (programmes in Utrecht, the Netherlands and Aachen, Germany); Two-year Part-time MBA (programmes in Utrecht, the Netherlands; and Bonn and Mainz, Germany); Two-year Part-time Executive MBA (modular programme with teaching locations in four countries).

Small-scale instruction enables students to participate significantly in class and facilitate increased interaction with the international teaching staff. The language of instruction is English. Its world-class curriculum, distinguished international faculty drawn from top academic institutions in Europe and North America and its many successful alumni, have earned NIMBAS an outstanding reputation for its MBA programmes, which draw candidates from all over the world. In the 23 February 1996 issue of *Management Team*, NIMBAS was rated Top Institution for Part-time MBA Degree Programmes. The European edition of 2/8 October 1997 included NIMBAS in its listing of Top European Business Schools.

Rotterdam School of Management, Erasmus Graduate School of Business

Address: PO Box 1738, 3000 DR Rotterdam, Netherlands
Tel: +31 (0)10 408 2222   Fax: +31 (0)10 452 9509
EMail: rsm@fac.rsm.eur.nl
Internet: www.rsm.eur.nl/rsm

Dean: Dr J W Foppen

MBA Admissions Officer: Ms Connie Tai

MBA Programmes
Full-time International MBA Programme in General Management; Full-time International MBA/MBI Program (Master of Business Administration/Master of Business Informatics); Part-time International MBA Program in General Management

Programme Details	Full-time MBA programmes ✔	Part-time MBA programmes
Duration	18 months	24 months
Commencement	mid-August	January
Application deadline	June 15, for August/September	November 30
GMAT Yes/No	Yes	Yes
Fees EC/Overseas	Dfl 67,500 MBA/MBI Prog: Dfl 46,000	
Annual student intake	125	80-100
Average student age	29	34
Min. required experience	2 years	4 years
%EC/Overseas	15/85	74
%Men/Women	76/24	85/15
Number of elective courses	2nd year over 50	12
Assessment: Exams/Assignments	Both	Both
Dissertation/Project	Both	Both

Additional Information
International Links: The RSM has exchange relations with a number of top business schools worldwide.

Library hours: Bus Info Centre (Mon-Thurs) 0900-2100; (Fri) 0900-1800; Erasmus Uni (Mon-Fri) 0800-2230; (Sat) 0900-1300

IT facilities: The RSM has excellent computer facilities consisting of six dedicated computer labs with 200 personal computers. Additionally, there are extensive dial-in services running state-of-the-art network access software.

Other information: Admission requirements: university degree; GMAT; 2 references; work experience required, 2-4 years preferred; interview. To be considered for admission to the part-time MBA applicants should currently be working and have minimum four years work experience. They must take the GMAT exam or the RSM's equivalent exam, be proficient in English, and hold a higher education degree. References and an interview with RSM staff or alumni will also be required. Motivation and further career development are taken into consideration.

School Description

The Rotterdam School of Management is the business school of Erasmus University, situated in the Netherlands. In recent rankings the RSM was consistently ranked among the European top five business schools and the top ten worldwide.

The RSM offers full-time and part-time MBA programmes, in-company programmes, and workshops on open management programs.

The Rotterdam School of Management offers three MBA programmes: full-time Master of Business Administration degree (MBA); full-time Master of Business Administration/Master of Business Informatics degree (MBA/MBI); part-time Master of Business Administration degree (MBA)

The curriculum of the International MBA Programme in General Management (MBA) covers all major aspects of general management. The first year consists of mandatory courses dealing with management basics and covers functional areas. The first semester includes communication workshops.

The International MBA/MBI Programme (Master of Business Administration/Master of Business Informatics) is designed for students who, in addition to a general management education, wish to receive theoretical and practical training in the managerial aspects of information technology. The MBA/MBI Programme is largely identical to the MBA Programme but offers MBI-exclusive class blocks later in the programme.

The first year course period ends with a project management and consulting workshop. During the summer, students are required to undertake an in-company project. MBI students follow required MBI courses, and subsequently perform an IT project.

The second year allows students to tailor their studies to areas of their interest. Through electives and mini-courses they can focus on areas such as investment banking, business in Eastern Europe, and management consulting. Additionally, the second year presents an opportunity to participate in the exchange programme with top business schools worldwide.

The RSM offers the high quality of its full-time International MBA Programmes in a part-time format to executives who want to earn the MBA degree while they continue to work. The programme minimises the number of days participants spend away from work. The part-time MBA Programme lasts 24 months, with classes on Friday evenings and Saturdays, every two weeks. Twice during the programme (in January of each year) there will be a Wednesday – Sunday block of classes, and there will be two one-week trips abroad. The language of instruction is, as in the full-time MBA Programmes, English. The programme is organised into three terms, with a one-month in-company project to be undertaken at the end of Term Two.

SDA Bocconi-Milano

Address: Masters Division, Via Balilla 16/18, 20136, Milano, Italy
Tel: +39 02 5836 3287   Fax: +39 02 5836 3275
EMail: mba@sda.uni-bocconi.it
Internet: www.sda.uni-bocconi.it

Dean: Elio Borgonovi
MBA Director: Mario Mazzoleni
MIEM Director: Guiseppe Ferraggio
MBA Admissions Officers: Rossana Camera; Luisa Negri

MBA Programmes
Full-time MBA (Master of Business Administration); Full-time MIEM (Master of International Economics and Management)

Programme Details	Full-time MBA ✔	Full-time MIEM
Duration	16 months	12 months
Class Contact	1700 hours + project	1100 hours
Commencement	September	January 1999
Application deadline	30 April	15 June/30 September
GMAT Yes/No	Yes	Yes (or GRE)
Fees EC/Overseas	Lit 34,000,000	Lit 28,000,000
Annual student intake	130	50
Average student age	29	26
Min. required experience	2	not required
%EC/Overseas	79/21	69/31
%Men/Women	79/21	60/40
Number of Professors	125	55
Number of Academic Staff	26	26
Number of elective courses	2 from 8	2 from 18
Assessment: Exams/Assignments	Both	Both
Dissertation/Project	P	Internship

Additional Information
International Links: MBA international exchange programme with approx 20 top universities and business schools around the world; MBA projects and MIEM internships in Italy and abroad; Joint Degree Programme MBA/MAIA (Master of Arts in International Affairs) with John Hopkins University

Library hours: 0830-2300 (Mon-Fri); 0900-1230 (Sat)

IT facilities: 100 personal computers networked wth commercial and proprietary software; email; Internet

Electives not readily available elsewhere: Includes MBA elective itineraries in Client Knowledge Based Marketing Management; Value Management; International Accounting and Tax Planning; Management Consulting; The Route to Internationalisation; Management of Small and Medium Enterprises; Merchant and Investment Banking; System Thinking on Management; Public Services Privatisation.

Other information: MBA delivered in English and Italian, MIEM delivered in English; Italian Language courses throughout the programme (3 levels). Recently refurbished building with 10 modern classrooms and 58 special group work areas; use of all Bocconi University facilities, including language laboratory and library (with over 600,000 volumes)

School Description

SDA is the Graduate School of Management of Milan's Bocconi University. It is Italy's leading management school and one of the most highly regarded Business School in Europe and in the world. SDA Bocconi was founded in 1871 and from the start it set itself the objective of joining forces with enterprises in the creation and dissemination of a true management culture. Apart from the 16-month, bilingual MBA Programme (English and Italian), the Masters Division of SDA Bocconi offers a one-year Master of International Economics and Management (MIEM), in English; a one-year Master of Small-Business Management (Master Piccole Imprese), in Italian; and a two-year evening Masters Programme (CEGA-Corso in Economia e Gestione d'Azienda), in Italian. The School also offers a full range of specialised executive courses and tailor-made initiatives for specific companies (more than 800 management education courses are organised annually and are attended by more than 10,000 executives, managers and entrepreneurs).

The MBA programme is a general management MBA which aims to give both a strong base in the concepts and techniques used in each of the functional areas of management (marketing, finance, strategy, etc.), and an understanding of the interfunctional mechanisms by which companies operate (processes). The 16-month course involves intensive classroom activity and interactive teaching methods for the first ten months. In the final part of the programme, participants follow elective itineraries and complete in-company projects in teams and may choose to follow one of the two focuses offered.

The MBA is bilingual, one class in English, one in Italian; small classes (65 participants approximately in each class), interaction among participants, cross-cultural exchange half of the students are non-Italians and come from approximately 30 different countries.

North America

Amos Tuck School of Business Administration at Dartmouth

Address: 100 Tuck Hall, Hanover NH 03755, USA
Tel: +1 603 646 3162   Fax: +1 603 646 1441
EMail: tuck.admissions@dartmouth.edu
Internet: www.dartmouth.edu/pages/tuck

Dean: Paul Danos

MBA Admissions Officer: Sally Jaeger

MBA Programmes
MBA Full-time

Programme Details	Full-time
Duration	2 years
Commencement	September
Application deadline	mid-April
GMAT Yes/No	Yes
Fees EC/Overseas	$24,900
Annual student intake	180
Average student age	27
Min. required experience	none
%EC/Overseas	17
%Men/Women	70/30
Number of Professors	49
Number of elective courses	50
Assessment: Exams/Assignments	Both
Dissertation/Project	Both

Additional Information
International Links: Exchange programmes with London Business School; The Instituto de Estudios Superiors de la Empresa in Barcelona, Spain; and the International University of Japan.

IT facilities: Whittlemore wing of Information Technology.

Electives not readily available elsewhere: Field Study in International Business

School Description
Founded in 1900, Tuck was the first graduate school of management in the United States. The school is small, with 363 students. It is known for its close-knit, cooperative spirit. The faculty are legendary for their accessibility and friendliness to students. The student to faculty ratio is ten to one. Tuck has a particularly strong worldwide network of alumni, who often stay closely involved with the school throughout their lives, recruiting students and interviewing applicants, sponsoring programmes, and serving as guest lecturers.

The School takes a general management approach to business education. Teamwork is central to the Tuck experience. All students take four or five courses in each term, with three terms in an academic year. A summer internship is encouraged between years. There are no areas of concentration. Year 1 consists of fourteen core courses. Year 2 consists of twelve electives chosen from over fifty offerings. Group projects and outside consulting with local businesses are part of the curriculum. Ninety-eight per cent of students have prior work experience before enrolment. Their ambitions include consulting, corporate management, entrepreneurship, investment banking, and the public sector.

Tuck's campus is comprised of seven interconnected buildings on thirteen rural acres on the western edge of the campus of Dartmouth College. Students use college facilities, including eight libraries, a cultural centre, and outstanding sport and recreational amenities. The Hanover, New Hampshire, area is rich with opportunities for outdoor activities, such as skiing, skating, water sports, hiking, climbing, and golf.

Tuck has its own library and sophisticated computing capabilities connected to a central campus network. The Whittlemore Wing for Information Technology is a new facility that offers the latest in desktop and mobile computing, along with facilities for video-conferencing, multimedia production, data visualisation, and group collaboration. First year students generally live in dormitories on campus. Second year students live in rented houses in Hanover and the surrounding communities.

The career counselling and placement office at Tuck works closely with each student to prepare them for their job search. Over 130 top companies recruit on Tuck's campus each year. More than 90 per cent of Tuck students have had one or more job offers by the time of graduation

---

Qualifies
for the
Association
of MBAs
Loan
Scheme

The Anderson School at UCLA

Address: MBA Admissions, 110 Westwood Plaza, Suite B201, Los Angeles CA 90095-1481, USA
Tel: +1 310 825 6944   Fax: +1 310 825 8582
EMail: mba.admissions@anderson.ucla.edu
Internet: www.anderson.ucla.edu

Dean: John Mamer

MBA Admissions Officer: Linda Baldwin

MBA Programmes
Full-time MBA; Computer Science MBA/MSCS; Law MBA/JD; Public Health MBA/MPH; Latin American Studies MBA/MLAS; Urban Planning MBA/MUP; Nursing MBA/MN; Library & Information Studies MBA/MLIS; Medicine MBA/MD; Fully-Employed MBA; Executive MBA; MS; PhD.

Programme Details	Full-time	Part-time	Executive MBA
Duration	2 years	3 years	2 years
Class Contact	16 hours/week	8-10 hours/week	30 hours/month
Commencement	June	June	September
Which evening/day		1 Sat section, 1 afternoon week + Sat section	Fri/Sat Alternate
Application deadline	April 3	May 1	May 1
GMAT Yes/No	Yes	Yes	Yes
Fees EC/Overseas	$20,093	$54,600	$55,800
Annual student intake	300	135	72
Average student age	27.9	30	39
Min. required experience	2 years	5 years	10 years
%EC/Overseas	25/75		

%Men/Women	73/27	72/28	81/19
Number of Professors	96	96	96
Number of elective courses	14	10/40	0
Assessment: Exams/Assignments	Both	Both	Both
Dissertation/Project	P	P	P

Additional Information

IT facilities: Incl 10 network servers, 4 workstation computation servers, and HP9000 super-minicomputer providing network services to AndersoNet (the School's ATM-based network); 2467 laptop computer ports; 3 laboratories, one 'computerless' for laptop users

School Description

The Anderson School at UCLA is ranked among the top graduate business schools in the US, and is especially well-known for its strengths in team problem-solving, entrepreneurial studies, global management, finance, and corporate renewal. Consisting of three components (the management core, advanced electives, and the management field study), the curriculum is regularly updated to address the evolving challenges today's business managers must meet. The School employs a broad range of teaching methods, maintaining a crucial balance between lecture and case study, and between individual and team approaches to management issues. The MBA programmes (one full-time and two for working professionals), eight concurrent degree programmes, and an MS/PhD programme are offered.

Through the Parker MBA Career Management Center (ranked #1 in the 1996 *Business Week* survey) the School offers sound guidance and multiple resources for career management. Students acquire the connections, skills and techniques needed to find a position that perfectly fits their career goals. Over 180 companies recruited in the campus interview program. 97.6% of Anderson students had job offers upon graduation in 1997, and students secured rewarding and challenging positions throughout the US and abroad.

Los Angeles, the second-largest city in the US, is the centre of one of the economically and culturally richest areas of the world. Los Angeles offers Anderson students the best of many worlds. Beach, mountain, and desert recreation areas are plentiful and easily accessible by car. The moderate Southern California climate makes outdoor activities such as tennis, skiing, biking, roller blading, sailing, and golf enjoyable year-round. Los Angeles museums house some of the finest art collections in the country, and theatres and the Music Centre offer the world's most acclaimed entertainment. Westwood Village, which adjoins the UCLA campus to the south, offers shopping, dining, and a wide range of services.

University of California, Berkeley, Haas School

Qualifies for the Association of MBAs Loan Scheme

Address: S440 Student Services Bldg, #1902, Berkeley CA 94720-1902, USA
Tel: +1 510 642 1405   Fax: +1 510 643 6659
EMail: mbaadms@haas.berkeley.edu
Internet: haas.berkeley.edu

MBA Programmes

Full-time MBA; Part-time MBA; JD/MBA; MBA/MPH in Health Services Management; MBA-MA in Asian Studies; MBA/MIAS in International Area Studies

Programme Details	Full-time	Part-time
Duration	2 years	3 years
Class Contact	56 credits	36 credits + 5 prere
Commencement	May	May
Which evening/day		Evening
Application deadline	February 14	April 1
GMAT Yes/No	Yes	Yes
Fees EC/Overseas	$38,756	$62,934
Annual student intake	235	100
Average student age	28	29.5
Min. required experience	2 years	2 years
%EC/Overseas	30	11
%Men/Women	68/32	68/32
Number of Professors	145	145
Number of Academic Staff	14	5
Number of elective courses	85	36
Assessment: Exams/Assignments	Both	Both
Dissertation/Project	Both	Both

Additional Information

International Links: Study abroad for one semester at 17 schools in Europe, Asia, and Latin America. International Business Development course with 3-week consulting projects in Southeast Asia, China, India, Russia, and Latin America

Library hours: 0745-2200 (Mon-Thurs); 0745-1700 (Fri); 1300-1700 (weekends)

IT facilities: Main computer lab: 20 HP Pentium/90 PCs, 20 HP 486DX2/66 PCs, 10 Apple Macintosh 6100s; Multimedia lab equipped to digitize almost anything; 2 computer classrooms with DOS compatible Apple Macintosh 6100/66 machines; Unix workstation lab (10 Sun SPARC Cla

Electives not readily available elsewhere: International Business Development, Global Strategy, and certificate programs in Global Management, Health Management, Management of Technology, and in Entrepreneurship

School Description

Business education in Berkeley dates from 1898, making the Haas School of Business the second oldest college school of business in the US. The school provides an unparalleled intellectual and physical setting for graduate management education. The faculty are considered among the best in their field, students are drawn from all walks of life, and the curriculum is comprehensive and interdisciplinary. Berkeley is across the bay from San Francisco and the Silicon Valley, two of the most dynamic centres of the nation's leading state economy.

In January 1995, the school moved into its new building overlooking the Berkeley campus and the San Francisco Bay. A mini-campus in its own right, this state-of-the-art complex consists of three pavilions set around a central courtyard and features three floors of classrooms, ultramodern computer labs, a career development centre, and a wired 21st century business and economics library.

The Haas School offers a strong general management programme that prepares its graduates to understand the economic, social, political and technological forces driving global competition and to become effective leaders of modern organisations. It is increasingly well-known nationally and internationally for its focus on international business, innovation and entrepreneurship, and the management of technology. Unusually flexible in its range of courses and electives for second-year students, the MBA programme emphasises cooperative work in teams and small groups.

The full-time programme, with approximately 30 per cent international students (evenly divided between Europe and Asia) reflects the diverse global environment in which it graduates will pursue their careers. More than 30 per cent are women. The diverse student body represents nearly 200 colleges and universities, 42 countries, and a wide range of academic and professional backgrounds. There are approximately 450 students in the two-year full-time programme and 250 students in the part-time evening programme.

In addition to the 17 international student exchange programmes, Berkeley students may participate in the Washington Campus Program in the nation's capital and the MBA Enterprise Corps in Eastern Europe.

Carnegie Mellon University Graduate School of Industrial Administration

Qualifies for the Association of MBAs Loan Scheme	

Address: Admissions Office, Schenley Park, Pittsburgh PA 15213-3890, USA
Tel: +1 412 268 2272   Fax: +1 412 268 7094
EMail: gsia.admissions@andrew.cmu.edu
Internet: www.gsia.cmu.edu
Dean: Dr Ilker Baybars

MBA Admissions Officer: Laurie Stewart

MBA Programmes
Full-time MSIA; Flex-time MSIA (evenings); JD/MSIA (with University of Pittsburgh); Collaborative Program in Private and Public Management and Policy (with Heinz School of Public Policy and Management)

Programme Details	Full-time	Part-time
Duration	2 years	3 years
Class Contact	20 hours per week	8 hours per week
Commencement	May	May
Which evening/day		Monday-Thursday
Application deadline	March 15	March 15
GMAT Yes/No	Yes	Yes
Fees EC/Overseas	$22,100	$16,704
Annual student intake	215	
Average student age	27	
Min. required experience	2 years preferred	2 years preferred
%EC/Overseas	40%	
%Men/Women	77/23	
Number of Professors	98	98
Number of elective courses	200	200
Assessment: Exams/Assignments	Both	Both
Dissertation/Project	P (optional)	P (optional)

Additional Information
International Links: Semester at one of: Koblenz (Germany); Lyon GSB (France); Manchester Business School (UK); Wirtschaftsuniversität Wien (Austria); Aoyama Gakvin University (Japan); ITESM (Mexico); Bradford (UK); Université de Nancy (France); Universitat Pompeu Fabra (Spain)
IT facilities: State-of-the-art PCs and workstations; real-time financial market information in Financial Analysis and Securities trading lab

Electives not readily available elsewhere: Financial Analysis and Securities Trading (FAST); Business Leadership in Changing Times; Managing Knowledge Intensive Businesses and Gold Collar Workers; French, German, Japanese, or Spanish for Business

School Description

The Graduate School of Industrial Administration (GSIA) was created in 1949 to provide a scientific approach to management education and practice. It gave managers new and creative approaches to solving old problems, and now sets the standard in educating world-class business leaders who can use technology to improve performance in an increasingly complex global environment. GSIA is known for providing students with quantitative general business knowledge, and offers particular strengths in the areas of: Manufacturing; Finance; Information Systems; Marketing; Entrepreneurship.

GSIA remains one of the smallest major business schools in the US; the annual student intake to the full-time programme is deliberately limited, thus offering unique opportunities for interaction with other students, faculty members, and administrative staff. GSIA has always promoted innovation and the dissemination of new knowledge; state-of-the-art technology is provided, through which students learn decision-making in simulated environments. This greatly enhances the traditional case studies.

GSIA emphasises teamwork, and encourages students to work closely together.

The School is located in the beautiful and historic East End of Pittsburgh, four miles from downtown. The School borders 500-acre Schenley Park, a wooded area of winding trails, with a public golf course, skating rink and swimming pools. The Carnegie Mellon campus includes GSIA's new business school building (opened 1993) and the multi-million dollar Student Center, which opened in August 1996. Pittsburgh also offers world-class ballet, opera, symphony, theatre, and three major league athletic teams.

Qualifies for the Association of MBAs Loan Scheme

University of Chicago Graduate School of Business

Address: 1101 East 58th Street, Chicago IL 60637, USA
Tel: +1 773 702 7369   Fax: +1 773 702 9085
EMail: admissions@gsb.uchicago.edu
Internet: www.gsb.uchicago.edu

Dean: Robert Hamada

MBA Admissions Officer: Donald C Martin

MBA Programmes

Full-time MBA; Evening MBA; Weekend MBA; Executive MBA (US and Barcelona); International MBA

Programme Details	Full-time	Part-time	Executive
Duration	2 years	2½-5 years	2 years
Class Contact	Apprx 12 hours	Apprx 6 months	7 hours
Commencement	All quarters – all programmes	All quarters – all programmes	All quarters – all programmes
Which evening/day		Evening	Friday/Saturday
Application deadline	January 16, March 20	January 23, April 17	March 31 (US), May 15 (Barcelona)
GMAT Yes/No	Yes	Yes	No

Fees EC/Overseas	$2,490 per course	$2,490 per course	$2,490 per course
Annual student intake	500	100 per quarter	80
Average student age	28	28	35
Min. required experience	n/a	n/a	10 years
%EC/Overseas	24	2	n/a
%Men/Women	80/20	55/45	n/a
Number of Professors	100	100	100
Number of elective courses	11	11	n/a
Assessment: Exams/Assignments	Both	Both	Both
Dissertation/Project	No	No	No

Additional Information

International Links: International Business Exchange Program; International Masters Business Administration; Executive Barcelona Program; Center for International Business, Education and Research

Library hours: 0800-0100 (Mon-Thur); 0800-2200 (Fri); 1200-0100 (Sun)

Electives not readily available elsewhere: Entrepreneurship; Strategic Management

Other information: First business school to have Nobel Laureate on its faculty. First to develop a programme aimed at encouraging liberal arts graduates to enter business school. First to establish a minority relations programme. First to adopt computerised bidding for placement interviews and class registration. First to offer an Executive MBA programme. First to publish a scholarly business journal. First to initiate a PhD programme in business.

School Description

Strengths in finance, marketing, accounting, international business. Thirteen concentrations: Accounting; Entrepreneurship; Economics; Econometrics and Statistics; Financial Management; Analytic Finance; General Management; Human Resource Management; International Business; Marketing Management; Production and Operations Management; Managerial and Organisational Behaviour; Strategic Management.

21 courses to complete the MBA degree 11 electives, 8 core courses, policy studies and LEAD. Total of 6 courses are allowed at any other graduate studies programme at the University of Chicago (i.e. law, divinity, social sciences, etc.).

Management Labs: Leadership Exploration and Development (LEAD) Laboratory; New Product Laboratory; Laboratory in Organisational Effectiveness; Laboratory in Organisational Excellence.

A balance between theory and practice

World class faculty, includes 4 nobel laureates

Urban setting (closely connected with the business community)

Fifteen professional interest groups for students – Business Students Association (BSA)

Ninety-eight per cent placement rate within 3 months of graduation – 99% within six months of graduation

Financial Aid available to US citizens (including minorities), and some merit based scholarships available to international students.

Columbia Business School

Address: Uris Hall, 3022 Broadway, Room 105, New York NY 10027, USA
Tel: +1 212 854 1961   Fax: +1 212 662 6754
EMail: gohermes@claven.gsb.columbia.edu
Internet: www.columbia.edu/cu/business/
Dean: Professor Meyer Feldberg
MBA Admissions Officer: Linda B Meehan

MBA Programmes
Full-time MBA; Accelerated MBA; Executive MBA

Programme Details	Full-time	Accelerated	Executive
Duration	20 months	16 months	20 months
Commencement	February, May, August	May	May, August
Which evening/day	n/a	n/a	Friday/Saturday
Application deadline	Mar 1, Oct 1, Feb 1	October 1	October 1/May 1
GMAT Yes/No	Yes	Yes	Yes
Fees EC/Overseas	$12,570 per semester	$12,570 per semester	$83,000
Annual student intake	488		180
Average student age	27		23
Min. required experience	2 years		5 years
%EC/Overseas	28		25
%Men/Women	63/37		78/22
Number of Professors	191	191	191
Number of elective courses	179	179	30
Assessment: Exams/Assignments	Both	Both	Both
Dissertation/Project	None	P	P

School Description
Columbia Business School's unique strengths are: its outstanding faculty; its location in the business and financial capital of the world; its resources as part of a great Ivy League University; and its worldwide relationships with business and academic leaders.

The pace, perspective and culture at Columbia Business School reflect the homogeneity, drive and unlimited opportunity of New York City. For students seeking to be global players, being in close proximity to New York's 3,000 internationally-owned firms, 300 foreign banks, the United Nations, the stock exchanges, scores of brokerage firms and investment banks enables them to explore countless industries at first hand.

The School's location and strong relationships allows it to draw to campus more than 300 business leaders a year – as teachers, speakers, adjunct lecturers and advisors. The opportunity to learn from those who have made an impact on the global business community adds to the School's unique academic and hands-on atmosphere.

The Columbia MBA equips students with the tools they need to be competitive and valuable in the international marketplace. The revised curriculum integrates the core disciplines of accounting, finance, management, marketing and operations, and incorporates four overarching themes: total quality management, ethics, human resource management and globalisation. To increase the understanding of interdisciplinary concepts and practices, the faculty uses combinations of lectures, group projects and case studies.

The School's proximity to Wall Street – and to leading international consulting, financial services, media, advertising, pharmaceutical, real estate and consumer packaging firms, provides unparalleled opportunity for students. Over 390 companies recruited on campus in 1997 and the school received over 3,500 correspondence opportunities from firms worldwide. The Career Services Offices provided close to 60 different workshops, seminars and panels on conducting effective job searches.

Cornell University's Johnson School of Management

> Qualifies for the Association of MBAs Loan Scheme

Address: 315 Malott Hall, Ithaca, New York 14853, USA
Tel: +1 607 255 4526   Fax: +1 607 255 0065
EMail: mba@cornell.edu
Internet: www.gsm.cornell.ed
Dean: Robert J Swieringht

MBA Programmes
Full-time MBA

Programme Details	Full-time
Duration	2 years
Commencement	May
Application deadline	Rolling
GMAT Yes/No	Yes
Fees EC/Overseas	$70,000/55,000
Annual student intake	250
Average student age	28
Min. required experience	2 years
%EC/Overseas	28
%Men/Women	70/30
Number of Professors	48
Number of Academic Staff	48
Number of elective courses	60
Assessment: Exams/Assignments	Both

Darden Graduate School of Business Administration

> Qualifies for the Association of MBAs Loan Scheme

Address: University of Virginia, PO 6550, Charlottesville, Virginia 22906-6550, USA
Tel: +1 804 924 7281   Fax: +1 804 924 4859
EMail: darden@virginia.edu
Internet: www.darden.edu
Dean: C Ray Smith
MBA Admissions Officer: A Jon Megibow

MBA Programmes

Full-time MBA programme in General Management; Executive Education programmes; joint degrees with Engineering, Nursing, Government/Foreign Affairs, Law and Asian Studies

Programme Details	Full-time
Duration	2 years
Class Contact	78 credit hours
Commencement	September
Application deadline	March 15
GMAT Yes/No	Yes
Fees EC/Overseas	$20,249 non-Virginia resident (tuition & fees)
Annual student intake	240-250
Average student age	27
Min. required	
%EC/Overseas	18% international
%Men/Women	70/30
Number of Professors	80
Number of Academic Staff	78
Number of elective courses	80
Assessment: Exams/Assignments	Both
Dissertation/Project	Directed study

Additional Information

Library hours: 0730-2400 (Mon-Fri); 0800-1800 (Sat); 1200-2400 (Sun)

IT facilities: Integrated computing environment supporting over 1,000 ports for student access; Major databases; Email; Access to Internet

School Description

The Darden School offers a two-year Master of Business Administration degree programme designed as a unified curriculum rather than a collection of courses. The programme, widely known for its general management orientation and intensive learning experience, prepares men and women for positions of leadership in today's complex business world.

Darden students are interested in a wide variety of careers in the private and public sectors. Many of the students accept positions that involve international assignments. Finance, marketing, consulting, and operations are traditionally the functions employing most Darden graduates at entry, with most aspiring to general management positions in manufacturing or the service sector. Starting salaries for Darden graduates are high, ranking in the top ten in the US.

The Darden School now occupies new facilities (5 new buildings) designed by Robert A M Stern and inspired by the Jeffersonian architecture of the University of Virginia.

The rigor and intensity of life at The Darden School find their complement in the easy-paced life of Charlottesville and the tranquil beauty of the nearby Blue Ridge Mountains.

Charlottesville and the surrounding Albermarle county have a combined population of more than 100,000. Newcomers find a remarkably cosmopolitan community wth friendly people, ample cultural and recreational opportunities, lovely rural surroundings, and a thriving economy. Such firms as General Electric and Sperry Marine have facilities in Charlottesville.

Harvard Business School

Qualifies
for the
Association
of MBAs
Loan
Scheme

Address: MBA Admissions, Dillon House, Boston MA 02163, USA
Tel: +1 617 495 6127   Fax: +1 617 496 9272
EMail: admissions@hbs.edu
Internet: www.hbs.edu
Director: Jill Fadule

MBA Programmes
Full-time MBA

Programme Details	*Full-time*
Duration	16 or 20 months
Class Contact	18 hours per week
Commencement	June
Application deadline	November 12, January 8, March 5
GMAT Yes/No	Yes
Fees EC/Overseas	$25,000
Annual student intake	880
Average student age	26
Min. required experience	2 years
%EC/Overseas	25
%Men/Women	71/29
Number of Professors	170
Number of elective courses	70
Assessment: Exams/Assignments	Both
Dissertation/Project	P

Additional Information
International Links: International Field Study Program

IT facilities: Two computer labs; internal website (communication centre for entire HBS community)

School Description
The MBA programme seeks to develop outstanding business leaders who will contribute to the well-being of society. Students are taught an integrative approach to managerial decision-making, which invovles the basic functions of business as well as social/political and economic factors. The School develops their analytical and problem-solving abilities to prepare them for the responsibilities of leadership in business, government, and non-profit organisations.

The programme takes four terms to complete. Terms I and II are a required curriculum; terms III and IV are all electives, Students may take courses throughout the University, and at Tufts' Fletcher School and MIT's Sloan School.

The MBA programme uses practical teaching methods including case method, business simulations, group projects, and small group discussion.

Harvard offers the largest business library in the world. On-campus accommodation is available.

Indiana University Kelley School of Business

Address: 1309 East 10th Street, Room 254, Indiana University, Bloomington IN 47405-1701, USA

Tel: +1 812 855 8006   Fax: +1 812 855 9039

EMail: mbaoffice@indiana.edu/mba

Internet: www.bus.indiana.edu/mba

Dean: Dan Dalton

MBA Admissions Officer: James Holmen

MBA Programmes
Full-time MBA

Programme Details

	Full-time
Duration	2 academic years
Class Contact	54 credit hours
Commencement	May
Which evening/day	Day
Application deadline	Dec 1, Feb 1; international students Dec 1, Jan 15,
GMAT Yes/No	Yes
Fees EC/Overseas	Roughly $30,000 per annum
Annual student intake	280
Average student age	28
Min. required experience	No minimum; four years average
%EC/Overseas	20
%Men/Women	74/26
Number of Professors	135
Number of Academic Staff	14
Number of elective courses	Variable
Assessment: Exams/Assignments	Both
Dissertation/Project	None

Additional Information

International Links: Study abroad available in England, Australia, France, Spain, Switzerland, Norway, Mexico. Summer programmes in Germany and Finland. Member of MBA Enterprise Corps

Library hours: 0800-2400 (Mon-Fri), 1000-2400 (Sat), 1100-2400 (Sun)

IT facilities: MBA students have access to four public computing facilities and a private lab which contains Pentium-based workstations with Internet access, flatbed scanner, Bloomberg terminal, Lexis/Nexis stations, and two high-speed network laser printers.

School Description

Indiana University Graduate School of Business offers study leading to the MBA degree. Accredited by the American Assembly of Collegiate Schools of Business, the programme takes two years and requires 54 credits. The Indiana MBA curriculum reflects a new direction in graduate management education. The first year of the MBA curriculum is designed to provide students with the basic business principles and management tools. Students participate in a foundations and functional core that includes integrative teaching methods, group work, and consideration of the global economy. The critical issues of cultural diversity, ethics, and communication are among the topics addressed in an integrated form across the curriculum.

The course work in the second year permits individual choice, and students are able to self-design their programme. Students choose from one of four options, ranging from all electives and a generalist's focus to a double major, completing requirements for two majors. In addition, computer literacy is a critical component of the programme. Every MBA student is required to own a personal computer and use technology to support their academic work.

As a major research institution, Indiana University maintains an extensive computer network providing access to mainframe computers and numerous databases. MBA students are actively involved with the electronic mail system, the world wide web and the Internet. The library in the School of Business complex provides much computer access and also has more than 150,000 volumes of research materials. The main library is conveniently located across the street from the business school and is internationally known as one of the best university libraries.

Approximately 35 per cent of Bloomington MBA students receive financial aid from the School of Business. Graduate assistantships are available; these provide a partial fee remission and stipend in return for a minimal work obligation with faculty members or within administrative departments in the School of Business. In addition, more than $150,000 in scholarship funds is awarded each year to MBA students. The Business School awards are based on merit, not need. The IU Office of Student Financial Assistance administers federal financial aid based on student need. (The cost of a personal computer is calculated into the student's financial aid budget). Indiana University participates in the Consortium for Graduate Study in Management, which offers substantial support for candidates from minority groups.

The MBA Association attracts high student participation in sponsoring a variety of activities such as the MBA newspaper, social events, guest speakers from industry, and athletic events. Bloomington offers a number of museums and galleries. Opera at the School of Music is available for viewing pleasure, and restaurants are in abundance.

Ivey Business School

Address: The University of Western Ontario, London, Ontario N6A 3K7, Canada
Tel: +1 519 661 3212   Fax: +1 519 661 3431
EMail: admiss@ivey.uwo.ca
Internet: www.ivey.uwo.ca
Dean: Lawrence (Larry) Tapp
MBA Admissions Officer: Larysa Gamula

> Qualifies
> for the
> Association
> of MBAs
> Loan
> Scheme

MBA Programmes
Full-time MBA; LLB/MBA; Executive MBA

Programme Details	Full-time
Duration	2 years
Commencement	Sept/April
Application deadline	April 1
GMAT Yes/No	yes
Fees EC/Overseas	Can $14,000 for international students
Annual student intake	200
Average student age	29
%EC/Overseas	20%
%Men/Women	75/25
Number of Professors	70

Number of Academic Staff	100
Number of elective courses	40/50
Assessment: Exams/Assignments	Both
Dissertation/Project	P

Additional Information

International Links: Extensive exchange programme worldwide

IT facilities: Student computer labs

Electives not readily available elsewhere: Doing Business in Europe, Asia, Latin America, China; Entrepreneurship and Consulting Streams

School Description

Founded in 1878, the University of Western Ontario is one of Canada's oldest and largest universities and has established a tradition of excellence in teaching and research.

The Ivey MBA has long been regarded as one of the leading MBA programmes in the world; it is highly integrated and focuses on the leadership skills and perspectives essential for success in a global marketplace. The faculty are dedicated to teaching and creating an intense and 'real world' learning environment. As the second largest producer of teaching cases in the world, Ivey uses a variety of interactive and experiential learning methods which capitalise on the rich base of experience the class. The MBA students are distinguished by the diversity of their educational and professional backgrounds and their history of outstanding achievement. They come from over 20 countries world-wide, about 40 per cent have substantial work or educational experience outside Canada, and about one-third speak at least two languages.

The first year core courses are the same for all students; they are also exposed to an intensive 'Managing Diversity' workshop to help them understand the impact of greater diversity on management and how to harness that diversity to obtain better organisational performance. The second year allows choice from an array of options; courses covering various international topics, such as 'Managing in Developing Countries', are available.

Class projects undertaken with corporations allow companies to show future managers how major institutions operate and implement key strategic changes; this interaction with executives and managers results in a strong integration of material in the first year. A programme of industry tours, seminars, and guest speakers at the School feature prominent business and government leaders, many of whom are Ivey graduates.

London, with a population of 320,000 is two hours by car or train from Toronto and Detroit; it is known as 'Forest City' in recognition of the many trees which line its streets and add beauty to its parks.

J L Kellogg Graduate School of Management

Address: Leverone Hall, 2001 North Sheridan Road, Evanston IL 60208-2003, USA

Tel: +1 847 491 3308   Fax: +1 847 491 4960

EMail: kellogg.admissions@nwu.edu

Internet: www.kellogg.nwu.edu

Dean: Donald P Jacobs

MBA Admissions Officer: Michele Rogers

MBA Programmes

Masters of Management (Full-time) – 6 quarters or 4 quarters; Manager's Program (Part-time)

Programme Details	Full-time	Part-time	Full-time Quarter
Duration	2 years	2½-5 years	1 year
Commencement	September	Quarterly	June
Which evening/day		Monday Saturday	
Application	November 14/ January 15/ March 15	Quarterly	November 14/ January 15
GMAT Yes/No	Yes	Yes	Yes
Fees EC/Overseas	$42,596		$55,941
Annual student intake	490		75
Average student age	27		
%EC/Overseas	25%		
%Men/Women	69/31		
Number of Professors	150		
Number of elective courses	14		11
Assessment: Exams/Assignments	Both		
Dissertation/Project	None		None

School Description

Widely recognised as one of the finest graduate business programmes in the United States, the J L Kellogg Graduate School of Management at Northwestern University is home to a renowned, research-based faculty and bright, ambitious management students from around the world. From its quiet beginning at the turn of the century as the undergraduate School of Commerce, Kellogg has risen to national prominence through a dedication to academic excellence, a lively spirit of innovation, a commitment to serving the needs of the marketplace, and, above all, a profound sense of fellowship. Throughout all of its incarnations, Kellogg's goals have remained the same: to educate masters students to assume responsible roles in management; to encourage rigorous faculty research; to promote education for senior and mid-level executives; to prepare doctoral students to teach and pursue research in the management sciences.

Kellogg's Master of Management degree can be attained through three different programmes, each of which is led by the same faculty using the same teaching methods. The one-year and two-year full-time programmes are conducted on Northwestern's Evanston campus; a part-time evening programme, called The Managers' Program, is held at Northwestern's downtown Chicago campus.

The Kenan-Flagler Business School

Qualifies for the Association of MBAs Loan Scheme

Address: The University of North Carolina at Chapel Hill, CB 3490, McColl Building, UNC Chapel Hill NC 27599-3490, USA
Tel: +1 919 962 3236   Fax: +1 919 962 0898
EMail: mba.info@unc.edu
Internet: www.bschool.unc.edu
Dean: Robert S Sullivan
MBA Admissions Officer: Aleta Howell

MBA Programmes

Full-time MBA; Executive MBA (evening); Program MBA/JD (MBA and Law); MBA/MRP (MBA and Master of Regional Planning); MBA/MHA (MBA and Master of Health Care Administration)

Programme Details	Full-time	Other EMBA	Other MBA/ JD	Other MBA/ MRP	Other MBA/ MHA
Duration	2 years	2 years	4 years	3 years	3 years
Commencement	May	September	May	May	May
Which evening/day		evening Mon-Thurs			
Application deadline	March 6	March 6	Feb 1	Jan 31	April 15
GMAT Yes/No	Yes	Yes	Yes	Yes	Yes
Fees EC/Overseas	$17,017	$29,800			
Annual student age	200	65			
Average student age	27	33			
Min. required experience	2 years	5 years			
%EC/Overseas	20% intern.	12% intern.			
%Men/Women	2:1	2.6:1			
Number of Professors	101				
Number of elective courses	68	15-20			
Assessment: Exams/Assignments	Both	Both	Both	Both	Both
Dissertation/Project	P	P	P	P	P

Additional Information

International Links: Incl Frank Hawkins Kenan Institute of Private Enterprise and Kenan Institute Asia (in Bangkok); member of Programme International de Management (PIM); MBA Enterprise Corps; North Carolina Global Center; International Summer Internship Program

Library hours: The School's Graduate Career Services Library is open seven days a week

IT facilities: The Price Waterhouse-Dell Computer-Cabletron Systems Technology Center features 68 desktop systems with CD-ROM capability and computer study rooms. All 18 classrooms in the new McColl Building feature multimedia consoles

Electives not readily available elsewhere: Competitive Strategy in an Environmental Age; East Asia Business: Asia's Most Dynamic Markets and Companies; Telecommunications and Electronic Commerce; The Mexican Economy: Opportunities and Prospects; Communication for Tomorrow's Leaders

Other information: Kenan-Flagler's new McColl Building is located next to the Kenan Center, which houses the School's Kenan Institute of Private Enterprise and many of its international activities. The Kenan Institute also has offices in Washington, D.C., and Bangkok. The School has broken ground with a new executive education complex at Meadowmont, a pastoral former family estate located in Chapel Hill. The new complex will feature residential and classroom buildings, and a social facility.

School Description

The Kenan-Flagler Business School's highly ranked MBA programme takes a small, diverse group of experienced professionals, places them in a collegial, team-oriented environment and gives them an innovative curriculum taught by world-class faculty. A hallmark of the programme is a collegial, supportive environment emphasising teamwork, diversity and partnership with students. Kenan-Flagler prepares students to succeed in a global marketplace by maintaining a diverse student body, a diverse faculty and an expanding array of international experiences and courses.

Central to the MBA programme are the study groups of five or six students, assigned for the duration of the first year. The lock-step coursework of the first year builds a strong foundation of key management and leadership competencies. Students hone their skills in the second year by choosing from a wide range of electives clustered into 'career tracks'. The Practicum Program allows students to address a significant business problem for domestic and international companies.

Faculty members are dedicated to the integrated curriculum, incorporating cross-functional collaboration, team teaching and input from student and business people. The faculty consistently are ranked nationally for teaching excellence, availability and responsiveness to students, and emphasis on applied research and case development.

The School's strong placement record includes one of the best recruiter-to-graduate ratio of any business school; a variety of organisations that come to campus to interview students for positions in industries such as consulting, investment banking and consumer goods; and a strong support system for students conducting independent job searches.

The MBA Student Association (MBASA) serves as a liaison between students and faculty on academic matters and sponsors special events throughout the school year. Within MBASA, specific clubs focusing on functional or industry areas allow student to associate with others who have similar career interests. Clubs often sponsor guest speakers former family estate located in Chapel Hill. The new complex will feature residential and classroom buildings, and a social facility.

The quaint, village atmosphere of Chapel Hill has earned it the reputation as 'the perfect college town'. Chapel Hill is centrally located within North Carolina, allowing weekend rips to both the mountains and the coast. Outdoor and performing arts events are complimented by UNC sports, including nationally ranked basketball, football and soccer.

The School moved into a new, state-of-the-art $44 million facility in October 1997. The 191, 234 square-foot McColl Building, which houses all of the School's programmes, is equipped with the latest classroom and communications technology to enhance business teaching and research.

Dr Robert S Sullivan, the School's new dean, will direst the School's effort to create a new model of business education for the 21st century. He is an acknowledged leader in global business education, the application of technology to learning, entrepreneurship, and the commercialisation of new technologies.

McGill University

Qualifies for the Association of MBAs Loan Scheme

Address: 1001 Sherbrooke St West Suite 454 Montreal DC H3A 165, Canada
Tel: +1 514 398 4066   Fax: +1 514 398 2499
EMail: mba@management.mcgill.ca
Internet: www.management.mcgill.ca
Dean: Dr David M Saunders
MBA Admissions Officer: Antoinette Molino

MBA Programmes
Full-time MBA; Part-time MBA; MBA/Law; MBA/Asian Studies; MBA/MD

Programme Details	Full-time
Duration	2 years
Class Contact	15 hours per week
Commencement	September
Application deadline	April 1
GMAT Yes/No	Yes
Fees EC/Overseas	Can $16,000
Annual student intake	150

Average student age	26
Min. required experience	1 year
%EC/Overseas	40%
%Men/Women	70/30
Number of Professors	55
Number of elective courses	65
Assessment: Exams/Assignments	Both
Dissertation/Project	None

Additional Information

International Links: Exchange option available in Year 2 with 20 European, American, South American or Asian universities. On site MBA programme in Japan

Library hours: 0900-2200 daily

IT facilities: Computer resources; each student is assigned a network account. Two multi-purpose rooms have been dedicated to MBA students' use to facilitate individual and group work

School Description

The Faculty of Management at McGill University is world-renowned as a leader in international management education. Students acquire an inherent understanding of international commerce and an appreciation for other cultures in McGill's mulitcultural learning environment, and those interested in international business enjoy exceptional opportunities to network and acquire experience.

The McGill curriculum offers a unique learning opportunity to students. The traditional graduate business teaching approach usually combines theory, case studies and team projects in a collection of separate foundation courses. However, the McGill programme views the understanding gained from these foundation disciplines as a core knowledge required by all students, regardless of the function, organisation or industry in which they work. The balanced teaching has therefore been redefined to include integrative instruction; as a result, professors can jointly plan, teach and grade first-year courses.

The full-time curriculum features an integrative first year; all students follow the same sequence of courses in three 10-week modules. The rapport that develops between students and professors enhances the flexibility, adaptability, and people-oriented skills developed by the curriculum. The second year is free of required courses, and individuals may choose or individually tailor a concentration. The programme also provides the opportunity for MBA students to learn about the socio-economic, commercial, and cultural context to other countries by participating in one of 20 international exchanges during the second year.

McGill Faculty of Management occupies a building specifically designed for its needs, complete with computer-assisted instruction, a student lounge, a computing centre and library with electronic database searching services. A Management Career and Placement Centre with an extensive resource library acts as a facilitator between companies and students during the placement process.

McGill has one of the highest percentage of international students of any Canadian university. In fact 42% of the students speak three or more languages.

University of Michigan Business School

Address: 701 Tappan Street, Room 2260, Ann Arbor, Michigan 48109-1234, USA
Tel: +1 734 763 5796   Fax: +1 734 763 7804
EMail: umbusmba@umich.edu
Internet: www.bus.umich.edu
Dean: B Joseph White
MBA Admissions Officer: Natalie Grinblatt

MBA Programmes
Full-time MBA; Evening MBA

Programme Details

Programme Details	Full-time	Part-time
Duration	2 years	4 years
Class Contact	3 hours	3 hours per course per week
Commencement	September	September/January
Which evening/day	Day	Evening
Application deadline	Dec/Jan/March	October/May
GMAT Yes/No	Yes	Yes
Fees EC/Overseas	$48,000	$600 per credit hour
Annual student intake	430	300
Average student age	27	28
Min. required experience	2 years preferred	2 years preferred
%EC/Overseas	22	2
%Men/Women	72/28	78/22
Number of Professors	170	
Number of elective courses	130	
Assessment: Exams/Assignments	Varies	Varies
Dissertation/Project	No	No

Additional Information
International Links: Incl. Wirtschaftsuniversität Wien: National University of Singapore; Erasmus University Rotterdam; Ecole des Hautes Etudes Commerciales; Universita Commercial Luigi Bocconi; London Business School; Stockholm School of Economics; St Gallen; Escuela Superior de doblenz Program, Africa Corps, William Davidson Institute.

Library hours: 0800-2400 (One of the nation's largest business libraries with over 140,000 volumes, almost 400,000 microfilms,

IT facilities: 170 advanced microcomputers housed in a student lab and two classrooms

Electives not readily available elsewhere: Entrepreneurial Track; Manufacturing Management; Corporate Environmental Management; Global Projects Course, International Multidisciplinary Action Project Information on other facilities

School Description
The School offers a strong global business programme; strong ties with the community (many student projects are community-based); very diverse student body and faculty; opportunities for specialisation; world-class computer, library and teleconferencing facilities; leadership skills from its top-ranked executive education group; a unique in-compnay learning programme.

MIT Sloan School of Management

Address: 50 Memorial Dr E52-126, Cambridge MA 02142, USA
Tel: +1 617 253 3730   Fax: +1 617 253 6405
EMail: mbaadmissions@mit.edu
Internet: web.mit.edu/sloan/www/

Dean: Glen Urban

MBA Admissions Officer: Rod Garcia

MBA Programmes
Full-time MBA; MS in Management

Programme Details	Full-time
Duration	2 years
Commencement	June
Application deadline	January 31
GMAT Yes/No	Yes
Annual student intake	350
Average student age	28
%EC/Overseas	38
%Men/Women	72/28
Number of Professors	100
Number of elective courses	125+
Assessment: Exams/Assignments	Both

Additional Information
International Links: Over 35% international students representing more than 50 countries; five international field trips (Japan/Korea; South America; Eastern Europe; Western Europe; Asia) offered to all students.

Library hours: Sloan students have access to all five divisional libraries

IT facilities: Excellent IT facilities both within the School and other parts of the Institute; Laboratory for Financial Engineering (a virtual trading floor of networked workstations and financial and other business-related databases)

School Description
The Sloan Master's Programme educates managers for the next century, leaders able to deal with the complexity of organisational, financial, and technological issues in an increasingly competitive and international business world. Students may elect to receive a general management education by assembling a series of courses in Finance, Marketing, Operations Management, Information Technologies, Management of Technology, Industrial Relations, Accounting, and Human Resource Management. Alternatively, students can choose an interdisciplinary 'management track', a programme of classroom learning, workshops, supervised field work, seminars, and summer internships tailored to give them cutting-edge competency for specific careers. Management tracks in Finance, Financial Engineering, Strategic Management and Consulting, Information Technology and Business Transformation, and New Product and Venture Development are offered.

Theoretical, case study, applied and practical teaching methods are employed throughout the programme; most courses will combine the methods. Sloan's philosophy is that theory must be understood before it can be applied. There is an open-door policy among Sloan faculty, and students are encouraged to take full advantage of this. Sloan's student body is extremely diverse, with representation from around the world. The School is small, which encourages students to work and interact closely together in classes, in job searches, and socially.

Teamwork is essential, and most Sloan students form study groups; many class projects involve teamwork, which is explored conceptually in organisational study courses.

The Career Development Office hosts recruiting employers (185 plus last year, with similar numbers expected in future) and receives several hundred job opportunities by mail. Employers are keen to employ the skills acquired by Sloan graduates, perhaps now more than ever.

New York University, Leonard N. Stern School of Business

Address: 44 West Fourth Street, Management Education Center, Suite 10-160, New York 10012-1124, USA
Tel: +1 212 998 0600   Fax: +1 212 995 4231
EMail: sternmba@stern.nyu.edu
Internet: www.stern.nyu.edu
Dean: George Daly
MBA Admissions Officer: Mary Miller

MBA Programmes
Full-time MBA; Evening MBA; Executive MBA

Programme Details	Full-time	Part-time	Executive/Executive Finance
Duration	2 years	3-6 years	2 years
Class Contact	800 hours	800 hours	702 hours
Commencement	May	May/January/September	June
Which evening/day		Monday-Thursday evenings + Saturday (optional)	Alternate Fridays & Saturdays + 6 x 1-week residentials
Application deadline	March 15	May 15/ September 15	March 15
GMAT Yes/No	Yes	Yes	Yes
Annual student intake	410	650	100
Average student age	27	27	36
Min. required experience	2 years	2 years	10 years
%EC/Overseas	31%	4%	25%
%Men/Women	64/36	70/30	66/34
Number of Professors	290	290	50
Number of Academic Staff	200+	200+	
Number of elective courses	200+	200+	
Assessment: Exams/Assignments	Both	Both	Both
Dissertation/Project	P	P	P

Individual programmes accredited by the Association of MBAs are indicated by a tick

Additional Information

Library hours: 0800-2300 daily

IT facilities: Numerous facilities throughout campus

Electives not readily available elsewhere: Financial Engineering; Management Consulting; Entertainment Media & Technology

Other information: Located in heart of New York City's famed Greenwich Village and midway between Wall Street and Midtown Manhattan

School Description

The Leonard N. Stern School of Business is a vital part of New York University. Established in 1831, NYU has 13 schools, colleges and divisions at five major centres in Manhattan. The MBA programme at Stern provides fundamental management skills as well as in-depth knowledge in a chosen area of specialisation. A choice of eight majors plus four co-majors is available. The Stern programme gives students: conceptual and analytical skills; comprehensive information in one or more functional areas; breadth of knowledge across functional areas; an holistic view of an enterprise; an ability to act strategically; a global vision and understanding; an understanding of today's latest technologies; the capability to anticipate and manage change; a commitment to ethical and legal business practices combined with practical business experience.

Full- and part-time study modes are available. Full-time students spend the first semester studying the core curriculum in 'blocks' of 65 new candidates. They will elect block leaders to liaise between students and School administrators. Stern's novel Multi-Disciplinary Exercise in Teambuilding (MET) organises students into five member teams which analyse a company, and create and present a corporate strategy based on real-world data to a 'Board of Directors' comprised of Senior Corporate Executives. Following a summer internship, students complete their major and elective course work in the second year. Special programmes include: Entrepreneurial Studies; Management Consulting; Entertainment, Media and Telecommunications; the International Management Program (IMP). Through IMP, students can spend a semester abroad at one of 28 top business schools worldwide.

The Office of Career Development offers recruiting, counselling, and career development services. Over 200 companies recruit Stern students for summer internships and for full-time employment. Stern alumni hold positions in every major industry worldwide. The alumni network of approximately 70,000 includes members located all over the world.

Qualifies for the Association of MBAs Loan Scheme

Stanford Graduate School of Business

Address: 518 Memorial Way, Stanford University, Stanford 94305-5015, USA
Tel: +1 650 723 2766   Fax: +1 650 725 7831
EMail: mbainquiries@gsb.stanford edu
Internet: www.gsb.stanford.edu

Dean: A Michael Spence

MBA Admissions Officer: Marie Mookini

MBA Programmes

Full-time MBA; Public Management Program MBA; Global Management Program MBA; Health Services Management Program MBA

Programme Details

	Full-time
Duration	21 months
Class Contact	at least 102 course credits
Commencement	September
Application deadline	November, January, March
GMAT Yes/No	Yes
Fees EC/Overseas	Tuition $23,100
Annual student intake	Approx 365
Average student age	26
Min. required experience	2 years average
%EC/Overseas	30%
%Men/Women	530/215
Number of Professors	115
Number of Academic Staff	175
Number of elective courses	110
Assessment: Exams/Assignments	Both

Additional Information

Library hours: 0750-2300 (Mon-Thurs); 0750-1700 (Fri); 0800-1700 (Sat); 1300-2200 (Sun)

IT facilities: Fully-equipped computer lab; Access to high-speed electronic network

Electives not readily available elsewhere: Entrepreneurship and Venture Capital, Environmental Management; Supply Chain Management; Derivative Securities; Trading and Risk Management; High Performance Leadership

School Description

Stanford's MBA programme is designed to give a foundation in management which is expected to be as valuable in 20 years' time as it is immediately after graduation. The curriculum is dynamic, forward-looking and innovative, and constantly enriched as it incorporates new ideas. A variety of teaching styles are used, including cases, lectures, online assignments, and independent study.

Students learn from their classmates as well as from the faculty. To ensure that student-to-student learning is dynamic and meaningful, the United States' most selective admissions process is used to gather students who represent a broad range of professional and personal achievement.

The School is noted for its course offerings in Entrepreneurship, a Public Management programme designed to prepare students for leadership roles in public service throughout their careers and for providing business and management expertise to public sector organisations. A Global Management programme helps students prepare for today's global business environment and enhances faculty efforts to increase international dimensions of teaching and research. The Center for Entrepreneurial Studies supports teaching and research in entrepreneurship.

The Business School's Career Management Center is dedicated to giving students tools and information to help them launch their careers. In recent years, MBA graduates have averaged three job offers per student; by graduation, 99 per cent of the 1997 graduates had received job offers, with 16 per cent taking their first job outside the United States. To help with job searches, the CMC organises recruiting receptions in several international cities, in addition to having more than 250 firms recruit on campus each year.

The School is located in northern California, in the heart of a region of high technology and biotech firms. Facilities include one of the nation's most complete business libraries, an extensive computer facility, and access to high-speed computer networks. In 1997, the Schwab Residential Center opened, a few blocks from the Business School, providing private apartments for MBA students during the academic year.

University of Texas at Austin
Graduate School of Business

Address: PO Box 7999, Austin TX 78713, USA
Tel: +1 512 471 7612   Fax: +1 512 471 4243
EMail: texasmba@bus.utexas.edu
Internet: texasinfo.bus.utexas.edu

Dean: Robert May

MBA Admissions Officer: Dr Carl Harris

MBA Programmes
Full-time MBA

Programme Details

	Full-time
Duration	2 years
Class Contact	60 hours
Commencement	May
Application deadline	April 15 domestic/February 1 International
GMAT Yes/No	Yes
Fees EC/Overseas	$2,686/semester (domestic) $7,366/semester (inter)
Annual student intake	425
Average student age	28
Min. required experience	2 years
%EC/Overseas	24%
%Men/Women	73/27
Number of Professors	175
Number of elective courses	175
Assessment: Exams/Assignments	Both
Dissertation/Project	Optional

Additional Information
Electives not readily available elsewhere: MBA Investment Fund

School Description
The School has strengths in: Accounting; Entrepreneurship; Information Management; Operations Management; Marketing

The Wharton School

Address: University of Pennsylvania, 3733 Spruce Street, Philadelphia PA 19104-6361, USA
Tel: +1 215 898 6182   Fax: +1 215 898 0120
EMail: mba.admissions@wharton.upenn.edu
Internet: www.wharton.upenn.edu/
Dean: Robert J Alig

MBA Programmes
Full-time MBA; Executive MBA

Programme Details	Full-time
Duration	2 years
Class Contact	20 total
Commencement	August
Application deadline	April 10
GMAT Yes/No	Yes
Fees EC/Overseas	$47,216
Annual student intake	750
Average student age	28
Min. required experience	2 years preferred
%EC/Overseas	17/29
%Men/Women	72/28
Number of Professors	182
Number of elective courses	200
Assessment: Exams/Assignments	Exams/Proj
Dissertation/Project	None

Additional Information
International Links: Overseas Offices in Paris, Tokyo, China, Korea and Thailand; Ten international exchange programmes available; Global Immersion Programme

Library hours: until midnight

IT facilities: Computer labs with laser printer, electronic mail, on-line career development scheduling

School Description
Wharton's curriculum is designed to generate innovative and creative thinking and to instill an excitement about learning. Students are challenged through their core courses, case studies, and leadership coursework to formulate and solve problems. The first year focuses on Wharton's business core, providing fundamental skill, knowledge, and perspectives. Traditional semesters are replaced by four tightly-focused six-week quarters to expose students to the greatest number of subjects and to allow faculty to co-ordinate material across courses. Cohorts of 60 students, who take core courses together in the first year, form a strong social and academic group.

Clusters of three cohorts form a 'class within a class'. The second year allows student to choose electives from one of the largest selections of courses of any business school to pursue one of two dozen majors, or create joint majors and individualised programmes.

Wharton students have outstanding records of professional achievement and bring a wide range of experience, insights, and interests to the classroom and to campus. Drawing on their experiences throughout the world, students offer diverse cultural viewpoints on business issues. They bring perspectives from undergraduate major that range from English to engineering and work experience that extends from non-profit management to marketing to corporate finance.

Wharton MBA students help shape the intellectual atmosphere of challenge and collaboration that is a central part of a Wharton education.

Wharton's curriculum has a strong international perspective, reinforced by a core course on global strategic management and a range of electives that provide insights into global business. In addition, the Wharton Global Immersion Program option offers four weeks of intense, hands-on experience and education abroad following size weeks of classroom study. Recent groups have travelled to Japan, Germany, Brazil, China, and Russia. Wharton also offers two international join degree programmes, exchange programmes with ten leading international business schools, and opportunities to develop foreign language skills. Students pursue individual interests through more than 125 professionals, social, and academic affairs clubs and task forces.

The University of Pennsylvania was sounded in 1740 by inventor, entrepreneur, and statesman Benjamin Franklin. The 260-acre Ivy League campus is located in University City, which contains several colleges, business and government offices, and one of the largest urban research parks in the nation. The campus provides a setting of tree-lined walks, spacious lawns, and a blend of modern and historic buildings. The Wharton School, the world's first collegiate school of management, was founded in 1881 by entrepreneur and industrial Joseph Wharton. Wharton provides undergraduate master's doctoral, and executive education programmes.

The Wharton Career Development and Placement Office co-ordinates over 35 different programmes for students – from identifying potential career areas and developing effective job search strategies, to interviewing, negotiating, and evaluating offers. Some programmes extend over several days, involving numerous events and dozens of recruiters and industry leaders. Programmes include career management classes in the first year, alumni career panels, videotaped interview training, and seminars on negotiating offers.

There are strong international student communities at Wharton, with resources and programmes to meet social, cultural, and professional interests. International students make up on third of the MBA student body and they represent over 60 nationalities. Many of the campus club activities are generated by the cultural interests of MBA students. International students who plan to visit Wharton and wish to meet with an international student may contact the Admissions Office.

Qualifies for the Association of MBAs Loan Scheme

Yale School of Management (SOM)

Address: 135 Prospect Street, Box 208200, New Haven CT 06520-8200, USA
Tel: +1 203 432 5832   Fax: +1 203 432 9991
EMail: admissions@addmin.som.yale.edu
Internet: www.som.admissions@yale.edu
Director: Richard A Silverman

MBA Programmes
Full-time Master's Public and Private Management (MPPM)

Programme Details	*Full-time*
Duration	2 years
Class Contact	varies
Commencement	May
Application deadline	March 16
GMAT Yes/No	Yes
Fees EC/Overseas	$25,250 tuition, $16,400 living costs
Annual student intake	226
Average student age	27.2
Min. required experience	no min; 4.3 years average
%EC/Overseas	35%

%Men/Women	74/26
Number of Professors	82
Number of elective courses	varies (substantial)
Assessment: Exams/Assignments	Both
Dissertation/Project	P

Additional Information
International Links: Many (though no formal exchange programmes)

Library hours: Minimal holiday closings

IT facilities: State-of-the-art facilities

School Description
The two-year Master's programme in Public and Private Management teaches general management through a course of study that unites the intellectual content of the most competitive traditional MBA curriculum with both the practical application and broad context essential for effective modern management.

SCM students receive Yale training in the analytical and institutional knowlege required of successful managers; Accounting; Finance; Economics; Marketing; Data Analysis and Statistics; Organisational Behaviour; and other fundamental management disciplines. In addition, SOM students are taught to consider political and environmental factors; and to understand the interactions and interdependencies of private, public, and non-profit institutions.

Since its founding in 1976, the Yale School of Management has gained international recognition as a training ground for managers with extraordinary leadership and decision- making capabilities. They are individuals who have a deep appreciation for the use and effects of management practice, not only for the specific organisations in which they work, but also in the larger social, political, and global economic contexts.

Another exciting element of the Yale management experience is the opportunity to enrol in joint degree programmes with other distinguished Yale schools and departments. Students in these programmes pursue collaboratively designed, carefully integrated courses of study that lead to two degrees one year earlier than would otherwise be required.

Founded in 1701, Yale is one of the world's leading universities. Over 10,000 students are enrolled during the academic year, and more than 2,000 faculty teach and administer programmes across the full range of academic disciplines in the humanities, sciences, and social sciences. Yale SCM students have access to many of the rich resources of this institution during the course of their two years in New Haven.

Since November 1995 when Dean Jeffrey E. Garten first took the helm, the Yale School of Management is clearly on the move. The School is enjoying a surge in applications and on-campus recruiting has increased more than 80% in the past two years. Among the many new initiatives Dean Garten has introduced are a penetrating international focus on emerging markets that is attracting the best and brightest applicant pool. He is committed to expanding the senior faculty by 60% within the next few years and has plans to inaugurate a new International Center for Finance at SOM, which will house world renowned economists at Yale.

Australasia

Melbourne Business School, University of Melbourne

Address: 200 Leicester Street, Carlton, Victoria 3053, Australia
Tel: +61 3 9349 8100   Fax: +61 3 9349 8133
EMail: a.sankey@mbs.unimelb.edu.au
Internet: www.mbs.unimelb.edu.au/

Dean: Professor John Rose

MBA Admissions Officer: Ms Ann Sankey

MBA Programmes
Full-time MBA; Part-time MBA

Programme Details	Full-time	Part-time
Duration	18 months	4 years
Class Contact	780 hours	780 hours
Commencement	January	January/September
Which evening/day		Monday-Saturday
Application deadline	November 30	November 30/June 30
GMAT Yes/No	Yes	Yes
Fees EC/Overseas	A$39,000	A$39,000
Annual student intake	140	140
Average student age	28	28
Min. required experience	2 years	2 years
%EC/Overseas	50%	20%
%Men/Women	65/35	65/35
Number of Professors	15	15
Number of Academic Staff	45	45
Assessment: Exams/Assignments	Both	Both
Dissertation/Project	None	None

Additional Information
International Links: Member of PIM group of schools for student exchange

Library hours: 0900-1800 (Mon-Fri); 1000-1700 (Sat)

IT facilities: 2 PC labs, each with 21 PCs

School Description
The Melbourne MBA is a product of the long and close relationship between Melbourne-based corporations and the University of Melbourne. Most of Australia's largest corporations were founded in Melbourne in the late nineteenth century. Today, Melbourne is the headquarters for seven of Australia's ten largest companies. The University was established in 1854 and is consistently ranked as the leading research university in Australia.

The University produced its first MBA graduates in 1964. From these early beginnings, the Melbourne-based companies have supported the School with advice, and finance, by providing access for student projects, and by employing its graduates. Today, the Melbourne Business School is a not-for-profit company controlled by a Board which includes the Vice-Chancellor of the University along with the chairman and directors of the leading Australian corporations.

The relatively small full-time faculty of the School is continuously supplemented by visiting faculty from other leading business schools around the world. Many of these visitors return each year to teach in their specialisation. One feature of the School is its diverse student population. International students from twenty countries make up around 35 per cent of its student population. The International Students Club is one of the most active on campus, its members greet students who are new to Australia, conduct a special orientation programme, and organise many international events during term. In addition, around one quarter of the MBA students at the School change places with students from other leading schools as a part of the international exchange programme.

Qualifies for the Association of MBAs Loan Scheme

Australian Graduate School of Management, University of New South Wales

Address: Sydney 2052, Australia
Tel: +61 2 9931 9222   Fax: +61 2 9662 1695
EMail: r.christie@agsm.unsw.edu.au
Internet: www.agsm.unsw.edu.au

Dean: Professor Peter Dodd

MBA Admissions Officer: Ms Rosamund Christie

MBA Admissions Officer: Ms Carolyn Pugsley

MBA Programmes
Full-time MBA; Executive MBA

Programme Details	Full-time	Part-time
Duration	18 or 21 months	3 years
Class Contact	18 hours per week	6 hours per subject
Commencement	February	February/July
Which evening/day	n/a	Mon/Tues/Wed
Application deadline	30 November	28 Nov/5 June
GMAT Yes/No	Yes	No
Fees EC/Overseas	A$45,000	n/a
Annual student intake	124	330
Average student age	29	35
Min. required experience	2 years	2 years
%EC/Overseas	27%	0%
%Men/Women	78/22	79/21
Number of Professors	22	22
Number of Academic Staff	44	44
Number of elective courses	41	0
Assessment: Exams/Assignments	Both	Both
Dissertation/Project	P (optional)	Both

Additional Information
International Links: The full-time MBA offers an international student exchange program with 17 leading international business schools in North America, Europe and Asia

Library hours: 0800-1900 (Mon-Thurs), 0800-1800 (Fri); 1200-1800 (Sat)

IT facilities: Email; 24 hour internet access; 45 terminals; 4 printers; On-line library access to Bloomberg, Reuters, F&S, AAP and UNSW. CD-RDM network of 90

Electives not readily available elsewhere: Modern development in Financial Management (Joel Shenn); Developing fast growth high value-added enterprise (Paul Martin)

School Description
The Australian Graduate School of Management at the University of New South Wales was founded in 1977 as Australia's first national business school. It offers both a full-time MBA in Sydney and an Executive MBA delivered part-time by open learning in six major Australian cities. A PhD program, both full-time and part-time, is also available.

The full-time MBA is designed for those planning a major career move, either into a new field or a significant advance in their current career. Offered over either 18 months or 21 months with an optional summer term, it provides 800 hours of face to face teaching by world renowned faculty, extensive exposure to business leaders and an exchange program with 17 leading North American, European and Asian business schools. The optional summer term includes a work project in which small teams of students complete a project for a firm, supervised by AGSM faculty and the firm's managers. From 1998, overseas projects will be among those selected.

The Executive MBA program offers a modular sequence of courses over a minimum of three years. It is delivered through a mix of self-directed study materials, with synchronised classes held in Sydney, Melbourne, Brisbane, Adelaide, Perth and Canberra. Managers can thus transfer between study locations without disruption. The final year features intensive residentials held at the AGSM.

Major firms recruit annually at the AGSM, which offers a placement service for graduates. A graduate resumé book is published annually and in 1997, for the first time, a separate Asian resumé book was published for recruiters seeking graduates for Asia and graduates seeking employment in Asia.

The AGSM is located in its own building, which houses the Frank Lowy Library, the most comprehensive collection of management and business information in the Asia-Pacific region. The building, which was extended, redesigned and refurbished in 1996, is on the campus of the University of New South Wales in Sydney. It is 20 minutes' drive from the Sydney CBD, close to a number of surfing beaches, as well as the 350 hectare Centennial Park; and close to major sporting venues and recreation facilities.

The Graduate School of Business, The University of Sydney

Qualifies for the Association of MBAs Loan Scheme

Address: Locked Bag 20, Newtown, New South Wales 2042, Australia
Tel: +61 2 9351 0000   Fax: +61 2 9351 0099
EMail: gsbinfo@gsb.usyd.edu.au
Internet: www.usyd.edu.au/su/gsb
Dean: Professor Chris Adam
MBA Admissions Officer: Jenny Woodward

MBA Programmes
Full and Part-time MBA; Professional Accounting MBA

Programme Details	Full-time	Part-time
Duration	1½ years	3 years
Class Contact	672 hours	672 hours
Commencement	Jan/March/July	Jan/March/July
Which evening/day		All

Application deadline	31 Oct/30 April	31 Oct/30 April
GMAT Yes/No	Yes	Yes
Fees EC/Overseas	A$24,000/A$32,000	A$24,000/A$32,000
Annual student intake	60	80
Average student age	31	31
Min. required experience	2 years	2 years
%EC/Overseas	25%	90%
%Men/Women	60/40	75/25
Number of Professors	10	10
Number of Academic Staff	44	44
Number of elective courses	min 10 required	min 10 required
Assessment: Exams/Assignments	Both	Both
Dissertation/Project	P	P

Additional Information

International Links: Exchanges with USA, Asia and Europe

Library hours: 0900-2200

IT facilities: Computer Lab with 30 computers; home email links

School Description

MBA students at the University of Sydney learn the latest in management theory and practice, are taught by extremely well-qualified faculty, are exposed to fellow students of a very high calibre, and are able to adapt their studies to suit their individual needs. The University's worldwide reputation ensures that its MBA qualification is valued in many countries by both industry and government.

The MBA programme's design is significantly flexible; only one-third of subjects are compulsory, and a wide range of electives is available (including those offered by other faculties). The MBA is based on a general structure of semester-based courses; each course typically involves 42 class hours of instruction during a 14-week semester.

The Australian Society of Certified Practising Accountants (ASCPA) and the Institute of Chartered Accountants in Australia (ICAA) have approved for admission purposes a programme combing the MBA programme and courses available from the University of Sydney's Centre for Continuing Education. Candidates complete the MBA programme and a further five courses from the Centre; graduates are then eligible to enter the CPA programme of the ASCPA or the Professional Year programme of the ICAA (provided that they also meet the other admission criteria of these organisations).

The School has established exchange programmes with several leading business schools in Asia, Europe and the USA; MBA students may participate in these exchanges with other major MBA degrees in other countries. Students normally spend the final semester in the overseas programme, taking courses in that degree to contribute to their MBAs; students from the overseas programme spend the same semester on the School's MBA.

The School has an Industry Placement programme, which enables students to seek voluntary placement in leading organisations at the end of each semester. There are also workshops on selecting a suitable career, job search skills, resume writing, and interviewing skills.

The University offers sports facilities, student unions, clubs and a library.

South Africa

The Graduate School of Business, University of Cape Town

Address: Private Bag, Rondebosch 7700, South Africa
Tel: +27 21 406 1339   Fax: +27 21 215608
EMail: mbaenqry@gsb2.uct.ac.za
Internet: gsb.uct.ac.za

Director: Professor Kate Jowell

Professor Michael Page

MBA Admissions Officer: Pat Boulton

MBA Programmes
Full-time MBA; Part-time MBA

Programme Details	Full-time	Part-time
Duration	1 year	2 years
Commencement	January	January
Which evening/day		Monday eve/Saturday morn
Application deadline	October	October
GMAT Yes/No	Yes	Yes
Fees EC/Overseas	approx US$9,500	approx US$9,500
Annual student intake	approx 70	approx 50
Average student age	29	30
Min. required experience	3 years	3 years
%EC/Overseas	33%	
%Men/Women	83/17	84/16
Number of Professors	7	
Number of Academic Staff	16	
Number of elective courses	c10	
Assessment: Exams/Assignments	Both	Both
Dissertation/Project	D	D

Additional Information
International Links: Exchange programmes with: UCLA; Fuqual/Duke University; Wharton; New York University; Warwick University; Erasmus University

School Description
Founded in 1965, the Graduate School of Business of the University of Cape Town has established a reputation for excellence in providing business education for managers from all over the world.

The UCT MBA aims to provide a solid general management education. During the first two terms, students concentrate on foundation courses essential to a broad understanding of general management, including the business fundamentals of Data Analysis, Accounting, Economics, and Human Behaviour in Organisations. The focus then becomes the functional aspects of management (particularly Marketing, Finance, Human Resource Management, Manufacturing and Operations Management). The second year concentrates on integrating all aspects of management through a series of cross-functional electives and core courses in Strategy, Management of Technology, and Company Analysis. Students conclude with a research report on a specific subject, in recognition of the importance of scientific rigour.

The teaching style (a dynamic three-phase sequence of learning involving private preparation followed by group discussion) encourages a high degree of student participation; this is also encouraged during formal lectures. The relatively small number of resident faculty are supplemented by colleagues from other departments at the University and a large number of visiting international academics and business experts.

The Career Development Service publishes and distributes a Graduates Guide containing the CVs of all students and arranges workshops on CV preparation and interview techniques, and on-campus presentations and interviews by companies seeking to employ MBA graduates.

All MBA graduates become life members of the Graduate School of Business Association, an international network of some 14,500 alumni. Interaction between MBA students continues outside the classroom with a wide range of social sport, and community-orientated activities.

Accommodation is available at the Breakwater Campus, the converted Breakwater Prison overlooked by Table Mountain, which also offers modern lecture theatres and seminar rooms, a self-service restaurant, and a cocktail bar with restaurant. The School is located at the Victoria and Alfred Waterfront (constructed around a working harbour), which offers a vibrant mix of restaurants, pubs, hotels, craft markets, theatres, shops, and outdoor entertainment venues.

Qualifies for
the
Association
of MBAs
Loan Scheme

Graduate School of Business, University of Stellenbosch

Address: PO Box 610 Bellville 7535, South Africa
Tel: +27 21 9184205   Fax: +27 21 9184112
EMail: ehjs@maties.sun.ac.za
Internet: www.sun.ac.za/local/academic/usb/usb.ht

Dean: Professor E vd M Smit

MBA Admissions Officer: Ms E H J Swart

MBA Admissions Officer: Ms M Willows

MBA Programmes
Full-time English MBA; Part-time evening English/Afrikaans MBA; Modular English MBA; Modular Afrikaans MBA; Modular Human Resources Management MBA

Programme Details	Full-time	Part-time	Modular
Duration	2 years	3 years	4 years
Class Contact	4 hours per day	2 hours/day	6 hours/day
Commencement	January	January	March/January
Which evening/day		Monday/ Wednesday/ Friday	3 sessions of 2 weeks for first 3 years
Application deadline	October 31		
GMAT Yes/No	Yes		
Fees EC/Overseas	R31,220	R31,220	R31,220
Annual student intake	40	50	140
Average student age	26	30	35
Min. required experience	2 years	2 years	2 years
%EC/Overseas	1%		

%Men/Women	70/30
Number of Professors	8
Number of Academic Staff	13
Number of elective courses	8
Assessment: Exams/Assignments	Both
Dissertation/Project	Both

Additional Information

International Links: Member of AACSB and EFMO

Library hours: 0800-2000 (Mon-Fri); 0900-1300 (Sat)

IT facilities: Access to Internet and International Electronic Mail Service; Variety of personal computers, printers, etc

School Description

The MBA course comprises four sections. The first, Foundations of Management, has three components: personal (where the emphasis is on the academic and experience-based study of personal and interpersonal behaviour, team work and communication skills); conceptual (in which students are exposed to organisation models and the systems approach); practical (which includes the development of technical and analytical skills, and in which students are expected to draw up a business plan for an enterprise as a practical application).

The second section, Functional and Integrated Management, is directed at knowledge which the manager should have in order to integrate the personal, functional and organisational elements of organisation management.

The third section, Management in Content, concentrates on the broader social and economic environment and transformation in which business is conducted. Strategy formulation, international management opportunities, and the social and moral aspects of doing business are highlighted.

The fourth section, the Research Report (study project), entails analysis of a real business problem and should comprise 60-120 typed pages. Students also have the opportunity to select two electives.

The Course is available in full-time, part-time, and modular modes. Students taking the Modular degree can choose between English presentation or a combination of English and Afrikaans; they also have the option to specialise in Human Resources (taking courses in Personnel Management and Industrial Relations in their third year). Alumni and students of the School manage the USB Club, which provides an opportunity for both alumni and present students to make a tangible contribution towards the development of the Business School. Continuous contact between alumni is ensured through meetings organised in different provinces, at which speakers discuss topical subjects. Club members receive a newsletter three times per year.

The School is conveniently situated for a wide variety of activities such as golf, squash, tennis, hiking, sailing, and volleyball. A local sports club offers gymnasium, swimming, and squash facilities.

It's a jungle out there.
Join the lions.

WITS BUSINESS SCHOOL

The Wits Business School (WBS) is located in Johannesburg in the heart of South Africa's rapidly transforming business community. Established as an integral part of the University of the Witwatersrand in 1968 and sharing its commitment to values and high academic standards, the WBS has proven to be highly effective in empowering individuals to handle local and global business challenges and continues to produce a significant number of the country's most outstanding business leaders.

Believing focused education to be central to effective management, the WBS aims to equip students with the theoretical knowledge and practical management skills necessary to assume a leadership role in the changing and challenging business environment. The school offers a highly interactive approach to management education that draws on the experience of all executives, companies and industries in the programmes.

The faculty is staffed by academics who are recognised authorities in their fields and have extensive experience in the private sector. The WBS also invites international faculty on a regular basis to teach on its programmes and enjoys a working relationship with a number of international business schools. The WBS is consistently ranked by local surveys as the leading business school in SA.

The Wits MBA is a focused, practical and future orientated programme. A choice of three formats is offered: a three year part-time programme; a twelve month full-time programme; and an eighteen month programme that allows students to complete the first half of the MBA in six months full-time and the second half of the programme (electives and research report) over twelve months part-time.

Through its course in International Business, which includes a significant overseas experience as part of the core curriculum, as well as its student exchange programmes, the Wits MBA offers a blend of a deeply relevant South African orientation to management practice as well as a critical component of international exposure and experience.

Students are selected from a large number of applicants who have already shown significant promise and success in business and are able to bring to the classroom their own wealth of experience and viewpoints about the practice of management. Constant feedback from students and companies shows that the Wits MBA provides a unique learning experience.

For more information, please contact the MBA course co-ordinator on tel: (2711) 488-5600; fax: (2711) 643-2336; e-mail: gierutj@zeus.mgmt.wits.ac.za

UNIVERSITY OF THE WITWATERSRAND
WITS BUSINESS SCHOOL
INNOVATION THROUGH INTERACTION

30th Anniversary

Wits Business School

Address: University of the Witwatersrand, PO Box 98, Wits, 2050, Johannesburg, South Africa
Tel: +27 11 488 5581   Fax: +27 11 643 2336
EMail: reg@zeus.mgmt.wits.ac.za
Internet: www/wits.ac.za/wbs

Dean: Professor Mike Ward

MBA Admissions Officer: Mrs Leslie Salter

MBA Programmes
Full-time MBA; Evening MBA

Programme Details	Full-time	Part-time
Duration	1 year	3 years
Class Contact	630 hours	630 hours
Commencement	June	January
Which evening/day		Varies
Application deadline	February 28	August 30
GMAT Yes/No	Yes	Yes
Fees EC/Overseas	R35,000	R35,000
Annual student intake	55	75
Average student age	29	31
Min. required experience	4 years	5 years
%EC/Overseas	5%	
%Men/Women	65/35	
Number of Professors	8	
Number of Academic Staff	22	
Number of elective courses	20	
Assessment: Exams/Assignments	Both	Both
Dissertation/Project	D	D

Additional Information
International Links: International Student Exchange Programme

IT facilities: Up-to-date computer laboratories, facilities and networks

Electives not readily available elsewhere: Issues in South African Management; Business in Asia; International Marketing; Labour Issues in SA

Other information: The John S Schlesinger Library is widely recognised as one of the leading management libraries in South Africa; it contains more than 6,000 volumes, subscribes to over 100 journals, and includes a significant collection of research projects accumulated over a 25-year period

School Description
The Wits Business School, rated the top school in South Africa in 1997, was established in 1968 and is located in the heart of the business community, with which it maintains close ties through consulting and teaching on executive programmes. The School is striving for increased global awareness. Some of the lecturers have lived overseas whilst teaching in foreign business schools, and several visiting professors are appointed annually.

The Full-time MBA programme commences in June each year. The first six months comprises core courses and students may opt to spread the second half (electives and research report) over a six month or twelve month period. A third option is to take the Evening MBA. A three year course, this is a post experience programme, with the average student age approximately 30 years.

Asia

The Chinese University of Hong Kong

Address: MBA Programmes, Chinese University of Hong Kong, G07, Leung Kau Kui Building, Shatin, New Territories, Hong Kong
Tel: +852 2609 7783   Fax: +852 2603 6289
EMail: cumba@cuhk.edu.hk
Internet: www.cuhk.edu.hk/baf/graduate.html
Director: Professor Japhet S Law
MBA Admissions Officer: Ms Lauren Lee

MBA Programmes
Full-time MBA; Part-time MBA; Executive MBA

Programme Details	Full-time	Part-time	Executive MBA
Duration	2 years	2 to 3 years	2 years
Class Contact	3	3	8
Commencement	September	September	late August
Which evening/day	5 day	variable	Friday eve, Saturday afternoon
Application deadline	February 28	February 28	January 2/April 9
GMAT Yes/No	Yes	Yes	No
Fees EC/Overseas	HK$44,500	HK$57,000	HK$98,010 plus HK10,700 residence fee
Annual student intake	40	90	40
Average student age	24	28	35
Min. required experience	n/a	3 years	7 years
%EC/Overseas	10%	0	0
%Men/Women	53/47	64/36	3/1
Number of Professors	100	100	100
Number of elective courses	53	53	n/a
Assessment: Exams/Assignments	Both	Both	Both
Dissertation/Project	P	P	n/a

Additional Information
International Links: Program exchanges with schools in USA, Canada, Europe, Asia and Australia
IT facilities: CD-ROM resources; on-line searches on overseas and local databases
Electives not readily available elsewhere: China's Trade and Enterprise; Business Practicum; Management: Competencies and Current Perspectives

School Description
The MBA courses in the curriculum will enable students to continue to explore in greater depth the issues and processes in their own field of expertise. Each term is filled with activities and events to motivate and stimulate students to think beyond themselves and their special interests.

Seminars and talks by business leaders create opportunities for students to learn vicariously about the challenge of constructing the corporate vision and fulfilling the mission and strategy despite obstacles. The International Exchange Programme and workshops on building cross-cultural skills promote awareness of cultural differences in a multicultural team or while working in another country. Public lectures by world-renowned experts bring to students state-of-the-art approaches to addressing current business issues at a global level.

The MBA Programme strives to provide a balanced MBA education through its Executive Development Series. The aim is to prepare graduates for society as well as for the business community. We want students to believe that caring for the social and physical environment are as important as enabling organizations become more profitable. Students are encouraged to devote part of their extra-curricular activities towards community service with non-profit organizations. Field visits to see environmental conservation projects are organized to increase their awareness of key environment issues and solutions.

The MBA Programme also encourages the students to become well-rounded individuals through developing awareness of the sciences, arts and humanities. To develop their critical thinking skills, students meet and interact with scholars and professionals from these disciplines. They are encouraged to apply what they learned from these disciplines into business situations.

Sports, games, and debating events are organized regularly to develop team and individual skills. Activities such as hikes through some of Hong Kong's mountain trails and the annual MBA homecoming event are an important part of the MBA student experience, These activities build a sense of belonging and identity with the MBA Programme that is essential for sustaining an active alumni.

In co-operation with many leading business firms in Hong Kong, the Programme arranges for work opportunities for student in the summer between their first and second year of study. These students are generally assigned meaningful projects under the supervision of the senior management of the firm which provides the employment opportunities. Thus, they are able to gain valuable experience related to their studies.

The MBA programme make every effort to assist each graduate in finding a position that matches their interests and abilities. The Chinese University's Appointment Service also helps graduates find suitable positions. The Appointment Service provides employments counseling services to all the students. MBA Students may register with this Service and make use of its numerous career services. The MBA Programmes career activities include the following: modules on career communication and interviewing skills in the course on Management Communication production of a resume book containing information of the graduating class and sent directly to companies in Hong Kong.

Scholarships, exchange student awards and financial assistance are available. Life beyond the CUMBA degree is filled with excitement and challenge for our 2,000 strong alumni. We take pride in the achievements of our alumni and follow their career growth. Our alumni are most valuable resource of our Programmes. Many of our MBA graduates are now in the forefront of Hong Kong's business community.

Part 3
APPENDICES

Useful contacts

United Kingdom

General

Association of MBAs, 15 Duncan Terrace, London N1 8BZ. Tel: 0171 837 3375. Internet: http://www.mba.org.uk.
Services to MBA members. Accreditation of MBA programmes. Offers impartial general information on MBA study. Administers Business School Loan Scheme. Does NOT offer scholarships.

Association for Management Education & Training in Scotland (AMETS), The Cottrell Building, University of Stirling, Stirling FK9 4LA. Tel: 01786 450906. Fax: 01786 465070. EMail: amets@stir.ac.uk.
Organisation for Scottish schools. Provides MBA fact sheet on Scottish schools. Details on Management Training.

Career Development Loans, Career Development, Employment Department, Steele House, Room 711, Tothill Street, London SW1H 9NF. Tel: 0800 585505.
Loans for vocational courses. Available for one year of study only.

Chartered Institute of Bankers, LoMBArd Scheme, Emmanual House, 4/9 Burgate Lane, Canterbury CT1 2XJ. Tel: 01227 762600. Fax: 01227 763788. Internet: cib@qmw.ac.uk.
For details about LoMBArd Scheme – MBA courses for Associates of the Institute.

Foundation for Management Education, Sun Alliance House, New Inn Hall Street, Oxford OX1 2QE. Tel: 01865 310570. Fax: 01865 310794.
Provides information about Management Teaching.

Women in Management, 5th Floor, 45 Beech Street, London EC2Y 8AD. Tel: 0171 382 9978. Fax: 0171 382 9979.
A network for women in management. Provides training and development and offers advice.

Scholarship & awards

Association of Commonwealth Universities, John Foster House, 36 Gordon Square, London WC1H 0PF. Tel: 0171 387 8572. Fax: 0171 387 2655. EMail: awards@acu.ac.uk.
Scholarships for study within the Commonwealth. Information on Commonwealth universities. Publications on undergraduate and postgraduate courses.

Economic & Social Research Council (ESRC), Polaris House, North Star Avenue, Swindon SN2 1UJ. Tel: 01793 413000. Fax: 01793 413001.
Funding for research degrees and some masters courses in the UK. Funding NOT available for MBA study.

The Grants Register, Globe Book Services Ltd., Macmillan Publishers Ltd., Brunel Road, Basingstoke, Hants RG21 2XS. Tel: 01256 817245.
Comprehensive listing of grants, scholarship and awards. Available in all academic and large libraries.

London Chamber of Commerce & Industry Examinations Board, Charles R.E. Bell Fund, 112 Station Road, Sidcup, Kent DA15 7BJ. Tel: 0181 302 0261. Fax: 0181 309 5169.
Scholarships tenable in the UK or abroad. Applicants must be UK residents and in employment.

The Lord Kitchener National Memorial Fund, The Secretary, Satters Green Farm, Mayfield, East Sussex TN20 6NP.
Scholarships available to sons and daughters of serving and retired members of HM Forces.

Rotary International of Great Britain & Ireland, Kinwarton Road, Alcester, Warwickshire B49 6BP. Tel: 01789 765411. Fax: 01789 765570.
Scholarships for study outside one's own country.

The Royal Academy of Engineering, Sainsbury Management Fellowship Scheme Office (MFS), 29 Great Peter Street, London SW1P 3LW. Tel: 0171 222 2688. Fax: 0171 233 0054. Internet: bowbricki@raeng.co.uk.
Scholarships for professionally qualified engineers aged 26–34. Tenable only at international schools.

United States

General Information

Graduate Management Admissions Council (GMAC), 8300 Greensboro Drive, Suite 750, McLean, Virginia 223102, USA. Tel: +1 703 749 0131. Fax: +1 703 749 0169.
Umbrella organisation for US schools. MBA forums. Publications.

Educational Advisory Service, Fulbright Commission (US–UK Educational Commission), Fulbright House, 62 Doughty Street, London WC1N 2LS.
Internet: http://www.fulbright.co.uk. Tel: 0171 404 6994 or for Test Information: 0171 404 6854.
General information of study in the USA including list of awards and MBA information sheet (send A4 s.a.e. for 60 grams). Library of university catalogues and business school guides. Provides GMAT application bulletin (send A4 s.a.e. with postage for 115 grams). GMAT preparation guides for sale and reference use, and computer facilities include computer-based GMAT practice software...

American Association of University Women USA, Educational Foundation
Programs, 1111 16th Street North West, Washington, DC 20036-4873, USA. Tel: +1
202 785 7700. Fax: +1 202 872 1425.
Scholarships for women currently studying in the USA.

British Universities North America Club (BUNAC), 16 Bowling Green Lane,
London EC1R 0BD. Tel: 0171 251 3472 Fax: 0171 251 0215. Internet:
http://www.bunac.org. EMail: bunac@co.uk.
"Topping up" awards for study in North America.

English Speaking Union of the Commonwealth, 37 Charles Street, London W1X
8AB. Tel: 0171 493 3328. Fax: 0171 495 6108. EMail: esu@mailbox.ultc.ac.uk.
Nelly Gwendolyn Lewis Scholarships for study in the USA. One award every
two years. Must have been born or educated in Wales.

Frank Knox Fellowships, 16 Great College Street, London SW1P 3RX.
Tel: 0171 222 1151. Fax: 0171 222 8550.
Scholarships for Harvard only. Closing date October 17th for following year. Applicants
must have graduated no earlier than two years prior to September of departure to the
USA. Scholarships only tenable from September start of academic year.

Fulbright Awards, Fulbright Commission, Fulbright House, 62 Doughty Street,
London WC1N 2LS. Tel: 0171 404 6880. Internet: http://www.fulbright.co.uk.
Scholarships for study in the USA, including several MBA awards. Must be UK citizen,
graduate with 2:1 degree or higher, outstanding academic ability and leadership skills.
MBA applicants must also show 2–3 years work experience. Academic exchanges.

Kennedy Memorial Trust, Kennedy Scholarships, 16 Great College Street,
London SW1P 3RX. Tel: 0171 222 1151. Fax: 0171 222 8550.
Scholarships for Harvard and M.I.T. only. Application deadline October 25th for
following year. Applicants must have graduated no earlier than three years prior
to September of departure to the USA. Scholarships only tenable from September
start of academic year.

The Sainsbury Management Fellowship Scheme, The Royal Academy of
Engineering, 29 Great Peter Street, London SW1P 3LW. Tel: 0171 222 2688.
Fax: 0171 233 0054.

Thouron Awards, Office of the Registrar, University of Glasgow, Glasgow
G12 8QQ. Tel: 0141 339 8855.
Scholarships for University of Pennsylvania only.

Thomas Angear Scholarship, The Dean, Office of Admissions, Johnson
Management School, Cornell University, Ithaca, NY 14853, USA. Tel: +1 607 255
8915.
For study at Cornell only. Open to EC nationals. Worth c. $5 000. Renewable for
2nd year.

(B) Aston University	0121 333 5940	Fax: 0121 333 4731
Brunel University	01985 203064	
(B) Durham University	0191 374 2219	Fax: 0191 374 3748
Institute of Finance, Bangor Banking	01248 382278	
(B) Henley Management College	01491 571454	Fax: 01491 410184
Heriot Watt University, Edinburgh Business School	0131 449 5111	
Keele University	01782 621111	
(B) Kingston University	0181 547 2000	Fax: 0181 547 7026
Leicester University Management School	0116 2523952	
Leicester University (Education)	01604 30180	
Napier University	0131 445 5016	
(B) Open University	01908 654321	Fax: 01908 563744
Oxford Brookes University	01865 485783	
Oxford Brookes University (Hospitality)	01865 483800	
Paisley University	0141 848 3921	
Reading University	01734 318180	
Stirling University (Retailing)	01786 467386	
(B) Strathclyde University	0141 553 6000	Fax: 0141 552 2501
Surrey European Management School	01483 259347	
(B) Warwick University	01203 523922	Fax: 01203 523719
Westminster University (Design Management)	0171 911 5000	

Association of MBAs accredited programmes

United Kingdom

Ashridge Management College
MBA – full & part-time

Aston Business School
MBA – full-time, part-time & distance
  learning
MBA – Public Sector Management

University of Bath
School of Management
MBA – full-time, modular, Executive
  part-time & MIM (Malaysian Institute
  of Management)/Bath Executive MBA

The Birmingham Business School
MBA – full-time (International Business &
  European Business)
MBA – part-time (Evening & Executive
  Modular)
MBA – part-time (Executive Modular,
  Singapore)

Bradford Management Centre
MBA – full & part-time

Bristol Business School
University of the West of England
MBA – part-time

University of Bristol
Graduate School of International Business
MBA in International Business (full-time &
  part-time)

The University of Cambridge
The Judge Institute of Management Studies
MBA – full-time

City University Business School
MBA – full & part-time
MBA – Engineering Management

Cranfield School of Management
MBA – full-time & part-time
MSc – Project Management

De Montfort University
School of Business
MBA – part-time

Durham University Business School
MBA – full, part-time & distance
  learning

**Edinburgh University Management
  School**
MBA – full & part-time

University of Glasgow Business School
MBA – part-time

Henley Management College
MBA – full-time, part-time, distance
  learning & modular
MBA – Project Management (modular &
  distance learning)

Imperial College Management School
MBA – full & part-time

Kingston Business School
MBA – part-time & open learning

Lancaster University
The Management School
MBA – full-time & part-time

Leeds University Business School
MBA – full-time
MBA – part-time Executive & Evening
MBA – part-time Executive (Health &
  Social Services)

London Business School
MBA – full & part-time
Sloan Fellowship Programme

Manchester Business School
MBA – full & part-time

The Manchester Metropolitan University
MBA – part-time

Middlesex University Business School
MBA – full & part-time

University of Newcastle School of Management
MBA – full & part-time

Nottingham University School of Management and Finance
MBA – General MBA full & part-time
MBA – Financial MBA full & part-time

Open University Business School
MBA – distance learning

Sheffield Business School Sheffield Hallam University
MBA – full & part-time

Sheffield University Management School
MBA – full-time

Strathclyde Graduate Business School
MBA – full, part-time & open learning (UK & International) & mixed mode

Warwick Business School
MBA – full, part-time, distance learning & modular

Westminster Business School University of Westminster
MBA – part-time

Continental Europe

SDA Bocconi – Milano
MBA – full-time

EAP, European School of Management
MBA – full-time

ENPC, Ecole Nationale des Ponts et Chaussées
The International MBA (full-time)

ESADE, Escuela Superior de Administración y Dirección de Empresas
MBA – full-time

ESCP, Ecole Superieure de Commerce de Paris
MBA – full-time

Helsinki School of Economics and Business Administration
The International MBA – full-time

IE, Instituto de Empresa
The International MBA (full-time)

IEP, Institut d'Etude Politiques de Paris MBA Sciences Po
MBA – full-time

IESE, International Graduate School of Management University of Navarra
MBA – full-time

IMD, International Institute for Management Development
MBA – full-time

INSEAD The European Institute of Business Administration
MBA – full-time

ISA at HEC School of Management
MBA – full-time

Katholieke Universiteit Leuven
MBA – full-time

EM Lyon
CESMA MBA (full-time)

Nijenrode University The Netherlands Business School
International MBA (full-time)

NIMBAS, Graduate School of Management
MBA – full, part-time & Executive

Rotterdam School of Management Erasmus Graduate School of Business
MBA – full-time
MBA/MBI – full-time

United States of America

The Association of MBAs recognises schools accredited by AACSB.
Association of MBAs Membership and Association of MBAs Loan Scheme: Applicants from a limited number of schools other than the UK, USA and Continental Europe may also be considered.

© The Association of MBAs, May 1998

**1996 Research Assessment Exercise: The Outcome.
December 1996 Ref RAE96 1/96**

1. The following points should be taken into account when reading the individual ratings:

a. The ratings reflect the panel's judgement as to the **quality of the research submitted** only. They are not a guide to any other aspect of an institution's work in the subject area concerned. It was for each HEI to decide which active researchers to submit for assessment and within which subject Unit of Assessment they should be returned.

b. This is a **peer review exercise** and the ratings reflect the professional judgement of a panel of practising researchers in the subject. Each panel's criteria for assessment and working methods were published in circular RAE96 2/95.

c. The HE funding bodies have made entirely separate arrangements for assessing the **quality of teaching** in HEIs.

2. The ratings are expressed in terms of a standard numerical scale defined as set out below.

3. Alongside each rating is shown the following information:

a. Proportion of staff selected: this is the proportion of all the HEI's staff, employed on academic contracts and working within the subject area, who were put forward for assessment ('Category A' staff). The letters indicate the following bands:

A: 95–100% staff submitted   D: 40–59%

B: 80–94%   E: 20–39%

C: 60–79%   F: below 20%

b. Category A Research Active Staff (FTE): the number (FTE) of academic staff employed by the HEI put forward for assessment in the UOA. This does not include 'Category C' staff – researchers not employed as academic staff by the HEI, but for whom the department is the focus of their research. Such staff may also have been put forward for assessment and contributed to the rating.

Interpretation of the ratings

4. These charts show, for each participating HEI:

a. How many academic staff it employs in total and the proportion of these returned as 'Category A' research active in the RAE.

b. The number and proportion of these selected staff in departments rated at each point of the rating scale.

Distribution of research active staff

In both cases the figures are taken from the institution's submissions and reflect its staffing on the census date (31 March 1996).

The rating scale

5* Research quality that equates to attainable levels of international excellence in a majority of sub-areas of activity and attainable levels of national excellence in all others.

5 Research quality that equates to attainable levels of international excellence in some sub-areas of activity and to attainable levels of national excellence in virtually all others.

4 Research quality that equates to attainable levels of national excellence in virtually all sub-areas of activity, possibly showing some evidence of international excellence, or to international level in some and at least national level in a majority.

3a Research quality that equates to attainable levels of national excellence in a substantial majority of the sub-areas of activity, or to international level in some and to national level in others together comprising a majority.

3b Research quality that equates to attainable levels of national excellence in the majority of sub-areas of activity.

2 Research quality that equates to attainable levels of national excellence in up to half the sub-areas of activity.

1 Research quality that equates to attainable levels of national excellence in none, or virtually none, of the sub-areas of activity.

Notes

1. The concept of a 'sub-area' of research activity is applicable to the work of individual researchers as well as to that of groups. A sub-area is a coherent sub-set of a unit of assessment, and could refer either to the research of a group of staff in a submission, for example high energy physics in a submission from a physics department, or to the disparate research interests of an individual, for example an individual studying both cosmology and high energy physics. The sub-areas relate only to the individual submission and will vary between submissions.

2. 'Attainable' levels of excellence refers to an absolute standard of quality in each unit of assessment, and should be independent from the conditions for research within individual departments.

3. The international criterion adopted equates to a level of excellence that it is reasonable to expect for the unit of assessment, even though there may be no current examples of such a level whether in the UK or elsewhere. In the absence of current examples, standards in cognate research areas where international comparisons do exist will need to be adopted. The same approach should be adopted when assessing studies with a regional basis against 'national' and 'international' standards.

4. For the Research Assessment Exercise, 'national' refers to the United Kingdom of Great Britain and Northern Ireland.

Institution	1996 Rating	Proportion of Staff Selected	Category A Research Active Staff (FTE)
Anglia Polytechnic University	2	E	15.4
Aston University	4	C	51.1
University of Bath	5	B	36.0
Bath College of HE	1	D	3.8
University of Birmingham			
A – School of Business	4	C	26.0
B – Public Policy	3a	A	70.9
Birkbeck College	3a	A	20.2
Bolton Institute of HE	2	E	6.0
Bournemouth University			
A – Business School and School of Finance and Law	2	F	2.0
B – School of Service Industries	2	D	12.0
University of Bradford	4	A	54.2
University of Brighton	3a	E	23.5
Brunel University	3b	C	10.0
Buckinghamshire College of HE	2	F	6.0
University of Cambridge	4	A	27.0
University of Central England in Birmingham	2	D	26.5
University of Central Lancashire	2	F	3.0
Cheltenham and Gloucester CHE	2	E	13.6
City University	4	B	51.8
Coventry University	2	F	12.0
Cranfield University	4	D	43.5
De Montfort University	3b	C	57.0
University of Derby	2	E	21.1
University of Durham	3a	D	28.0
University of East Anglia	2	C	8.0
University of East London	2	E	11.3
University of Exeter	2	D	7.0
University of Greenwich	2	F	6.7
Harper Adams Agricultural College	1	E	2.0
University of Hertfordshire	3b	C	37.0
University of Huddersfield	2	C	46.9
University of Hull	3b	B	19.3
Imperial College of Science, Technology and Medicine	4	C	24.8
Keele University	4	A	30.2
University of Kent at Canterbury	3a	C	15.0
King's College London	3b	C	6.3
Kingston University	3b	D	27.0
Lancaster University	5*	B	69.3
University of Leeds	4	C	48.2
Leeds Metropolitan University	2	E	15.7
University of Leicester	2	A	9.0
University of Lincolnshire and Humberside	3a	F	8.0
Liverpool John Moores University	2	E	12.8
London Business School	5*	A	86.5

Institution	1996 Rating	Proportion of Staff Selected	Category A Research Active Staff (FTE)
London School of Economics and Political Science	5	A	34.5
London Guildhall University	1	F	7.0
Loughborough University	3a	B	39.0
University of Luton	2	F	12.0
University of Manchester	4	B	42.3
UMIST	5*	A	65.3
Manchester Metropolitan University	3b	E	41.0
Middlesex University	2	E	13.0
Nene College	1	E	10.0
University of Newcastle upon Tyne	2	D	8.0
University of North London			
A – Business and Management Studies	2	E	12.0
B – CELTS	3a	C	10.0
University of Northumbria at Newcastle	2	F	14.0
University of Nottingham	4	B	25.3
Nottingham Trent University	3a	F	15.0
Open University	3a	E	19.0
University of Oxford	4	B	16.0
Oxford Brookes University			
A – Business and Management Studies	1	E	17.0
B – Hospitality Management	2	D	10.0
University of Plymouth	2	D	15.6
University of Portsmouth	3b	E	20.5
University of Reading	5	B	14.0
Royal Holloway, University of London	3a	A	19.0
Salford College of Technology	1	F	7.0
University of Sheffield	4	B	38.0
Sheffield Hallam University	3b	F	28.0
University of Southampton	5	B	19.3
Southampton Institute	1	E	12.0
South Bank University	3b	E	8.0
Staffordshire University	2	E	17.0
University of Surrey	3a	D	20.4
University of Teesside	1	E	16.0
Thames Valley University	1	F	2.0
Trinity & All Saints	1	E	4.5
University of Warwick	5	A	113.0
University of Westminster	3b	E	22.8
University of West of England, Bristol	2	F	12.0
University of Wolverhampton	2	F	9.8
University of Aberdeen	3b	C	8.6
University of Abertay Dundee	1	D	8.0
University of Edinburgh	4	A	33.7
University of Glasgow	4	B	18.0
Glasgow Caledonian University	3b	E	28.0
Heriot-Watt University	3a	C	16.2

Institution	1996 Rating	Proportion of Staff Selected	Category A Research Active Staff (FTE)
University of Paisley	2	E	7.0
Queen Margaret College	1	E	2.0
Robert Gordon University	3b	F	4.0
University of St Andrews	4	B	7.0
University of Stirling	3a	C	36.0
University of Strathclyde	5	C	66.0
University of Glamorgan	2	E	8.9
University College of North Wales, Bangor	3b	B	15.0
University of Wales, Swansea	3a	C	12.3
University of Wales, Cardiff	5	B	73.9
University of Wales Institute, Cardiff	1	F	5.0
University of Ulster	3a	E	51.5

There are certain instances where the panel wished to draw attention to a body of work within the submission which it judged to stand out by virtue of its higher quality. These are as follows:

University of Huddersfield – Corporate/Environmental Management
University of North London (Business Management Studies) – Transport Studies
University of Oxford – Accounting and Finance
Sheffield Hallam University – Management Accounting
South Bank University – Marketing Research
Glasgow Caledonian University – Accounting and Finance

This report was the outcome of an assessment of research conducted by the Higher Education Funding Council for England, the Scottish Higher Education Funding Council, the Higher Education Funding Council for Wales (Cyngor Cyllido Addsyg Uwch Cymru) and the Department of Education Northern Ireland. Reprinted with the permission of the HEFCE.

TABLE OF SPECIALIST MBAs

The Schools below offer a specialist MBA – i.e. the title of the MBA Programme

	Aberystwyth	Aston	Bangor	Birmingham Univ.	Birmingham B. Sch	Brighton	Bolton	Canterbury	Cranfield	Cheltenham & Glos	City University	Coventry	Cranfield	Dundee University	Dundee Bus. School	East London	Exeter	Glasgow University	Greenwich University	Henley
Agribusiness	•																			
Banking/Finance			•		•					•	•						•		•	
Business Economics																				
Construction																				
Criminal Justice																				
Design																				
Education																				
Engineering																				
Environment																				
European						•		•				•			•					
Food																				
Football																				
Health								•										•		
Housing																		•		
Human Resources											•									
Hospitality																				
Industrialisation																				
Information																				
Info. Technology											•									
International					•						•	•					•	•		
Law																				
Local Government																				
Marketing											•					•	•		•	
Mineral Resources														•						
Museums & Heritage																				
Operations										•										
Oil, Gas, Petroleum														•						
Procurement					•															
Project Management									•											•
Public Sector		•	•					•						•			•			
Real Estate																				
Retailing																				
Small Business						•														
Sport & Leisure																				
Technology											•									
Telecommunications																				
Transport																				
Tourism & Hospitality																				
TQM/Quality																				
Voluntary Sector																				
Water														•						
Women Returners																				

This is a dot-matrix chart. Columns are not labelled on the page, so they are numbered 1..22 from left to right. Each row is labelled at the right edge.

Institution	1	2	3	4	5	6	7	8	9	10	11	12	13	14	15	16	17	18	19	20	21	22
Hull												•										•
Imperial								•							•							
Leeds Univ.			•					•		•					•							•
Leicester Univ.		•						•											•			•
Liverpool LIPAM											•			•		•						
Loughborough				•							•											
Luton			•		•			•		•				•								•
Manchester BS						•				•												
Nene College	•																					
Newcastle B. Sch																	•					
Newcastle Univ.					•																	
North London												•					•					
Nottingham Univ.		•						•		•		•					•		•	•		•
Oxford Brookes													•									
Paisley		•					•		•													
Plymouth							•															
Royal Agri. College																						•
Royal Holloway										•												
Robert Gordon										•												
Sheffield Univ.								•		•												•
South Bank							•									•		•				
Stirling							•		•							•						
Strathclyde										•						•						
Sunderland		•						•		•				•							•	
U.C.W.I. Cardiff			•								•		•									•
Westminster																				•		

Starting dates for full- and part-time MBA programmes

= Full-time courses * = part-time courses

UNIVERSITY/COLLEGE	JAN	FEB	MAR	APR	MAY	JUN	JLY	SEP	OCT	NOV
Aberdeen University								*		
Aberystwyth, Univ. College of Wales								#		
Anglia Business School		#						#*		
Ashridge Management College	#								*	
Aston Business School	*			*					#*	
Bath, University of								#	*	
Birmingham, University of	*			*		*		#*		
Birmingham, School of Pub. Policy								#	*	
Bolton Business School	*					*			*	
Bournemouth University	*							#		
Bradford University								#*		
Brighton University								#*		
Bristol BS, Univ. of West England								#*		
Bristol University	#*							#*		
Brunel University								#*		
Buckinghamshire College								*		
Cambridge University									#	
Canterbury Business School									#*	
Cardiff Business School								#*		
Central England Business School								#		
Cheltenham & Gloucester	*								#*	
City College Norwich										
City University		*							#*	
Coventry University								#	*	
Cranfield Business School	*								#	
De Montfort University	*								#*	
Dearne Valley Business School									*	
Derby, University								#*		
Dundee University									#*	
Durham Bus. School. Abertay Univ.								#*		
Durham Univ. Business School	*							#		
East Anglia, University of									*	
East London University		#*						#*		
Edinburgh B.S., Heriot Watt Univ.								#*		
Edinburgh University	*							#		
Exeter University									#*	
Glamorgan University								#*		
Glasgow Caledonian University								#*		
Glasgow University								#*		
Greenwich University								#*		
Henley Management College					*			#*		
Hertfordshire Business School									#*	
Huddersfield Univ. Business School	#							#*		
Hull University									#	
Imperial College	*								#	

UNIVERSITY/COLLEGE	JAN	FEB	MAR	APR	MAY	JUN	JLY	SEP	OCT	NOV
Keele University	*							#		
Kingston University		*						*		
Lancashire Business School								#*		
Lancaster University								#*		
Leeds Metropolitan University		#*							*	
Leeds University	*			*				#*	*	
Leicester Univ. (Education)	#*			*				#		
Leicester Univ. Management Centre	*			*	*			#	*	
Lincolnshire & Humberside Univ.								#*		
Liverpool Business School (JMU)	*			*				*		
Liverpool University (LIPAM)									#	
London Business School	*								#	
London Guildhall University		*						*		
Loughborough University									*	
Luton University				*					#*	
Manchester Business School	*			*				#*		
Manchester Metropolitan Univ.					*					
Middlesex University								#	*	
Napier University								*		
Nene College of Higher Educ.	*							*	#	
Newcastle University								#*		
Newcastle B. Sch. Univ. Northumbria								#*		
North London University		#*						#*		
Nottingham Business School								#*		
Nottingham University								#		
Oxford Brookes University								#*		
Oxford University									#	
Plymouth Business School								#*		
Portsmouth University		*						#*		
Robert Gordon University								#*		
Roffey Park Management Institute				*						
Royal Agricultural College								#		
Royal Holloway College								#		
Salford University									#*	
Sheffield Hallam University								*		
Sheffield University								#	*	
South Bank University		*						#*		
Southampton Institute								#	*	
Southampton University		*						#*		
Staffordshire University								#*		
Stirling University								#		
Strathclyde Graduate School									#*	
Suffolk Man. Dev. Centre									*	
Sunderland University	*							#		
Surrey European Man. School								#*		
Swansea Business School								#*		
Teesside University									*	
Thames Valley		#							#*	
Ulster Business School								#*		
Univ. of Wales College Newport								#*		
Univ. of Wales Institute Cardiff		#*						#*		
Warwick Business School				*					#	
Westminster University		#*						#*		
Wolverhampton Business School	#*							*		

Starting dates for distance and open learning MBA programmes

\# = commencement date

OBL = course has an obligatory residential element   OPT = optional residential element

UNIVERSITY/COLLEGE		JAN	FEB	MAR	APR	MAY	JUN	JLY	SEP	OCT	NOV
Aston University		#			#					#	
Bangor, Inst. of Finance	OBL	#						#			
Brunel University				#					#		
Durham Business School	OPT	#	#	#	#	#	#	#	#	#	#
Henley Man. College		#	#	#	#	#	#	#	#	#	#
Heriot Watt Univ. Edinburgh B.S.	OPT	#	#	#	#	#	#		#	#	#
Keele University	OBL	#									
Kingston University	OBL			#					#		
Leicester Univ. Mngt. Centre	OPT	#			#			#		#	
Leicester Univ. (Education Mngt.)	OPT	#			#			#		#	
Napier University	OBL									#	
Open University	OBL		#								
Oxford Brookes University	OBL			#					#		
Oxford Brookes (Hospitality)			#						#		
Paisley University	OBL	#			#			#		#	
Reading University	OBL	#		#			#			#	#
Stirling Univ. (Retail)	OBL						#				
Strathclyde Grad. School	OBL				#					#	
Surrey European Man. School	OPT								#		
Warwick Business School	OBL	#						#			
Westminster Univ. (Design Mngt.)	OBL			#						#	

Directions: Each passage in this group is followed by questions based on its content. After reading a passage, choose the best answer to each question. Answer all questions following a passage on the basis of what is stated or implied in that passage. One sample reading passage follows.

Studies of the Weddell seal in the laboratory have described the physiological mechanisms that allow the seal to cope with the extreme oxygen deprivation that occurs during its longest dives, which can extend 500 metres below the ocean's surface and last for over 70

(5) minutes. Recent field studies, however, suggest that during more typical dives in the wild, this seal's physiological behaviour is different.

In the laboratory, when the seal dives below the surface of the water and stops breathing, its heart beats more slowly, requiring less oxygen, and its arteries become constricted, ensuring that the seal's blood

(10) remains concentrated near those organs most crucial to its ability to navigate underwater. The seal essential shuts off the flow of blood to other organs, which either stop functioning until the seal surfaces or switch to an anaerobic (oxygen-independent) metabolism. The latter results in the production of large amounts of lactic acid which can

(15) adversely affect the pH of the seal's blood, but since the anaerobic metabolism occurs only in those tissues which have been isolated from the seal's blood supply, the lactic acid is released into the seal's blood only after the seal surfaces, when the lungs, liver and other organs quickly clear the acid from the seal's bloodstream.

(20) Recent field studies, however, reveal that on dives in the wild, the seal usually heads directly for its prey and returns to the surface in less than twenty minutes. The absence of high levels of lactic acid in the seal's blood after such dives suggests that during them, the seal's organs do not resort to the anaerobic metabolism observed in the laboratory,

(25) but are supplied with oxygen from the blood. The seal's longer excursions underwater, during which it appears to be either exploring distant routes or evading a predator, do evoke the diving response seen in the laboratory. But why do the seal's laboratory dives always evoke this response, regardless of their length or depth? Some biologists speculate

(30) that because in laboratory dives the seal is forcibly submerged, it does not know how long it will remain underwater and so prepares for the worst.

1. The passage provides information to support which of the following generalisations?
   (A) Observations of animals' physiological behavior in the wild are not reliable unless verified by laboratory studies.
   (B) It is generally less difficult to observe the physiological behavior of an animal in the wild than in the laboratory.
   (C) The level of lactic acid in an animal's blood is likely to be higher when it is searching for prey than when it is evading predators.
   (D) The level of lactic acid in an animal's blood is likely to be lowest during those periods in which it experiences oxygen deprivation.
   (E) The physiological behaviour of animals in a laboratory setting is not always consistent with their physiological behaviour in the wild.

2. It can be inferred from the passage that by describing the Weddell seal as preparing "for the worst" (lines 31-32), biologists mean that it
    (A) prepares to remain underwater for no longer than twenty minutes
    (B) exhibits physiological behaviour similar to that which characterises dives in which it heads directly for its prey
    (C) exhibits physiological behaviour similar to that which characterises its longest dives in the wild
    (D) begins to exhibit predatory behaviour
    (E) clears the lactic acid from its blood before attempting to dive

3. The passage suggests that during laboratory dives, the pH of the Weddell seals' blood is not adversely affected by the production of lactic acid because
    (A) only those organs that are essential to the seal's ability to navigate underwater revert to an anaerobic mechanism
    (B) the seal typically reverts to an anaerobic metabolism only at the very end of the dive
    (C) organs that revert to an anaerobic metabolism are temporarily isolated from the seal's bloodstream
    (D) oxygen continues to be supplied to organs that clear lactic acid from the seal's bloodstream
    (E) the seal remains submerged for only short periods of time

4. Which of the following best summarises the main point of the passage?
    (A) Recent field studies have indicated that descriptions of the physiological behaviour of the Weddell seal during laboratory dives are not applicable to its most typical dives in the wild.
    (B) The Weddell seal has developed a number of unique mechanisms that enable it to remain submerged at depths of up to 500 metres for up to 70 minutes.
    (C) The results of recent field studies have made it necessary for biologists to revise previous perceptions of how the Weddell seal behaves physiologically during its longest dives in the wild.
    (D) Biologists speculate that laboratory studies of the physiological behaviour of seals during dives lasting more than twenty minutes would be more accurate if the seals were not forcibly submerged.
    (E) How the Weddell seal responds to oxygen deprivation during its longest dives appears to depend on whether the seal is searching for prey or avoiding predators during such dives.

5. According to the author, which of the following is true of the laboratory studies mentioned in line 1?
    (A) They fail to explain how the seal is able to tolerate the increased production of lactic acid by organs that revert to an anaerobic metabolism during its longest dives in the wild.
    (B) They present an oversimplified account of mechanisms that the Weddell seal relies on during its longest dives in the wild.
    (C) They provide evidence that undermines the view that the Weddell seal relies on an anaerobic metabolism during its most typical dives in the wild.
    (D) They are based on the assumption that Weddell seals rarely spend more than twenty minutes underwater on a typical dive in the wild.
    (E) They provide an accurate account of the physiological behaviour of Weddell seals during those dives in the wild in which they are either evading predators or exploring distant routes.

6. The passage suggests that because Weddell seals are forcibly submerged during laboratory dives, they do which of the following?
    (A) Exhibit the physiological responses that are characteristic of dives in the wild that last less than twenty minutes.
    (B) Exhibit the physiological responses that are characteristic of the longer dives they undertake in the wild.
    (C) Cope with oxygen deprivation less effectively than they do on typical dives in the wild.

(D) Produce smaller amounts of lactic acid than they do on typical dives in the wild.

(E) Navigate less effectively than they do on typical dives in the wild.

Directions: For each question in this section, select the best of the answer choices given.

7. There are fundamentally two possible changes in an economy that will each cause inflation unless other compensating changes also occur. These changes are either reductions in the supply of goods and services or increases in demand. In a prebanking economy the quantity of money available, and hence the level of demand, is equivalent to the quantity of gold available.

    If the statements above are true, then it is also true that in a prebanking economy

    (A) any inflation is the result of reductions in the supply of goods and services

    (B) if other factors in the economy are unchanged, increasing the quantity of gold available will lead to inflation

    (C) if there is a reduction in the quantity of gold available, then other things being equal, inflation must result

    (D) the quantity of goods and services purchasable by a given amount of gold is constant

    (E) whatever changes in demand occur, there will be compensating changes in the supply of goods and services

8. Which of the following best completes the argument below?

    One effect of the introduction of the electric refrigerator was a collapse in the market for ice. Formerly householders had bought ice to keep their iceboxes cool and the food stored in the iceboxes fresh. Now the iceboxes cool themselves. Similarly, the introduction of crops genetically engineered to be resistant to pests will

    (A) increase the size of crop harvests

    (B) increase the cost of seeds

    (C) reduce demand for chemical pesticides

    (D) reduce the value of farmland

    (E) reduce the number of farmers keeping livestock

9. Since 1975 there has been in the United States a dramatic decline in the incidence of traditional childhood diseases such as measles. This decline has been accompanied by an increased incidence of Peterson's disease, a hitherto rare viral infection, among children. Few adults, however, have been affected by the disease.

    Which of the following, if true, would best help to explain the increased incidence of Peterson's disease among children?

    (A) Hereditary factors determine in part the degree to which a person is susceptible to the virus that causes Peterson's disease.

    (B) The decrease in traditional childhood diseases and the accompanying increase in Peterson's disease have not been found in any other country.

    (C) Children who contract measles develop an immunity to the virus that causes Peterson's disease.

    (D) Persons who did not contract measles in childhood might contract measles in adulthood, in which case the consequences of the disease would generally be more severe.

    (E) Those who have contracted Peterson's disease are at increased risk of contracting chicken pox.

Questions 10-11 are based on the following.

An annually conducted, nationwide survey shows a continuing marked decline in the use of illegal drugs by high school seniors over the last three years.

10. Which of the following, if true, casts most doubt on the relevance of the survey results described above for drawing conclusions about illegal drug use in the teenage population as a whole?

    (A) Because of cuts in funding, no survey of illegal drug use by high school seniors will be conducted next year.

    (B) The decline uncovered in the survey has occurred despite the decreasing cost of illegal drugs.

(C) Illegal drug use by teenagers is highest in those areas of the country where teenagers are least likely to stay in high school for their senior year.

(D) Survey participants are more likely now than they were three years ago to describe as "heroic" people who were addicted to illegal drugs and have been able to quit.

(E) The proportion of high school seniors who say that they strongly disapprove of illegal drug use has declined over the last three years.

11. Which of the following, if true, would provide most support for concluding from the survey results described above that the use of illegal drugs by people below the age of 20 is declining?

(A) Changes in the level of drug use by high school seniors are seldom matched by changes in the level of drug use by other people below the age of 20.

(B) In the past, high school seniors were consistently the population group most likely to use illegal drugs and most likely to use them heavily.

(C) The percentage of high school seniors who use illegal drugs is consistently very similar to the percentage of all people below the age of 20 who use illegal drugs.

(D) The decline revealed by the surveys is the result of drug education programmes specifically targeted at those below the age of 20.

(E) The number of those surveyed who admit to having sold illegal drugs has declined even faster than has the number who have used drugs.

12. In elections in the United States, the proper role of the press is to cover only those factors in the campaign which bear on the eventual outcome. Since the outcome is invariably a victory for the candidate of one of the two major parties, the press should not cover the campaigns of candidates of minor parties.

The argument above relies on which of the following assumptions?

(A) The press has an obligation to cover the candidates of the two major parties because these candidates are likely to be better known to the public than are candidates of minor parties.

(B) It is unlikely that there will be more than three candidates in any given race.

(C) Many eligible voters do not bother to vote, and of those who do not vote, some would probably have supported a candidate of a minor party.

(D) The number of votes cast for a candidate of a minor party is not likely to affect the outcome of the contest between the candidates of the two major parties.

(E) Supporters of candidates of minor parties are less likely to be influenced by the press than are supporters of candidates of the two major parties.

Data sufficiency

Directions: Each of the data sufficiency problems below consists of a question and two statements, labeled (1) and (2), in which certain data are given. You have to decide whether the data given in the statements are *sufficient* for answering the question. Using the data given in the statements *plus* your knowledge of mathematics and everyday facts (such as the number of days in July or the meaning of *counterclockwise*), you are to answer

A if statement (1) ALONE is sufficient, but statement (2) alone is not sufficient to answer the question asked;

B if statement (2) ALONE is sufficient, but statement (1) alone is not sufficient to answer the question asked;

C if BOTH statements (1) and (2) TOGETHER are sufficient to answer the question asked, but NEITHER statement ALONE is sufficient;

D if EACH statement ALONE is sufficient to answer the question asked;

E if statements (1) and (2) TOGETHER are NOT sufficient to answer the question asked, and additional data specific to the problem are needed.

Numbers: All numbers used are real numbers.

Figures: A figure in a data sufficiency problem will conform to the information given in the question, but will not necessarily conform to the additional information given in statements (1) and (2).

You may assume that lines shown as straight are straight and that angle measures are greater than zero.

You may assume that the positions of points, angles, regions, etc., exist in the order shown.

All figures lie in a plane unless otherwise indicated.

Note: In questions that ask for the value of a quantity, the data given in the statements are sufficient only when it is possible to determine exactly one numerical value for the quantity.

Example:
In $\triangle PQR$, what is the value of x?
(1) $PQ = PR$
(2) $y = 40$

Explanation: According to statement (1), $PQ = PR$; therefore, $\triangle PQR$ is isosceles and $y = z$. Since $x + y + z = 180$, it follows that $x + 2y = 180$. Since statement (1) does not give a value for y, you cannot answer the question using statement (1) alone. According to statement (2), $y = 40$; therefore $x + z = 140$. Since statement (2) does not give a value for z, you cannot answer the question using statement (2) alone. Using both statements together, since $x + 2Y = 180$ and the value of y is given, you can find the value of x. Therefore, the answer is C.

13. What was the gross income of Corporation C for year X?
   (1)   For year Y, the gross income of Corporation C was $8,300,000.
   (2)   The gross income of Corporation C for year X represented a 5 percent increase over the gross income for year Y.

14. If x is a positive number, what is the value of x?
   (1) $|x - 2| = 1$
   (2) $x^2 = 4x - 3$

15. During the first year after a homeowner had installed a solar-powered attic fan, the cost of air-conditioning her home was x dollars less than it was the previous year. What was the value of x?
   (1)   The total cost of purchasing and installing the fan was $350.
   (2)   During the first year after the fan was installed, the home-owner's cost for air-conditioning was reduced by 24 percent of the previous year's cost.

16. Are the integers p, q, and r consecutive integers?
   (1)   The sum of p, q, and r is 15.
   (2) r is 1 greater than q and q is 1 greater than p.

17. A wire 22 metres long is cut into three pieces. How long is the longest piece?
   (1)   Two pieces are each 1 metre shorter than the longest piece.
   (2)   One piece is 7 metres long.

18. What is the ratio of the areas of circular region A to the area of circular region B?
   (1)   The ratio of the circumference of A to the circumference of B is 3 to 1.
   (2)   The radius of A is 9 centimetres and the circumference of B is 6π centimetres

19. If t and r are positive integers and r is a divisor of t, is r a prime number?
   (1) $5r = t$
   (2)   The smallest divisor of t that is greater than 1 is r.

Directions: In this section solve each problem, using any available space on the page for scratchwork. Then indicate the best of the answer choices given. **Problem solving**

Numbers: All numbers used are real numbers.

Figures: Figures that accompany problems in this section are intended to provide information useful in solving the problems. They are drawn as accurately as possible EXCEPT when it is stated in a specific problem that its figure is not drawn to scale. All figures lie in a plane unless otherwise indicated.

20. An earth science class had a 50-minute laboratory period during which 5 minutes were spent in distributing and collecting material and 10 minutes were spent in discussing the project for the day. If the remaining time was spent in work on the project, what percent of the period was devoted to work on the project?
(A) 80% (B) 75% (C) 70% (D) 60% (E) 50%

21. On the number line, what is the number that is $\frac{1}{4}$ of the distance from 5.1 to 5.3?
(A) 5.125 (B) 5.15 (C) 5.2 (D) 5.25 (E) 5.35

22. One-third of the rooms in the Chateau Hotel have a harbour view, and the rate for each of these is 1.2 times the rate for each of the remaining 180 rooms. If the rate for the rooms without a harbour view is d dollars per day, what is the hotel's maximum income in dollars, from room rentals for the day?
(A) 204d (B) 234d (C) 240d (D) 270d (E) 288d

23. $\frac{1}{x} - x = \frac{3}{2}$ and $x > 0$, then $x =$
(A) $\frac{1}{2}$ (B) 1 (C) $\frac{3}{2}$ (D) 2 (E) $\frac{5}{2}$

24. If the volume of cube X is 8 cubic metres, what is its total surface area in square metres?
(A) 8 (B) 16 (C) 24 (D) 48 (E) 64

25. If all of the telephone extensions in a certain company must be even numbers, and if each of the extensions uses all four of the digits 1, 2, 3 and 6, what is the greatest number of four-digit extensions that the company can have?
(A)   4
(B)   6
(C)   12
(D)   16
(E)   24

26. A car travelled 462 miles per tankful of petrol on the motorway and 336 miles per tankful in the city. If the car travelled 6 fewer miles per gallon in the city than on the motorway, how many miles per gallon did the car travel in the city?
(A)   14
(B)   16
(C)   21
(D)   22
(E)   27

Sentence correction

Directions: In each of the following sentences, some part of the sentence or the entire sentence is italicised. Beneath each sentence you will find five ways of phrasing the underlined part. The first of these repeats the original; the other four are different. If you think the original is the best of these answer choices, choose answer A; otherwise, choose one of the others. This is a test of correctness and effectiveness of expression. In choosing answers, follow the requirements of standard written English; that is, pay attention to grammar, choice of words, and sentence construction. Choose the answer that produces the most effective sentence; this answer should be clear and exact, without awkwardness, ambiguity, redundancy, or grammatical error.

27. As farmland has continued to erode, farmers have applied more fertilizer both *so that eroded topsoil will be substituted for and fertility should be enhanced.*
(A)   so that eroded topsoil will be substituted for and fertility should be enhanced
(B)   to substitute for eroded topsoil and to enhance fertility
(C)   that eroded topsoil might be substituted for and fertility enhanced
(D)   so as to substitute for eroded topsoil and fertility will be enhanced
(E)   to substitute for eroded topsoil and that fertility might be enhanced

28. As researchers continue to probe the highly expressively vocal and postural language of wolves, *their close resemblance to dogs has become* ever more striking.
(A)   their close resemblance to dogs has become
(B)   the closeness of their resemblance to dogs has become

(C) the close resemblance between them and dogs has become
(D) the close resemblance between wolves and dogs becomes
(E) the close resemblance of wolves with dogs becomes

29. As the British criminologist Radzinowiez maintains, the harsher the penalties formally required by statute, *judges and juries are less willing to impose them.*
(A) judges and juries are less willing to impose them
(B) imposing them becomes something judges and juries are less willing to do
(C) judges and juries become less willing about imposing them
(D) the less willing does imposing them by judge and jury become
(E) the less willing judges and juries are to impose them

30. Perhaps only among populations that have raised dairy animals for the past 10,000 years or so *people retain beyond childhood the ability that they can produce* lactase, the enzyme that enables them to digest milk products.
(A) people retain beyond childhood the ability that they can produce
(B) people retain beyond childhood the ability to produce
(C) is the ability of people retained beyond childhood to produce
(D) do people retain beyond childhood their ability for producing
(E) do people retain beyond childhood the ability to produce

31. *The effect of the earthquake that caused most of Port Royal to sink into the Caribbean was* like the eruption that buried ancient Pompeii: in each case a slice of civilization was instantly frozen in time.
(A) The effect of the earthquake that caused most of Port Royal to sink into the Caribbean was
(B) As the result of an earthquake, most of Port Royal sank into the Caribbean; the effect was
(C) In its effects, the sinking of most of Port Royal into the Caribbean was the result of an earthquake
(D) The earthquake that caused most of Port Royal to sink into the Caribbean was, in its effects,
(E) Most of Port Royal sank into the Caribbean because of an earthquake, the effect of which was

32. *Cleveland that Sarah Short Austen, former vice president of the National Urban Coalition, remembers* was a progressive city, the first of its size to elect a Black man, Carl Stokes, as a mayor.
(A) Cleveland that Sarah Short Austen, former vice president of the National Urban Coalition, remembers
(B) The Cleveland that Sarah Short Austen, former vice president of the National Urban Coalition, remembers
(C) The city of Cleveland that Sarah Short Austen, who has been a former vice president of the National Urban Coalition, remembered
(D) The Cleveland that Sarah Short Austen, once a former vice president of the National Urban Coalition, has remembered
(E) Cleveland, a city remembered by Sarah Short Austen, once a former vice president of the National Urban Coalition,

33. *Like John McPhee's works, Ann Beattie painstakingly assembles in her works* an interesting and complete world out of hundreds of tiny details about a seemingly uninteresting subject.
(A) Like John McPhee's works, Ann Beattie painstakingly assembles in her works
(B) Like John McPhee, Ann Beattie's works painstakingly assemble
(C) Like John McPhee, Ann Beattie painstakingly assembles in her works
(D) Just as John McPhee's, so Ann Beattie's works painstakingly assemble
(E) Just as John McPhee, Ann Beattie painstakingly assembles in her works

**Answer key
for sample
questions**

1.E	6.B	11.C	16.B	21.B	26.B	31.D
2.C	7.B	12.D	17.A	22.E	27.B	32.B
3.C	8.C	13.C	18.D	23.A	28.D	33.C
4.A	9.C	14.E	19.B	24.C	29.E	
5.E	10.C	15.E	20.C	25.C	30.E	

**Analytical
writing**

ANALYSIS OF AN ISSUE – SAMPLE TOPIC

Directions: In this section, you will need to analyze the issue presented below and explain your views on it. The question has no "correct" answer. Instead, you should consider various perspectives as you develop your own position on the issue.

Read the statement and the directions that follow it, and then make any notes in your test booklet that will help you plan your response. Begin writing your response on the separate answer sheet. Make sure that you use the answer sheet that goes with this writing task.

> In matching job candidates with job openings, managers must consider not only such variables as previous work experience and educational background but also personality traits and work habits, which are more difficult to judge.

> What do you consider essential in an employee or colleague? Explain, using reasons and/or examples from your work or worklike experiences, or from your own observations of others.

ANALYSIS OF AN ARGUMENT – SAMPLE TOPIC

Directions: In this section, you will be asked to write a critique of the argument presented below. *You are NOT being asked to present your own views on the subject.*

Read the argument and the instructions that follow it, and then make any notes in your test booklet that will help you plan your response. Begin writing your response on the separate answer sheet. Make sure that you use the answer sheet that goes with this writing task.

> The following appeared in the editorial section of a US local newspaper:

> "This past winter, 200 students from Waymarsh State College traveled to the state capitol building to protest against proposed cuts in funding for various state college programs. The other 12,000 Waymarsh students evidently weren't so concerned about their education: they either stayed on campus of left for winter break. Since the group who did not protest is far more numerous, it is more representative of the state's college students than are the protesters. Therefore the state legislature need not heed the appeals of the protesting students."

Discuss how well reasoned you find this argument. In your discussion, be sure to analyze the line of reasoning and the use of evidence in the argument. For example, you may need to consider what questionable assumptions underlie the thinking and what alternative explanations or counterexamples might weaken the conclusion. You can also discuss what sort of evidence would strengthen or refute the argument, what changes in the argument would make it more sound and persuasive, and what, if anything, would help you better evaluate its conclusion.

Reading list

Cameron, S, *The MBA Study Handbook*, Third Edition (Pitman Publishing)

Carpenter, P & C, *Marketing Yourself To The Top Business Schools* (Wiley)

Crainer, S, & Tate, R, *Key Management Ideas* (Pitman Publishing)

Crainer, S, & Hamel, G, *The Ultimate Business Library: 50 Books That Made Management* (Capstone)

Dickson, T, *Mastering Management* (Pitman Publishing)

Micklethwaite, J, & Wooldridge, A, *The Witch Doctors* (Butterworth Heinemann)

Handy, C, *Understanding Organisations* (Penguin)

Kennedy, C, *Guide to the Management Gurus* (Century)

Prahalad, CK and Hamel, G, *Competing for the Future* (Harvard Business School Press)

Robinson, P, *Snapshots From Hell* (Nicholas Brealey)

Background reading

Many business schools also suggest that prospective students should, if they do not do so already, regularly read *The Economist*, the *Financial Times* and the business sections of at least one quality daily and Sunday newspaper.

Atkinson, J, *Better Time Management* (Kogan Page)

Giles, K, & Hedge, N, *The Manager's Good Study Guide* (The Open University)

Gill, J, & Johnson, *Research Methods for Managers* (Paul Chapman)

Mandel, S, *Effective Presentation Skills* (Kogan Page)

Moroney, M, *Facts From Figures* (Penguin)

Morris, C, & Thanassoulis, E, *Essential Mathematics, A Refresher Course for Business and Social Studies* (Macmillan)

Rowntree, D, *Statistics Without Tears* (Penguin)

Vaitilingam, R, *The Financial Times Guide to Economics and Economic Indicators* (Pitman Publishing)

Walsh, W, *Key Management Ratios* (Pitman Publishing)

Skills development

Index of Schools

United Kingdom

Europe

North America

Australasia

South Africa

Asia

The Association of MBAs official multimedia directory of MBAs worldwide

StudyLink MBA

Special Offer
CD ROM – £9.95 (normally £14.95)

Find the right MBA course for you quickly and easily by using StudyLink's powerful search to shortlist the right programme.

Search through programmes accredited by the Association of MBAs and many more programmes offered worldwide.

View multimedia presentations from many of the world's leading business schools and get a better understanding of the MBA programme they offer, their facilities and what past students have to say about the course.

Suitable for Windows 3.1, Windows 95 and Macintosh.

StudyLink MBA CD ROM is offered to you, as a valued book purchaser, at a special price of only £9.95. Ensure you receive this worldwide listing of MBAs on an easy-to-use CD ROM.

www.studylink.com/mba

To order, please complete this form and return it to:

Amelia Lakin, FT Management, 128 Long Acre, London WC2E 9AN
Tel: (00) +44 171 447 2248
Fax: (00) +44 171 240 5771
e-mail: amelia.lakin@ftmanagement.com

Please send me _____ copy/ies of the StudyLink MBA CD Rom directory at the special price of £9.95 each (normally £14.95) inclusive of p&p.

I enclose a cheque payable to Learning Information Systems, for £_____

Mr/Mrs/Miss/Ms   Initials _____

Name   _____

Address   _____

Town   _____

Postcode   _____

Country   _____

Further reading available from your local bookseller

Mastering Management

ISBN 0273627295

The challenge facing today's high performers is to pursue creative, life-long learning, *FT Mastering Management* is the solution, enabling you to develop your own management learning programme.

This book provides you with a logical, cohesive and easy-to-use source of management excellence. Building on the core of the latest MBA programmes, *FT Mastering Management* delivers a unique synthesis of the most important disciplines of management. It brings together insights and perspectives of three of the world's leading business schools: IMD, London Business School and Wharton.

A world class management companion and the ideal launch pad for an MBA, *FT Mastering Management* is an investment in your own future.

The MBA Handbook – 3rd edition

ISBN 027362346X

The MBA Handbook is the most comprehensive, down-to-earth study skills handbook tried and tested on MBA students. It is recommended reading for anyone considering a postgraduate management qualification.

This new edition includes details on new modes of delivery of programmes, for example, through the Internet, or by video conferencing. It also includes information on the relevance of management qualifications in an increasingly insecure job market, and provides material on self-employment.

The FT Management Masterclass Series

– putting the ideas that will change the management world into the hands of those who need to implement them.

Available in the series:

Key Management Ratios
2nd edition
ISBN 0273635298

Key Management Ideas
2nd edition
ISBN 027363531X

Key Management Solutions
2nd edition
ISBN 0273635301

Key Management Decisions
ISBN 0273630091